Multiple Stressors in Ecological Risk and Impact Assessment: Approaches to Risk Estimation

Multiple Stressors in Ecological Risk and Impact Assessment: Approaches to Risk Estimation

Edited by:

Susan A. Ferenc
ILSI Risk Science Institute, Washington, DC

Jeffery A. Foran
Wisconsin Aquatic Toxicology and Environmental Research Institute,
Milwaukee, WI

SETAC Special Publications Series
Current Coordinating Editor of SETAC Books
C.G. Ingersoll
U.S. Geological Survey

Publication sponsored by the Society of Environmental Toxicology and Chemistry
(SETAC) and ILSI Risk Science Institute

Cover by Michael Kenny Graphic Design and Advertising
Indexing by IRIS

Library of Congress Cataloging-in-Publication Data

Multiple stressors in ecological risk and impact assessment: approaches to risk estimation / edited by
Susan A. Ferenc, Jeffery A. Foran.
    p. cm. -- (SETAC Special Publications Series)
  Includes bibliographical references and index.
  ISBN 1-880611-40-6 (alk. paper)
    1. Ecological risk assessment. 2. Ecological assessment (Biology) I. Ferenc, Susan A.
(Susan Adele), 1957- II. Foran, Jeffery Allen, 1953- III. Series.

QH541.15.R57 M86 2000
333.7'14--dc21

                    00-030125

© 2000 Society of Environmental Toxicology and Chemistry (SETAC)
SETAC Press is an imprint of the Society of Environmental Toxicology and Chemistry.
No claim is made to original U.S. Government works.

International Standard Book Number 1-880611-40-6
Printed in the United States of America
06 05 04 03 02 01 00 99   10 9 8 7 6 5 4 3 2 1

♾The paper used in this publication meets the minimum requirements of the American National
Standard for Information Sciences—Permanence of Paper for Printed Library Materials, ANSI
Z39.48-1984

Reference Listing: Ferenc SA Foran JA, editors. 2000. Multiple stressors in ecological risk and impact
assessment: approaches to risk estimation. Published by the Society of Environmental Toxicology and
Chemistry (SETAC), Pensacola, Florida, USA. 264 p.

The SETAC Special Publications Series

The SETAC Special Publications Series was established by the Society of Environmental Toxicology and Chemistry (SETAC) to provide in-depth reviews and critical appraisals on scientific subjects relevant to understanding the impact of chemicals and technology on the environment. The series consists of books on topics reviewed and recommended by the SETAC Board of Directors for their importance, timeliness, and contribution to multidisciplinary approaches to solving environmental problems. The diversity and breadth of subjects covered in the series reflect the wide range of disciplines encompassed by environmental toxicology, environmental chemistry, and hazard and risk assessment. These volumes attempt to present the reader with authoritative coverage of the literature, as well as paradigms, methodologies, and controversies; research needs; and new developments specific to the featured topics. All books in the series are peer reviewed for SETAC by acknowledged experts.

SETAC Special Publications are useful to environmental scientists in research, research management, chemical manufacturing, regulation, risk assessment and education, as well as to students considering careers in these areas. The Series provides information for keeping abreast of recent developments in familiar subject areas and for rapid introduction to principles and approaches in new subject areas.

SETAC would like to recognize the past SETAC Special Publications Series editors:

T.W. La Point, Institute of Applied Sciences,
University of North Texas, Denton, TX

B.T. Walton, U.S. Environmental Protection Agency,
Research Triangle Park, NC

C.H. Ward, Department of Environmental Sciences and Engineering,
Rice University, Houston, TX

Contents

Chapter 1
Assessment of Multiple Stresses at Regional Scales 1
Lawrence W. Barnthouse, David R. Marmorek, Calvin N. Peters

Chapter 2
Effects-driven Assessment of Multiple Stressors Using Fish Populations 27
Kelly R. Munkittrick and Mark E. McMaster

Chapter 3
Multivariate Statistical Applications for Addressing Multiple Stresses in Ecological Risk Assessments 67
Anne Fairbrother and Richard S. Bennett

List of Figures

List of Tables

Acknowledgments

The material presented in this book is the result of a cooperative project conducted by the U.S. Environmental Protection Agency (USEPA), Office of Water, and the International Life Sciences Institute (ILSI) Risk Science Institute. ILSI is a nonprofit, worldwide foundation established in 1978 to advance the understanding of scientific issues relating to nutrition, food safety, toxicology, risk assessment, and the environment by bringing together scientists from academia, government, industry, and the public sector to solve problems with broad implications for the well-being of the general public.

The ILSI Risk Science Institute (RSI) was established in 1985 to advance and improve the scientific basis of risk assessment. RSI serves as a catalyst for consensus on complex scientific issues in risk assessment by facilitating discussion and cooperation among scientists from all sectors.

We are grateful for the financial support of the USEPA, Office of Water, which provided funding through its cooperative agreement with the ILSI Risk Science Institute. The content of this publication does not necessarily reflect the position or policy of the U.S. Government, and an official endorsement should not be inferred.

The use of trade names and commercial sources in this document is for purposes of identification only, and does not imply endorsement by ILSI or the USEPA. In addition, the views expressed herein are those of the individual authors, and do not necessarily reflect those of their respective organizations or ILSI.

We thank Don DeAngelis, University of Miami; Peter deFur, Center for Environmental Studies; Dave Fisher, Bayer Corporation; Mike Johnson and John Muir, Institute of the Environment; Wayne Landis, Western Washington University; Michael Power, University of Manitoba; Randy Wentsel, USEPA; Fred Wrona, National Hydraulic Resource Center; Al Maki, Exxon Company; Keith Solomon, University of Guelph; and Glenn Suter, USEPA, for the time and effort extended in their peer review of the manuscripts in this publication. We also thank Eugenia Macarthy, Stephanie Carter, and Diane Dalisera of the ILSI Risk Science Institute for their support throughout the project.

About the Editors

Dr. Susan A. Ferenc is a Senior Scientist with ILSI Risk Science Institute. She received a Doctorate of Veterinary Medicine degree from Michigan State University in 1984 and a Ph.D. in Agricultural Economics from the University of Florida in 1994. She then joined the USDA's new Office of Risk Assessment and Cost-Benefit Analysis, where her initial activity was to facilitate and coordinate the two first-ever, nationwide ecological risk assessments. Dr. Ferenc has extensive experience in conducting site-based ecological, human-health, and agricultural risk assessments. She is currently involved in environmental and food safety risk assessment issues and serves as a Special Advisor to the World Health Organization.

Dr. Jeffery A. Foran is the Director of the Wisconsin Aquatic Technology and Environmental Research (WATER) Institute, part of the University of Wisconsin system. He received a Ph.D. in Environmental Sciences from the University of Florida and served as a Post-Doctoral Fellow at that institution. Along with his responsibilities at the WATER Institute, Dr. Foran continues to hold faculty positions at the University of Michigan School of Natural Resources and Environment and George Washington University School of Medicine. He is also a Senior Fellow at the George Washington University Center for Health Policy Research. Dr. Foran is a broadly trained environmental scientist with expertise in ecology, toxicology, risk assessment, and environmental policy. Dr. Foran has served as a member of the Steering Committee for the International Congress on Health and Ecological Effects of Hazardous Waste, as a Senior Advisor to the World Resources Institute, and as a member of the Board of Directors of the Society of Environmental Toxicology and Chemistry.

Foreword

Most risk and impact assessments have evaluated the effects of a single stressor (e.g., a chemical) on an ecosystem or its components. In 1996, the USEPA recognized this deficiency and, in the Agency's guidelines for ecological risk assessment (USEPA 1996), encouraged a move away from single stressor analyses to an approach that recognizes and evaluates the multitude of stressors that influence ecosystems, both singly and cumulatively. While explicitly citing the value of multiple stressor assessments, however, the USEPA's guidelines were not the first to recognize the importance of assessing the effects of multiple stressors in ecosystems. Barnthouse et al. (1990), Harris (1993), Crawford et al. (1994), Savage (1994), and Spaling and Smit (1995) all cited the influence of multiple stressors in both aquatic and terrestrial systems. Even earler, conceptual models had been developed for multiple stressor assessments, although they were referred to as cumulative impact or cumulative effects assessments (Preston and Bedford 1988).

In 1997, the Society of Environmental Toxicology and Chemistry (SETAC) conducted a Pellston workshop that, for the first time, attempted to develop a framework for assessments of multiple stressors. The framework derived from the workshop (Foran and Ferenc 1999) addressed questions such as how to identify disparate stressors in an ecosystem; how to assess, both qualitatively and quantitatively, the impact of multiple stressors; how to characterize risks associated with multiple stressors; and, how to manage risks and impacts of multiple, disparate stressors in ecosystems. The framework presented conceptual approaches to multiple stressor assessments; it did not present a set of detailed methods to evaluate the comparative or relative impacts of several individual stressors, to assess the integrated or cumulative impact of multiple stressors on ecosystems and their components, and to assess the indirect effects of multiple stressors.

One of the constraints on progress toward the development of an approach to address multiple stressors has been the terms used to provide the context for the assessment. Quite simply, the terms reduce to "risk assessment for multiple stressors," and "cumulative effects" or "cumulative impacts" assessment. The editors and authors of this book, and the scientists who reviewed early drafts of the chapters, discussed terminology that provides the context for the assessment of multiple stressors in ecosystems. During the initial phases of this discussion, two camps evolved around the different terms. What differentiates these assessments, argued the camps, is the time frame over which the assessment is conducted—risk assessment being primarily retrospective and impact assessment being primarily prospective. Upon further discussion, however, the camps agreed that both risk and impact assessments can be either or both retrospective and prospective, with the time frame for the assessment driven by the stimulus for the assessment itself, such as a particular law or statute. Another difference between risk and impact assessments, argued the camps, is the approach to the process. Risk assessments have been traditionally stressor-driven, while, as described by Foran and Ferenc (1999) and by

Munkittrick and McMaster in Chapter 2 of this text, impact assessments have been driven by effects analyses. While these difference are not universally applicable and may not clearly differentiate risk and impact assessments, it may be important in shaping the outcome of the assessment; therefore, stressor-driven and effects-driven approaches have been discussed in both Foran and Ferenc (1999) and in this text. Regardless of the assessment type, however, all participants in the discussion agreed that a variety of stressors shape ecosystems and must be considered in either risk assessments or in impact and effects assessment. Equally important is the absolute requirement that consideration of multiple stressors move beyond consideration of single or even multiple chemicals to consideration of chemical, biological, and physical stressors of both anthropogenic and natural origin. Exactly how multiple, disparate stressors are or should be considered is the subject of this text.

We commissioned the development of five chapters to address the methods development phase of assessments that tackle multiple stressors. In Chapter 1, Larry Barnthouse presents two case studies, the Chesapeake Bay and the Columbia River Basin assessments, that address multiple stressors. The approaches to these assessments and their outcomes differ, but the case studies provide useful examples of how a variety of stressors affect ecosystems and their components, and the critical need for methods that facilitate assessments of multiple stressors. In Chapter 2, Munkittrick and McMaster describe some of the deficiencies of stressor-based analyses, and argue for the use of effects-driven approaches to cumulative impact assessment. Included in this chapter is a thorough description of the effects-based approach to impact assessment, which builds on the description of the approach provide by Munkittrick and others in Foran and Ferenc (1999). In Chapter 3, Fairbrother and Bennett discuss the use of multivariate statistical applications to address multiple stressors in ecological risk assessment. A variety of tools are presented that can be used to describe, quantitatively, stressor/response or stressor/effect relationships in complex ecosystems. While this chapter applies statistical methods in the context of ecological risk assessment, it seems likely that the methods also have utility in the conduct of impact assessments as well. In Chapter 4, Moore and Bartell discuss the use of uncertainty analysis and ecological modeling in the assessment of multiple stressors. These methods are data-intensive and generally are intended for higher-level, more-refined assessments (as discussed in Chapter 5).

The methods presented in Chapters 2 through 5 are supplemented with short case studies of their application, as well as with brief discussions of the management implications for use of the methods. However, the methods are somewhat disparate because the authors developed the chapters independently. Chapter 5, by Harwell and Gentile, was commissioned to provide an integration of the methods and observations presented in Chapters 1 through 4. Harwell and Gentile provide this integration, both directly and through the development of a unified framework for the assessment of multiple stressors in risk and impact assessments. Additionally, Harwell and Gentile discuss the methods presented in the first four chapters in the context of a large-scale ecological risk assessment conducted in South Florida. We hope that the South Florida assessment in Chapter 5, along with the case studies presented in Chapter 1 and the methods presented in Chapters 2 through 4, will provide both guidance and impetus for the inclusion of consideration of multiple stressors in all future ecological risk assessments and cumulative impact and effects assessments.

References

Barnthouse LL, Suter GW, Rosen AE. 1990. Risks of toxic contaminants to exploited fish populations: influence of life history, data uncertainty and exploitation intensity. *Environ Toxicol Chem* 9:297–311.

Crawford DW, Bonnevie NL, Gillis CA, Wenning RJ. 1994. Historical changes in the ecological health of the Newark Bay Estuary, New Jersey. *Ecotoxicol Environ Safety* 29:276–303.

Foran JA, Ferenc SA, editors. 1999. Multiple stressors in ecological risk and impact assessment. Pensacola FL: Society of Environmental Toxicology and Chemistry (SETAC). 100 p.

Harris HJ. 1993. The state of the bay: a watershed perspective. Green Bay WI: Institute for Land and Water Studies, University of Wisconsin-Green Bay.

Preston EM, Bedford BL. 1988. Evaluating cumulative effects on wetland functions: a conceptual overview and generic framework. *Environ Manage* 12:565–583.

Savage M. 1994. Anthropogenic and natural disturbance and patterns of mortality in a mixed conifer forest in California. *Can J For Res* 24:1149–1159.

Spaling H, Smit B. 1995. A conceptual model of cumulative environmental effects of agricultural land drainage. *Agricul Ecosyst Environ* 53:99–108.

[USEPA] U.S. Environmental Protection Agency. 1996. Proposed guidelines for ecological risk assessment; notice. *Federal Register* 61(175):47552–47631.

CHAPTER 1

Assessment of Multiple Stresses at Regional Scales

Lawrence W. Barnthouse, David R. Marmorek, Calvin N. Peters

Sorting out the influences of multiple stressors is one of the most difficult challenges faced by ecologists involved in restoration and management of ecological resources. In this context, the term "multiple stressors" refers not to responses of individual organisms to multiple chemical exposures, but to combined effects of multiple human influences on populations and ecosystems. Such influences frequently include conventional water pollution, toxic chemicals, land-use change, harvesting, and many other qualitatively different disturbances. The challenge to ecologists is to 1) determine among all of the possible stressors which particular combination is responsible for observed adverse conditions, and 2) design effective restoration strategies to eliminate or ameliorate those conditions.

Regional-scale resources such as estuaries, watersheds, and anadromous fish species are especially likely to be influenced by multiple stressors because of the many and diverse human activities that occur on regional scales. The Great Lakes, Chesapeake Bay, San Francisco Bay, the Columbia River Basin, and southern Florida are all examples of regional resources that have been adversely affected by multiple stressors. Federal and state agencies have devoted significant efforts over a decade or more to understanding the various influences on these ecosystems and on developing restoration strategies.

The premise of this paper is that the successes and failures of these efforts provide instructive lessons for U.S. Environmental Protection Agency (USEPA) and other organizations interested in developing general procedures for assessing ecological

Multiple Stressors in Ecological Risk and Impact Assessment: Approaches to Risk Estimation. Susan A. Ferenc and Jeffery A. Foran, editors.
©2000 Society of Environmental Toxicology and Chemistry (SETAC). ISBN 1-880611-40-6

risks of multiple stressors. The principal lesson provided by the two cases examined here are that 1) risk assessments for multiple environmental stressors involves the same array of scientific methods already used to assess ecological risks of single stressors, and 2) the prospects for successful restoration of ecological resources adversely affected by multiple stressors are likely to be enhanced if management actions are viewed as experiments designed in part to identify the causes of observed degradation.

Common Types of Regional-scale Environmental Stressors

The most common types of stressors encountered in regional-scale assessments include the following elements.

- Overharvesting of natural resources, especially of fish and shellfish. Overharvesting leads to the depletion or even the disappearance of the harvested species. Overharvesting also can lead to a variety of indirect effects related to the loss of the ecological functions provided by the depleted species. An example would be the increase in turbidity of Chesapeake Bay that has been attributed to a reduction in water-column filtration provided by now-depleted oyster beds.

- Modification of natural hydrology as a result of dam construction, channelization, or water withdrawals for industry and agriculture. The construction of multiple hydroelectric dams on the Columbia and Tennessee Rivers created chains of reservoirs that destroyed habitat for some species and created habitat for others.

- Land-use change resulting from land clearing for agriculture and urban/suburban development. These changes, which include drainage of wetlands and clearing of riparian forests, can alter temperature regimes and increase sediment loads in tributary streams. Poor forestry practices in parts of the Pacific northwest have contributed to reductions in spawning success of Pacific salmon. Increased sediment loads in Chesapeake Bay are believed to have contributed to reductions in the area of the bay occupied by submerged aquatic vegetation.

- Point-source and nonpoint-source inputs of nutrients and conventional pollutants, often resulting in eutrophication, localized or widespread oxygen depletion, and outbreaks of nuisance organisms.

- Toxic chemicals, especially persistent organochlorine chemicals. Releases of these chemicals have led to depletion of many sensitive bird species and to widespread restrictions on human consumption of contaminated fish.

- Exotic species (both accidentally and deliberately introduced) , including fish, mollusks, and zooplankton. Introductions or invasions of these species have irreversibly altered the species compositions of the Great Lakes and San Francisco Bay.

Although all of these stressors are common, they have very little in common other than the fact that they all are byproducts of human-population growth and economic development. For this reason, they tend to develop over the same or similar time periods. The temporal confounding of stressors is one of the more difficult aspects of multiple-stressor problems because it obscures linkages between causes and effects.

The next sections examine approaches to multiple stressor assessments that have evolved in two major North American ecosystems: the Columbia River Basin and Chesapeake Bay. Both of these ecosystems have been affected by overharvesting, land-use change, point and nonpoint source pollutant discharges, and toxic chemicals. The approaches taken to addressing and managing the multiple stressors in these two regions have, however, been quite different.

The Columbia River Basin

Pacific salmon (*Onchorhyncus* spp) are among the most aesthetically appealing, scientifically interesting, and economically important of all North American fish species. The ecosystem occupied by Pacific salmon spans most of North America west of the Rocky Mountains and the Sierra Nevada Range, Northeastern Asia, and the entire northern Pacific Basin. The many species and races of salmon have developed subtle variations in life history that have enabled them to colonize virtually every type of native aquatic habitat that they could reach. Salmon are a major food source for many terrestrial bird and wildlife species and have supported intensive harvesting by Native American tribes and by modern commercial and recreational fishermen.

Historically, the Columbia River Basin was among the largest single sources of salmon. The entire watershed, which occupies most of the states of Washington, Oregon, and Idaho, as well as parts of Montana and Canada, was occupied by salmon. As recently as the 1930s, millions of pounds of fish were harvested annually. Major species included the chinook, coho, sockeye, and steelhead. Many of these fish originated in spawning streams in the mountains of the Snake River Basin in Idaho, more than 900 miles from the ocean.

As the population of the Pacific Northwest increased and economic development ensued, salmon production declined. By the 1970s, fisheries managers finally took action, and fishing on several species—notably chinook salmon—was severely restricted. Hatcheries were built to replace the production formerly provided by native populations. By 1990, coho salmon had been extirpated from the Snake River Basin, and the sockeye run had been reduced to a literal handful of fish returning annually to Redfish Lake, Idaho. The remaining populations of chinook and steelhead have, one by one, been listed as endangered or threatened under the federal Endangered Species Act (ESA). At present, all wild salmon and steelhead populations in the Snake River Basin are listed, and chinook and steelhead in the middle and upper Columbia Basins have been proposed for listing. Virtually all of the salmon that return annually to the mouth of the river are now derived from hatcheries.

Many factors may have contributed to the decline of salmon in the Columbia River Basin. Harvesting is an obvious suspect. Along with the "in-river" fishery, i.e., the fishery directed at the returning spawners, a significant "ocean-intercept" fishery for salmon developed after World War II. In the 1950s and 1960s it is estimated that approximately half of the total population of salmon was harvested each year.

Logging, mining, and land clearing also contributed to the decline of salmon. Clear-cutting of watersheds that provide spawning and rearing habitat for salmon increases water temperatures and causes silt deposition in spawning gravel beds. Mining also leads to siltation and, in extreme cases, reduced stream pH and contamination by heavy metals. Agriculture and grazing lead to nutrient enrichment. Most of the original forest within the interior Columbia River Basin has been logged, and much of the nonforested landscape is devoted to rangeland or farming.

Many scientists believe that the hatcheries designed to supplement salmon production actually have contributed to their demise (NRC 1996). The availability of hatchery fish maintains harvesting at a level that would not be economically supportable if only wild fish were available. Hatchery-derived fish may mix on the spawning grounds with wild fish and dilute or modify the gene pool of the native fish. Hatchery fish are also subject to a wide variety of infectious diseases, which can be transmitted to wild fish. Some hatchery-derived fish are large enough to prey on young wild salmon.

Aside from harvesting, the most obvious potential stress on salmon populations is the system of dams constructed on the mainstem Columbia and Snake Rivers since the 1930s (Figure 1-1). Grand Coulee Dam on the upper Columbia River and Hell's Canyon Dam on the Snake River block upstream migration of salmon and have eliminated salmon from a significant fraction of their former range. Fish ladders at the remaining dams—10 on the Columbia and four on the Snake—permit upstream migration of adults. However, the dams have changed the nature of the migration corridors from a free-flowing river to a chain of reservoirs. The survival of down-stream-migrating juvenile salmon appears to have been significantly reduced by passage through or around dams, by predation within the reservoirs, and by other stressors related to reduced freshwater flow rates and increased downstream travel times. Since the 1980s, young salmon have been collected at the Snake River dams and transported downstream by barge and truck.

Oceanic conditions also may have contributed to the decline. Oceanographers have documented cyclical changes in the circulation of the North Pacific that occur over a

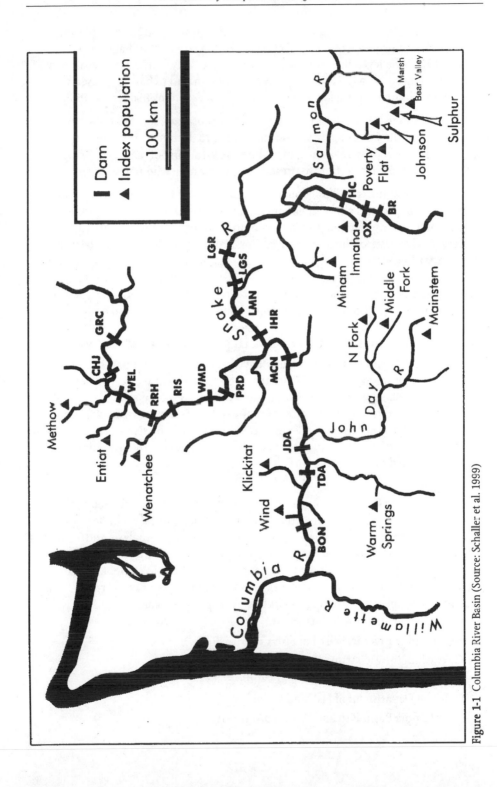

Figure 1-1 Columbia River Basin (Source: Schaller et al. 1999)

period of several decades. This cycle may affect the growth and survival of salmon during the oceanic phase of their life cycle. A shift in circulation that occurred around 1975 is believed by some scientists to have adversely affected the survival of salmon produced from the Columbia River and south and to have increased the survival of salmon produced by more northerly river systems (Anderson 1996).

Despite the extensive efforts already devoted to restoration, most of the salmon populations in the Columbia basin are continuing to decline. Expensive and economically disruptive measures, including the breaching of dams, are being considered in a last-ditch effort to preserve the remaining wild populations.

More than one hundred million dollars per year are now spent on research and demonstration projects aimed at enhancing salmon production. Many of the funds support hatchery production, habitat restoration, or other activities intended to address single causes of the decline in salmon production. However, the federal, state, and tribal agencies charged with salmon restoration and management also have supported a multi-agency quantitative assessment project intended to elucidate, as far as is possible from existing information, the specific processes responsible for the decline of chinook and steelhead populations in the Snake River Basin.

The Plan for Analysis and Testing of Hypotheses Project

Quantitative data analysis and modeling have been an important part of salmon management for many years. The "Ricker" stock-recruitment model (Ricker 1975) found in most ecology textbooks was developed from studies of salmon-population dynamics. Stock-recruitment models for many of the remaining chinook salmon populations have been developed from decades of data on the size and composition of the salmon harvest and on the numbers of fish returning to the spawning streams. Detailed models of the survival of juvenile chinook during downstream migration have been developed by several agencies.

In 1992, the agencies responsible for these efforts began to compare their models so that differences between the predictions made from the models could be understood and reduced. In 1995, a new project called the Plan for Analysis and Testing of Hypotheses (PATH) Project was initiated with the objectives of 1) testing the many alternative hypotheses concerning the causes of the declines in chinook and steelhead populations in the Snake River Basin and 2) evaluating potential restoration strategies. The agencies participating in the PATH project include
- Bonneville Power Administration,
- Columbia River Inter-Tribal Fish Commission,
- Washington Department of Environment,
- Oregon Department of Fish and Wildlife,
- Idaho Department of Fish and Game,
- Columbia Basin Fish and Wildlife Authority,

- National Marine Fisheries Service (NMFS),
- U.S. Army Corps of Engineers, and
- U.S. Fish and Wildlife Service (USFWS).

Other agencies, notably the U.S. Forest Service, have participated informally by contributing results from their own assessments. Several independent scientists with expertise in fish- population dynamics and quantitative decision analysis participate as active members of the PATH core team; a Scientific Review Panel consisting of four other independent scientists reviews all PATH products.

The initial focus of PATH was on spring/summer chinook spawning in the tributaries of the Snake River in Oregon and Idaho. These were the first populations to be listed under the ESA. Moreover, they have other characteristics that make them especially amenable to quantitative analysis. Spring/summer chinook spawn primarily in small headwater streams. The aggregate population is subdivided into many discrete spawning stocks occupying different watersheds. Information on long-term trends in juvenile production and adult returns are available for many of these so-called "index stocks." In 1996, the PATH project team produced a "retrospective analysis" based on these data (Marmorek 1996, Marmorek and Peters 1996). The retrospective analysis provided initial quantitative tests of a set of nested hypotheses concerning differences between stocks spawning in the Snake River Basin and stocks spawning in other parts of the Columbia Basin.

The Plan for Analysis and Testing of Hypotheses retrospective analysis

The PATH retrospective analysis (Marmorek and Peters 1996) addressed three hierarchical questions (Figure 1-1):

1) Do all of the spring/summer chinook salmon stocks above Bonneville Dam shown a similar pattern of recent change in stock indicators? If they did, then broad regional influences, rather than sub-basin-specific or stream-specific factors might have been responsible for the decline.

2) If all stocks have not shown the same trends, is there a difference in performance between upriver and downriver stocks or between the pre-1970 and post-1975 time periods? This question addresses the major geographic and temporal patterns of change within the Columbia Basin. It focuses on two critical time periods: the period prior to 1970, which is considered to be a relatively stable "baseline" period, and the period from 1976 through the present, when the decline in production of spring/summer chinook apparently accelerated. The Lower Granite, Little Goose, Lower Monumental, and Ice Harbor dams on the lower Snake River were constructed during the transition period of 1970 through 1974.

3) What do the retrospective analyses indicate about the contributions of the five major factors—hydropower, habitat, hatchery, harvest, and climate—to the observed spatial/temporal differences? This question relates directly to

the likelihood of success of the alternative restoration options available to the agencies. It was not expected that the retrospective analysis would provide definitive answers to this question. The objective of the third question was to provide guidance for structuring a "prospective analysis" of future management options, to be carried out in a later phase of the project.

Quantitative methods in the retrospective analysis

The "index stocks" used in the analysis are derived from three major sub-basins (Figure 1-2): the Snake River Basin, the upper Columbia Basin (the river above its confluence with the Snake), and the lower Columbia Basin (the river below its confluence of the Snake).

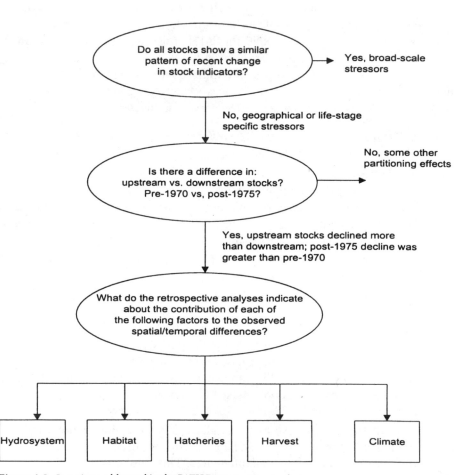

Figure 1-2 Questions addressed in the PATH Retrospective Analysis

Four independent quantitative analyses were performed to support the retrospective analysis. Schaller et al. (1999) analyzed trends in spawner-recruit data for index stocks in all three of the above sub-basins. "Spawners" were defined as the number of adults reaching the spawning streams in any given year; "recruits were defined as the number of progeny produced by those spawners that survive to return to the spawning grounds themselves (usually 5 years later). The authors used analysis of covariance to test for differences in spawner-to-recruit survival 1) between sub-basins and 2) over time within sub-basins.

Deriso et al. (1996) developed a suite of empirical models of the mortality of juvenile fish during downstream passage, using the method of "maximum likelihood estimation" (MLE). The different models reflected different assumptions concerning the influence of 1) the number of dams passed and 2) differences between sub-basins on the rate of mortality of salmon from the time they begin downstream passage until the time they return as adults. The goodness-of-fit of the alternative models was assessed using model-evaluation criteria that account for both the closeness of model predictions to the measured data and the number of parameters used in the fitting process.

Paulsen (1996a) performed a cluster analysis of year-to-year variations in juvenile survival data for the 16 index stocks. The purpose of this analysis was to determine the spatial scale of the factors influencing survival. This scale could be large, if the stocks clustered according to known geographic relationships (e.g., if stocks within the same sub-basin clustered together), or small, if variations in survival were independent of geographic relationships. Paulsen (1996b) also performed multiple regression analyses that attempted to relate variations in survival to a variety of indices of habitat quality and climatic indices.

Petrosky and Schaller (1996) examined the relationship between the numbers of juveniles emigrating from spawning streams and the numbers of spawners that produced them. The purpose of this analysis was to test the hypothesis that reductions in the quality of spawning and rearing habitat, rather than reductions in the survival of emigrating juveniles, were responsible for the observed decline in survival of spring/summer chinook over their full life cycle.

The above analyses provided relatively clear and unambiguous answers to the first two questions posed in the retrospective analysis. Schaller et al. (1999) found that recruit survival from the Snake River Basin had declined significantly between the "pre-dam" period and the "post-dam" period. Although the survival of fish from the upper Columbia and lower Columbia had also declined, the rate of decline in these two sub-basins was much more gradual. Similarly, Deriso et al. (1996) found that the best-performing of their alternative models assumed that 1) the rate of survival of juveniles during downstream passage was inversely related to the number of dams passed and 2) there were no other systematic differences in survival rate between juveniles originating in different sub-basins. The cluster analysis performed by Paulsen et al. (1996a) grouped the index stocks by sub-basin, indicating that annual variations in survival were more closely related to factors that influenced all fish derived from the same sub-basin than to factors that influenced different stocks within each sub-basin. The multiple regressions performed by Paulsen et al. (1996b) explained relatively little of the total variance in survival between stocks; however, the factor most strongly correlated with juvenile survival was the number of dams passed by juveniles originating in each index stream. Petrosky et al. (1996) found that the number of emigrating juveniles produced by each spawner in the Snake River index stocks was essentially the same during the pre-dam period as during the post-dam period.

In short, spring/summer chinook stocks above Bonneville dam have not exhibited similar patterns of change since the 1950s. The survival rate of fish throughout the basin has declined since the 1950s. The survival rate of fish spawned in the Snake River Basin has declined more than the survival rate of fish from other sub-basins, especially after the mid-1970s. Changes in survival of young fish between spawning and emigration, a period of about 18 months for spring/summer chinook, do not appear to have been large enough to account for the observed decline in overall life-cycle survival.

Five alternative hypotheses were proposed as possible explanations for the observed patterns in stock productivity:

1) The construction of the federal hydropower system, especially the four dams on the lower Snake River, decreased the survival rates of out-migrating smolts and returning adults.

2) Habitat degradation in the Snake River Basin reduced the productivity of the spawning and rearing stream.

3) Competition and disease transmission related to hatchery production decreased the survival rate of wild fish.

4) Overharvesting reduced the number of fish surviving to reproduce.

5) Cyclical changes in ocean conditions reduced the survival of fish during the oceanic phase of their life cycle.

Evaluation of alternative hypotheses

Quantitative information for testing these hypotheses was extremely limited; the retrospective analysis focused instead on qualitative analysis using a weight-of-evidence approach. Qualitative evidence was especially important for hypotheses dealing with local-scale factors such as habitat quality and hatchery influences.

Evidence that the construction of four dams on the lower Snake River was an important factor contributing to the decline was considered relatively strong. The quantitative analyses were consistent with a hydropower-related effect because the observed changes in productivity and survival coincided in space and time with the construction of the dams. Available estimates of survival rates for downstream-migrating smolts were also consistent with a hydropower-related effect; however, the specific mechanisms responsible for the effect could not be determined.

A variety of studies have documented widespread habitat change within the Columbia basin. The U.S. Forest Service recently completed an assessment of stream habitat quality for the entire basin east of the Cascade Range (Quigley and Arbelbide 1996). A majority of the watersheds in the basin are rated as less-than-pristine quality. Studies of spawning and rearing stress in individual streams have documented a variety of adverse effects of mining and forestry on salmon reproduction. However, no basin-wide changes in habitat quality have been documented that could explain the timing and spatial pattern of change documented in the retrospective analysis. Moreover, most of the habitat degradation that could have affected the index stocks is believed to have occurred prior to 1950. The power analysis performed by Petrosky et al. (1996) showed that the productivity of these streams could not have declined by more than 25% since the 1970s, and a decline of this magnitude would not have been sufficient to cause the observed decline in survival over the full life cycle.

A variety of studies have documented potential adverse effects of hatchery operations on wild salmon stocks, but quantitative data are scarce. Moreover, large-scale hatchery production within the Snake River Basin did not begin until the 1980s and was initiated in response to the observed decline in wild salmon production. Hatchery production was, on this basis, tentatively discounted as a significant cause of the decline. Harvest was similarly discounted as a contributing factor because rates of harvest of spring/summer chinook have been drastically reduced from the high levels observed in the 1950s and 1960s. The annual catch rate has been reduced from as high as 50% per year to 15% per year or less. This reduction should have produced a large and readily detectable increase in survival of spring/summer chinook rather than the decrease that actually occurred.

Influences of climate were less-readily discounted. Anderson (1996) summarized recent literature relating to 1) cyclical changes in climate and ocean circulation patterns in the North Pacific and 2) the possible influences of those changes on salmon production. Recent analyses cited by Anderson appear to show that abrupt changes in circulation occur with periodicity of approximately 30 years, and a shift between warm/dry and cold/wet conditions can cause ocean temperatures in the North Pacific to oscillate (Anderson 1996). Data indicate that a shift from cold/wet to warm/dry conditions occurred between 1976 and 1977. According to Anderson (1996), this shift may have lead to increased ocean survival of salmon originating in Alaska and to reduced survival of salmon originating in the Columbia Basin. Anderson's hypothesis is roughly consistent with results of the MLE analysis performed by Deriso et al. (1996). This analysis identified a "year effect" that appeared to influence all of the index stocks. The sign of the "year effect" was generally positive during the 1950s and 1960s and negative since 1970s with the exception of a few years in the early 1980s.

In summary, the retrospective analysis concluded the following with respect to the multiple stressors affecting spring/summer chinook stocks in the Snake River Basin:

- the aggregate effects of the hydrosystem probably contributed to reduced survival rates of Snake River stocks during the post-1974 period, as compared to the pre-1970 period;

- climatic conditions have probably contributed to observed differences in stock indicators between the pre-1970 and post-1970 periods, but there are no consistent differences in response between upriver and downriver stocks;[1]

- habitat modification and harvesting historically have been important influences on the stocks, but these stressors do not appear to have significantly contributed to the post-1974 decline; and

- hatcheries do not appear to have significantly contributed to the decline.

The Plan for Analysis and Testing of Hypotheses preliminary decision analysis

To address the implications of the retrospective analysis for decision-making concerning future hydrosystem management actions, the PATH project performed a quantitative decision analysis for spring/summer chinook salmon (Marmorek and Peters 1998). The purpose of the decision analysis was to estimate the probability of success of alternative management options in a way that explicitly accounted for existing uncertainty concerning the factors influencing salmon survival.

The analysis involved three steps: 1) specification of decision options, 2) development of quantitative models that link decision options to population responses, and 3) definition of performance measures for evaluating the decision alternatives.

The decision alternatives, which were defined by an interagency, policy-level working group termed the "Implementation Team," involve various combinations of mainstem hydrosystem actions ranging from continuation of current operations to breaching of four Snake River dams and drawdown of the John Day Dam on the lower Columbia River. The models consist of a set of three linked simulation models. A hydro-regulation model translates each management option into the mean monthly flows which would be observed in the Snake and Columbia Rivers at various locations. A passage model translates the projected set of flows for a given year into the estimated passage survival of both transported and non-transported fish through the migration corridor from the head of the uppermost reservoir on the Snake (Lower Granite Reservoir) to the tailrace of the lowermost dam on the Columbia (Bonneville Dam). A life-cycle model generates a range of possible spawner abundances for each stock and year, under each management option.

---

[1] Some PATH scientists still maintain that differential effects of climate on upriver versus downriver stocks could be responsible for the comparatively severe decline in Snake River Basin stocks. The proposed hypothesis involves differential ocean distributions of fish derived from different basins; available data are inadequate to test this hypothesis.

A wide variety of performance measures was defined by the PATH team, both for alternatives evaluation and for model verification and sensitivity analysis. The most important of these, from the decision perspective, is the NMFS Jeopardy Standard for the Snake River index stocks (BRWG 1994). The standard is based on stock-specific survival and recovery thresholds defined for each of the seven index stocks. The survival threshold is the minimum number of spawners required to ensure the persistence of the stock. This threshold, defined as either 150 spawners or 300 spawners depending on the characteristics of the stock and the stream, was chosen because NMFS believes that below these levels spawner/recruit relationships are poorly known and unpredictable changes in population behavior are likely to occur. The recovery threshold is the minimum number of spawners that would permit delisting of the stock. This threshold is defined, for each spring/summer chinook stock, as 60% of the average spawner count prior to 1971. The standard is expressed in probabilistic terms. To meet the jeopardy standard, an action must result in a "high percentage" of available populations having a "high likelihood" of being above the survival threshold and a "moderate likelihood" of being above the recovery level. "High" and "moderate" likelihoods have been operationally defined as being 0.7 for survival standards and 0.5 for recovery standards. NMFS has defined "high percentage" of stocks as being 80% of the available populations. Hence, since there are seven index stocks in the Snake River Basin, an action can meet the overall jeopardy standard only if it is predicted to result in six stocks having probability of 0.7 or greater of being above the survival threshold and a probability of 0.5 or greater of being above the recovery threshold. In the PATH decision analysis, these probabilities were estimated by using Monte Carlo analysis to propagate the uncertainties concerning the factors influencing salmon survival and reproduction.

A wide variety of uncertainties was quantified as part of the decision analysis. The available historical record of Snake and Columbia River flows was used to generate random flow-time series for simulating future conditions. Probability distributions were placed on all simulation model parameters, based in part on empirical measurements and in part on expert judgements. Because several of the alternative hypotheses concerning downstream passage and life-cycle mortality are too complex to be represented as individual parameters, alternative versions of both passage and life-cycle models were incorporated in the decision analysis.

Monte Carlo uncertainty analysis was used to express the individual uncertainties as aggregate probabilities of meeting or exceeding the NMFS jeopardy standard over future periods of 24, 48, and 100 years. Sensitivity analyses were performed to isolate the specific hypotheses (i.e., models and parameters) having the greatest influence on the outcome of the analysis. In the initial calculations, every alternative model and assumption was given equal weight. To refine the results, members of the PATH Scientific Review Panel (SRP) were asked to weight the alternatives according to their relative likelihood (PATH SRP 1998). The decision outcomes were then revised to reflect the weights given to the hypotheses by the SRP members.

The decision analysis is still a "work in progress." Preliminary results have been communicated to the Implementation Team, but a final report will not be published until parallel analyses for other salmon species are completed.

Remaining uncertainties and future directions

The PATH project is among the most comprehensive and rigorous analyses of fish population data that has ever been or are performed; however, the results to date have a number of significant limitations. The existing analyses focus on only one specific species and life-history type of the many that have been depleted and are in need of restoration. Conclusions regarding the relative influences of multiple stressors that are valid for spring/summer chinook may not be valid for other stocks. Retrospective and prospective analyses for both of these stock groups are currently underway. In principle, the quantitative methods used in the spring/ summer chinook analyses are applicable to all salmon populations. However, the available data for fall chinook and steelhead are much more limited than the data for spring/summer chinook. It is likely that qualitative rather than quantitative methods will be emphasized in assessments for these stocks.

Although the retrospective analyses for all species are quite broad and examine all of the potential influences on survival and reproduction, the prospective analyses are focused on mainstem passage issues. This narrowing of scope was directed by the Implementation Team because the NMFS is required by court order to issue an opinion about whether the configuration and operation of Snake and Columbia River dams must be modified to ensure recovery of endangered salmon stocks. Prominent reviews of the status of salmon in the Pacific Northwest sponsored by the National Research Council (NRC 1996) and the Northwest Power Planning Council (NPPC) (ISG 1996) have argued that a comprehensive management strategy that focuses on restoring the entire corridor from the spawning streams to the ocean rather than on individual components of the life cycle is the only approach likely to lead to long-term restoration of salmon production in the basin.

The structured approach to hypothesis testing and decision analysis employed in the PATH Project could, in principle, be applied at any spatial scale and could address any of the issues raised in the above reviews. The primary limiting factor is availability of appropriate data. Extending the analysis to other scales and stressors would require a focused data collection program. The existing models and prelimi- nary conclusions could be used to design such a program. In fact, one of the original goals of the PATH Project was to use the models to design "adaptive management experiments" (Walters 1986) that would enable resource managers to obtain an improved understanding of the factors influencing salmon production while implementing actions intended to restore the depleted stocks. The PATH team initiated an adaptive management task in October 1998; no results are available at this time.

The Chesapeake Bay

Chesapeake Bay is the largest and most productive estuary in the U.S. The Bay's fish and shellfish resources have been intensively exploited for decades. The Bay watershed, including tributary rivers in three states, contains several large urban centers and extensive agricultural development. By the 1970s, incipient signs of large-scale degradation of the Bay's biological resources were apparent. Major adverse changes included

- widespread loss of oyster beds due in part to over-exploitation and in part to diseases;
- reductions in the reproductive success of several finfish species, especially the striped bass;
- increases in nutrient loading, leading to eutrophication and seasonal anoxia in certain parts of the Bay;
- reductions in the area of the Bay occupied by submerged aquatic vegetation;
- increases in toxic chemicals loadings; and
- observations of potentially toxic levels of pH and aluminum in some tributaries, apparently associated with acid deposition.

A number of programs were initiated to investigate the causes of these adverse changes and to identify appropriate management actions. Most of this work was performed under two "umbrella" programs: 1) the interagency Emergency Striped Bass Study, intended to investigate the causes of the catastrophic decline in the striped bass fishery that occurred between 1970 and 1985, and 2) the joint federal/state Chesapeake Bay Program, which has the more general charge of restoring all of the Bay's biological resources. Both of these programs have addressed influences of multiple stressors, although the approaches adopted are quite different.

The Emergency Striped Bass Study

The striped bass supports the Atlantic Coast's most valuable commercial and recreational fishery. Chesapeake Bay is the most important spawning and nursery for striped bass, accounting for up to 90% of all striped bass caught from North Carolina to Maine (Merriman 1941; Boreman and Lewis 1987). Striped bass can live for 30 years or more and attain a size of up to 100 pounds. Female fish typically become sexually mature between 5 and 7 years of age and reproduce annually throughout the remainder of their lives. The reproductive success of the spawning females varies markedly between years, for reasons that are very poorly understood. Historically, large year classes (termed "dominant year classes") have been produced every 5 to 7 years. Both the fishery and the striped bass population itself are sustained by these dominant year classes.

The 1970 striped bass year class in Chesapeake Bay was the largest that had ever been recorded and supported an intensive fishery throughout the decade. However, after 1970 no more dominant year classes were produced. Catches began to decline, and because few young fish were being produced, it was clear by 1980 that catches would decline even further. A variety of hypotheses were proposed for the continued low rate of striped bass production, and in 1979 Congress amended the Anadromous Fish Conservation Act to request a study to identify causes for the decline. The study was conducted jointly by the USFWS and the NMFS.

Three general sets of hypotheses were investigated. One set related to changes in the physical environment of the fish caused by effects of toxic chemicals, agricultural runoff, municipal sewage, modified stream flow, and natural climatic variation. The second set related to biological processes such as disease, starvation, predation, and competition with other species. The third set related to mortality associated with fishing, including overharvesting, incidental catches of striped bass by fishermen targeting other species (known as "bycatch" in fisheries terminology), and hook-and-release mortality in the recreational fishery. In addition to research related to these various hypotheses, the Emergency Striped Bass Study supported intensified monitoring of both juvenile and adult striped bass.

Both laboratory experiments and field research were conducted over more than a decade to test the individual hypotheses (Table 1-1). Results of the research are summarized in the Final Report from the study (Young-Dubovsky et al. 1996). Almost all of the putative causal factors were found to be potential contributors at least in certain locations at certain times, but the quantitative contributions of individual stressors to the baywide decline could not be estimated.

The Final Report did not discuss reasons for the inability to quantify contributions of different stressors, but several reasons can be inferred from the information provided in Table 1-1. First, most of the studies, both field and laboratory, dealt with individual stressors. These studies were primarily investigations of whether and under what conditions a particular stress could affect striped bass survival (e.g., laboratory experiments on pH and metal toxicity, starvation, and predation) or whether ambient water at specific sites was toxic to striped bass (in situ bioassays in various spawning rivers). Second, except for studies of historical data on pH trends, no attempts were made to determine the baywide distribution of particular stressors. Third, the intensities of the stressors were not directly linked to the annual rates of survival or reproduction in the striped bass population as a whole.

It is possible that, had the program continued, attempts would have been made to quantify the population-level consequences of one or more of the stressors being investigated. However, by the mid-1980s the continued decline in striped bass recruitment convinced fisheries scientists that immediate action was necessary to preserve the population. A series of empirical and theoretical analyses of the relationships between potential stressors, year-class abundance, and catch in striped bass (Goodyear 1985a, 1985b; Goodyear et al. 1985) provided a rationale for a management experiment that ultimately determined the most likely cause of the

Table 1-1 Summary of Striped Bass Study research conducted on factors responsible for the decline of striped bass in the Chesapeake Bay

Hypothesis	Research	Summary
Contaminants	In-situ and on-site bioassays in spawning rivers	
	Maryland:	Toxic conditions in some rivers in some
	Nanticoke 1984–90	years. No single contaminant is consistently
	Upper Bay 1985–90	responsible for mortality. Point source
	Choptank 1987–90	discharge has been implicated.
	Potomac 1986, 1988–90	
	Virginia:	Survival generally high. Metals
	Rappahannock 1989–90	concentrations much lower than in
	Mattaponi 1989–90	Choptank and Nanticoke Rivers.
	Pamunkey 1989–90	
	James 1989–90	
	Laboratory experiments:	Highly sensitive to pH below 6.0 and
	pH, aluminum and metals for various life	aluminum concentrations. Salinity and
	stages	organic acids ameliorate effects.
Starvation	Laboratory studies	Limited evidence of impact except perhaps in Potomac River.
Fishing mortality	Extensive management changes	Strong evidence of over exploitation that
	Simulation modeling	reduced recruitment. Difficult to distinguish from effects of other factors.
Predation/competition (larval stage)	Exposed larvae to variety of predators in laboratory	Numerous potential predators, but evidence infield is lacking
Climatic events	Evaluated historical data on pH trends in major spawning rivers	No evidence of systematic decrease in pH or increased frequency of low pH. Historical information is insufficient to detect small changes.
Water use practices	Evaluated flow conditions in Chesapeake and Delaware Canal	Evidence of transport out of bay and entrainment of larvae. Overall impact is uncertain. Canal may serve as major egress for juveniles and adults from Chesapeake Bay.
Disease	Laboratory studies of IPN virus	Nonlethal, but striped bass can act as carriers. Potential disease problems in intensive culture, but much lesser problem in nature.

Source: Young-Dubovsky et al. (1996)

decline. First, Goodyear (1985a) demonstrated that values of the striped bass juvenile-abundance index estimated annually by the Maryland Department of Natural Resources were strongly correlated with subsequent commercial landings. Second, Goodyear (1985b) used a striped bass population model to show that chemicals or other stressors affecting the survival of early striped bass life stages would reduce the potential growth rate of the population in exactly the same way that population growth is affected by fishing-related mortality. Finally, Goodyear et al. (1985) used both the model and the available time series of juvenile index values to show that the average number of young striped bass being produced each year was lower than the number required to replace the adult population.

Goodyear argued that only a significant increase in survival of striped bass eggs and larvae or a significant reduction in fishing mortality could prevent further decline of the Chesapeake Bay striped bass population. Years of research might be required in order to determine which factors might be influencing early life-stage survival and to devise effective restoration measures. Fishing-related mortality, however, could be quickly reduced by imposing restrictions on the harvest. Even if fishing had not been responsible for the decline, reduced fishing effort would permit more fish to spawn. More young fish would be produced, stabilizing the population while research continued.

Goodyear's arguments were endorsed by other fisheries scientists, and the recommendation to reduce fishing effort was adopted by both federal and state fisheries managers. In 1985, Maryland unilaterally imposed a moratorium on fishing for striped bass in state waters. The moratorium would be lifted only when the Maryland Juvenile Index showed that striped bass recruitment had returned to the average level observed during the 1950s and 1960s. New York enacted a similar moratorium in 1986. Other states followed by either eliminating or severely restricting fishing for striped bass.

Observations of the age composition of the spawning stock over the next several years showed a steady increase in the relative proportion of young spawners, demonstrating that reduced fishing had, in fact, increased the number of fish surviving to maturity. The annual values of the Maryland Juvenile Index also rose. The juvenile index for 1989 was nearly as high as the 1970 index, signaling the production of the first dominant year class in two decades. The Atlantic States Marine Fisheries Commission (ASMFC) and the states partially lifted restrictions on striped bass the following year (ASMFC 1990), and in 1994 the population was declared fully restored. As noted in the Striped Bass Study Final Report (Young-Dubovsky et al. 1996), the contributions of other stressors to the decline in striped bass abundance may never be known. However, the immediate response of the population to reduced fishing effort demonstrates that overfishing was almost certainly the primary cause. The threats to Chesapeake Bay posed by other stressors continue to be addressed on an ecosystem rather than a population basis through the Chesapeake Bay Program.

The Chesapeake Bay Program

The Chesapeake Bay Program is a regional partnership established to promote restoration of all of the Bay's biological resources. Participants in the program, which was established in 1983, include the states of Maryland, Pennsylvania, and Virginia; the District of Columbia; the Chesapeake Bay Commission (a tri-state legislative body); and USEPA. The program promotes both research and restoration actions.

Environmental concerns pursued by the program involve two principal types of activities: habitat protection/restoration and pollution abatement. Obviously, multiple stressors are involved, but formal risk assessments are not in most cases performed to prioritize the program's activities. The original drivers of the first program activities were observations of overt degradation: nutrient enrichment; reduced areal extent of submerged aquatic vegetation; and the presence of toxic chemicals in sediment, water, and fish/wildlife tissue. The principal response has been source control, monitoring, and active restoration. For example, submerged aquatic vegetation (SAV) has probably declined for a number of reasons, including increased sediment loads due to land clearing, inputs of nutrients leading to eutrophication, and direct physical disturbance. The program has not attempted an assessment of the roles of the various influences. Instead, it has implemented management actions to address the potential causes, including 1) mandating reductions in phosphate loadings to the Bay, 2) encouraging revegetation of riparian areas to reduce sediment loading, 3) protecting existing and potential SAV beds, 4) planting SAV vegetation in suitable areas, and 5) instituting a baywide vegetation-monitoring program to measure progress in restoration of SAV.

The Chesapeake Bay Agreement (USEPA 1988) called for the development of a baywide toxic chemicals reduction strategy. A list of toxics of concern (TOCs) was developed (USEPA 1991) and subsequently revised (USEPA 1996). A research program was initiated to identify areas of the bay watershed that were affected by toxic chemicals and to characterize the risks associated with specific TOCs. This research has demonstrated that toxic chemicals are present at various locations within the bay watershed, but it has not conclusively determined the ecological significance of these chemicals.

Hall et al. (1995) performed ambient toxicity tests, with concurrent measurements of toxic chemical concentrations, using water samples collected from five sites within the watershed. Apparent toxicity, measured in one or more of four test systems, was found in at least some samples collected from most sites, but no sites were found to be consistently toxic, and no chemicals were consistently associated with the observed toxicity.

Hall et al. (1998) used baywide data on water-column concentrations of cadmium and copper to perform a preliminary watershed-level risk assessment for these chemicals. Potential risks due to copper exposure were identified in the Chesapeake and Delaware Canal, the Middle River, and selected locations in the Choptank and Potomac Rivers. However, since the effects benchmarks used in the assessment were derived from single-species laboratory tests and were not supported by biological surveys or ambient toxicity testing, Hall et al. (1998) could not infer that toxic effects due to copper exposure were actually occurring at these sites.

Hartwell (1997) and Hartwell et al. (1997) developed a risk-ranking index for sediment and water from correlations between ambient toxicity test results and indicators of fish community integrity. In general, the fish-community indices were more strongly correlated with sediment toxicity than with water-column toxicity. Toxic sediments and depauperate fish communities were clearly associated with heavily urbanized sites; however, no specific chemical or suite of chemicals could explain the observed degradation. No attempt has been made to apply Hartwell's approach throughout the watershed; therefore, the actual extent of ecologically significant contamination is still highly uncertain.

Even though the baywide significance of sediment and water contamination has never been firmly established, toxic chemicals have been perceived as a problem of sufficient importance to warrant a baywide risk-reduction program. The strategy relies primarily on reductions in inputs of chemical contamination from control-lable sources and on selective remediation of areas, termed "regions of concern", deemed to be the most severely contaminated. Currently, designated regions of concern are limited to areas located near urban centers close to the bay, specifically, the Patapsco, Anacostia, and Elizabeth Rivers.

Future directions

Chesapeake Bay now supports a large and growing population of striped bass. The Bay Program has documented decreased loadings of nutrients and toxic chemicals to the bay, decreases in the frequency and spatial extent of anoxic conditions related to eutrophication, and increases in the abundance of SAV. Recently, however, outbreaks of the dinoflagellate *Pfiesteria* have caused localized fish kills. Runoff from industrial-scale poultry farms has been implicated in the *Pfiesteria* outbreaks, and, in response to the outbreaks, a new program aimed at controlling nutrient inputs from these farms has been established.

The signatories to the original Chesapeake Bay Agreement continue to cooperate through sharing of research results, coordination of databases, and development of joint programs to restore habitat, and further reduce nutrient, pesticide, and toxic chemical loadings. These programs are believed to be targeted at the major sources of stress affecting the Chesapeake Bay ecosystem; however, no formal risk assessments are performed to support these programmatic decisions.

Conclusions

The assessments described in the two previous case studies are clearly very different from typical risk assessments performed by USEPA and other regulatory agencies. The disparate nature of the stressors and the very large spatial scales of the affected resources render conventional assessment approaches infeasible. It may not be possible to design an experiment or a monitoring program to measure the effects of multiple stressors, acting through different mechanisms at different times and at different locations, on an entire river basin or estuary. Both quantitative and qualitative methods were employed by the agencies responsible for developing and implementing restoration programs. In both cases, models of the responses of fish populations to multiple stressors were used to express the effects of multiple stressors in common units of survival and reproductive success. In neither case, however, did quantitative assessment provide fully satisfactory answers to key questions regarding the responses of the systems to management actions. In both the Columbia River Basin and Chesapeake Bay, responsible parties have advocated the use of "adaptive management" (Holling 1978).

The use of process-level ecological models to express responses in common units

In quantitative assessments performed for both the Columbia River Basin and Chesapeake Bay, effects of all of the stressors were expressed in common units relating to population responses. In the PATH retrospective analysis, effects of all of the influences on salmon survival were expressed in terms of the percent of down-stream-migrating juveniles that return as spawners. Decision criteria for the prospective analysis were also expressed in a common unit: the probability the future population sizes will be sufficient to meet jeopardy standards set by the NMFS. These common units have permitted a variety of tradeoffs to be explored among various management alternatives involving qualitatively different effects on the life cycle of the fish. These tradeoffs were made possible by the use of 1) down-stream-passage models that link the various biological and physical factors that influence juvenile salmon to the survival rate during emigration and 2) life-cycle models that project changes in survival to changes in the long-term abundance of the populations.

In the case of Chesapeake Bay, a key component of the argument supporting striped bass fishing restrictions was the demonstration that fishing and toxic chemicals both affect the lifetime reproductive potential of individual fish; thus, effects of toxic chemicals could be offset by reductions in fishing effort.

In both of the above cases, understanding of the processes linking the responses of organisms to responses of populations was the key to integrating responses to multiple stressors. At least in theory, all stressors that affect survival, reproduction, and growth of organisms, including all possible combinations of chemical and nonchemical stressors, can be integrated into effects on population growth. Relationships between individual-level population-level phenomena can be quantified using theoretically sound and empirically testable models. Recently developed techniques for "individual-based" and "spatially explicit" population modeling have greatly expanded the range of problems for which quantitative assessment of population responses is feasible (Barnthouse 1998).

Analogous methods for community- or ecosystem-level assessment are much less well-developed. Water-quality models that can predict the influence of nutrient enrichment on the potential eutrophication of water bodies have been available for many years (Barnthouse et al. 1986). The Chesapeake Bay Program currently uses a model of this type to predict the influence of nutrient loadings in tributaries on oxygen depletion in the Bay; the results are used to prioritize source-reduction actions within the watershed.

Comparable approaches do not exist for biological community structure. "Biocriteria," indicators of community health derived from standardized measures of community characteristics in "impaired" versus "reference" ecosystems, have become popular tools for measuring the responses of aquatic communities to stress (Karr 1991; Karr and Chu 1999). As noted in the Chesapeake Bay Program section, ambient toxicity test results have been linked to fish community indices for contaminated and uncontaminated locations within Chesapeake Bay (Hartwell 1997; Hartwell et al. 1997). Two decades of research on and applications of biocriteria have demonstrated the value of this approach for identifying aquatic ecosystems that have been degraded by human activities such as urban development, agriculture, and mining. However, the diagnostic and predictive power of the approach is limited because the index values have no theoretical foundation in biological or chemical processes. They are simply arithmetic combinations of empirical measurements. Approaches based on multivariate analysis (e.g., Johnson 1988; Van den Brink and ter Braak 1999; Kedwards et al. 1999) avoid many of the perceived weaknesses of single-valued indices (Suter 1993) but, like biocriteria, they are not derived from functional relationships between causes and effects and do not produce predictive models. Measures of ecological conditions derived from biological sampling can identify locations where management action is needed, but they cannot identify the type or extent of management action that should be pursued.

The importance of adaptive management

Even the best-supported ecological assessments, based on large datasets and well-tested quantitative methods, contain large residual uncertainties. In reviewing the results of the preliminary decision analysis for spring/summer chinook salmon, the PATH SRP overseeing the PATH Project concluded that relatively little was left to be gained through additional analyses of existing data and models (PATH SRP 1998). The approach used in the prospective analysis was judged suitable for evaluating the relative benefits and risks of a limited set of hydrosystem actions under a relatively narrow range of hypotheses. However, the models were judged to be inadequate for addressing the full range of plausible hypotheses or management actions.

In the face of this uncertainty, the panel concluded that it was "unrealistic and imprudent" to expect that decisions based on the results of the modeling would necessarily lead to recovery of the depleted stocks. The panel recommended that, rather than pursuing further research, the agencies implement an experimental management program in which large-scale changes in management practices would be accompanied by intensive observation to determine the responses of the stocks to management actions. The panel argued that this adaptive approach would provide the best means of sorting out the influences of the multiple stressors affecting Columbia River Basin salmon populations and developing an effective recovery program.

The idea of adaptive management is not new. The principle that the best way to determine the influences of human actions on biological resources is to treat resource management itself as an experiment was first proposed 20 years ago (Holling 1978) and has been the subject of numerous articles and books (e.g., Walters 1986; Lee 1993). The concept has been officially endorsed in the Columbia Basin Fish and Wildlife Program (NPPC 1987).

The restrictions on striped bass fishing imposed during the 1980s may be viewed as an adaptive-management experiment. In fact, the restrictions are viewed as a bay wide management experiment by the authors of the Emergency Striped Bass Fund Final Report (Young-Dubovsky et al. 1996). The Atlantic States Marine Fisheries Commission still views its management approach to striped bass as "adaptive." A target spawning-population size has been established, year-class production and spawning-stock size are estimated annually, and annual adjustments to fishing regulations are made based on measured fishing mortality rates and projected future spawning-stock sizes.

Implications for other multiple-stressor assessments

The two case studies examined in this paper are probably typical in terms of the scale and complexity of issues involved in assessment and management of stressors at regional scales. No new or unique approaches were used to assess the effects of multiple, rather than single, stressors. Quantitative modeling was a key ingredient in both cases, but the models used were straightforward extensions of methods routinely used in assessments of single, well-understood stressors.

A second key ingredient in both cases was long-term monitoring of the condition of the resources and of the various potential stressors influencing those resources. The availability of many years of stock-productivity estimates for Snake River spring/summer chinook enabled the agencies to develop models capable of providing quantitative assessments of restoration alternatives. Similarly, the existence of a long-term series of estimates of striped bass recruitment permitted fisheries scientists to identify the decline in reproductive success and make a case for reduced fishing effort. Although biocriteria clearly provide long-term indicators of general ecosystem quality, monitoring the status of specific populations is still beneficial because causal relationships can be investigated and predictive methods can be developed.

Regardless of the availability of models and data, actions still have to be taken before scientific analysis is complete. Well-designed adaptive-management programs would appear to provide the best opportunity to obtain information about the importance of multiple stressors while at the same time restoring the degraded ecological resources. Scientists can contribute to this process by providing a conceptual framework within which the questions can be properly defined and a set of assessment tools that can be used to answer the questions. The available tools include empirical measurements, databases, GIS systems, process-level models, and various types of quantitative decision-analysis techniques. Agencies and regional stakeholders can contribute by providing the resources necessary to establish and maintain the long-term data-collection programs needed to define appropriate management actions and monitor ecological responses to those actions.

In short, although it may well be useful to develop improved scientific tools for characterizing ecological risks of multiple stressors, the most important barriers to progress may be institutional rather than technical.

References

Anderson JJ. 1996. Review of the influence of climate on salmon. In: Marmorek DR, editor. Plan for Analyzing and Testing Hypotheses (PATH): Final report on retrospective analyses for fiscal year 1996. Vancouver BC: ESSA Technologies, Ltd.

[ASMFC] Atlantic States Marine Fisheries Commission. 1990. Source document for the supplement to the striped bass FMP, Amendment 19, No. 4. Atlantic States Marine Fisheries Commission. Fisheries Management Report No. 16.

Barnthouse LW, O'Neill RV, Bartell SM, Suter II GW. 1986. Population and ecosystem theory in ecological risk assessment. In: Poston TM, Purdy R, editors. Aquatic toxicology and environmental fate: 9th volume. Philadelphia PA: American Society for Testing and Materials. STP 921. p 82–96.

Barnthouse LW. 1998. Modeling ecological risks of pesticides: a review of available approaches. In Schüürmann H, and Markert B, editors. Ecotoxicology. Heidelberg, Germany: Spektrum Academic Publishers. p 769–798

Boreman J, Lewis RR. 1987. Atlantic coastal migrations of striped bass. *Am Fish Soc Symp* 1:331–339.

[BRWG] Biological Requirements Work Group. 1994. Analytical methods for determining requirements of listed Snake River salmon relative to survival and recovery. Progress Report of the Biological Requirements Work Group. Washington, DC: National Marine Fisheries Service, Idaho Department of Fish and Game.

Deriso R, Marmorek D, Parnell I. 1996. Retrospective analysis of passage mortality of spring chinook of the Columbia River. In: Marmorek DR, editor. Plan for Analyzing and Testing Hypotheses (PATH): Final report on retrospective analyses for fiscal year 1996. Vancouver BC: ESSA Technologies, Ltd.

Goodyear CP. 1985a. Relationship between reported commercial landings and abundance of young striped bass in Chesapeake Bay, Maryland. *Trans Am Fish Soc* 114:92–96.

Goodyear CP. 1985b. Toxic materials, fishing, and environmental variation simulated effects on striped bass population trends. *Trans Am Fish Soc* 114:107–113.

Goodyear CP, Cohen JE, Christensen SW. 1985. Chesapeake Bay striped bass: recruitment declining below replacement. *Trans Am Fish Soc* 114:146–151.

Hall LW, Ziegenfuss MC, Anderson RD, Killen Jr WD. 1995. Use of estuarine water column tests for detecting toxic conditions in ambient areas of the Chesapeake Bay watershed. *Environ Toxicol Chem* 14:267–278.

Hall LW, Scott MC, Killen, Jr. WD. 1998. Ecological risk assessment of copper and cadmium in surface waters of Chesapeake Bay watershed. *Environ Toxicol Chem* 17:1172–1189.

Hartwell SI. 1997. Demonstration of a toxicological risk ranking method to correlate measures of ambient toxicity and fish community diversity. *Environ Toxicol Chem* 16:361 371.

Hartwell SI, Dawson CE, Durrell EQ, Alden RW, Adolphson PC, Wright DA, Coelho GM, Magee JA, Ailstock S, Norman M. 1997. Correlation of measures of ambient toxicity and fish community diversity in Chesapeake Bay, USA, tributaries—urbanizing watersheds. *Environ Toxicol Chem* 16:2556–2567.

Holling CS, editor. 1978. Adaptive environmental assessment and management. Chichester, UK: J Wiley. 377 p.

[ISG] Independent Scientific Group. 1996. Return to the river: restoration of salmonid fishes in the Columbia River ecosystem. Report to the Northwest Power Planning Council, Portland, OR. Report No. 96-6.

Johnson AR. 1988. Diagnostic variables as predictors of ecological risk. *Environ Manage* 12:515–523.

Karr JR. 1991. Biological integrity: a long-neglected aspect of water resource management. *Ecol Appl* 1:66–84.

Karr JR, Chu EW. 1999. Restoring life in running waters. Washington DC: Island Press. 206 p.

Kedwards TJ, Maund SJ, Chapman PF. 1999. Community-level analysis of ecotoxicological field studies. I. Biological monitoring. *Environ Toxicol Chem* 18:149–157.

Lee KN. 1993. Compass and gyroscope: integrating science and politics for the environment. Washington DC: Island Press. 243 p.

Merriman D. 1941. Studies on the striped bass (*Roccus saxatilis*) of the Atlantic Coast. *Fish Bull* 50:1–77.

Marmorek DR, editor. 1996. Plan for Analyzing and Testing Hypotheses (PATH): Final report on retrospective analyses for fiscal year 1996. ESSA Technologies, Ltd., Vancouver, BC, Canada.

Marmorek DR, Peters CN, editors. 1996. PATH—Plan for Analyzing and Testing Hypotheses. Conclusions of fiscal year 96 retrospective analyses. Vancouver BC: ESSA Technologies.

Marmorek DR, Peters CN, editors. 1998. Plan for Analyzing and Testing Hypotheses (PATH): Preliminary decision analysis report on Snake river spring/summer chinook (Draft). Vancouver BC: ESSA Technologies, Ltd.

[NRC] National Research Council. 1996. Upstream—salmon and society in the Pacific Northwest. Washington DC: NRC.

[NPPC] Northwest Power Planning Council. 1987. Columbia River Basin fish and wildlife program. Portland OR: NPPC.

[PATH SRP] PATH Scientific Review Panel. 1998. Conclusions and recommendations from the PATH Weight of Evidence Workshop; 8–10 September 1998; Vancouver, BC, Canada. Vancouver BC: ESSA Technologies, Ltd.

Paulsen CM. 1996a. Level 1 hypotheses. In: Marmorek DR, editor. Plan for Analyzing and Testing Hypotheses (PATH): Final report on retrospective analyses for fiscal year 1996. Vancouver BC: ESSA Technologies, Ltd.

Paulsen CM. 1996b. Level 2 hypotheses. In: Marmorek DR, editor. Plan for Analyzing and Testing Hypotheses (PATH): Final report on retrospective analyses for fiscal year 1996. Vancouver BC: ESSA Technologies, Ltd.

Petrosky CE, Schaller HA. 1996. Evaluation of productivity and survival rate trends in the freshwater spawning and rearing life stage for Snake River spring and summer chinook. In: Marmorek DR, editor. Plan for Analyzing and Testing Hypotheses (PATH): Final report on retrospective analyses for fiscal year 1996. Vancouver BC: ESSA Technologies, Ltd.

Quigley T, Arbelbide S, editors. 1996. An assessment of ecosystem components of the interior
    Columbia River Basin and portions of the Klamath and Great Basin: general technical report.
    Portland OR: USDA Forest Service, Pacific Northwest Research Station. PNW-GTR-XXX.

Ricker WE. 1975. Computation and interpretation of biological statistics of fish populations. *Fish Res
    Board Can Bull* 191:1–333.

Schaller HA, Petrosky CE, Langness OP. 1999. Contrasting patterns of productivity and survival rates
    for stream-type chinook salmon (*Oncorhynchus tshawytscha*) populations of the Snake and
    Columbia Rivers. *Can J Fish Aquat Sci* 56:1031–1045.

Suter II GW. 1993. A critique of ecosystem health concepts and indexes. *Environ Toxicol Chem*
    12:1533–1540.

[USEPA] U.S. Environmental Protection Agency. 1988. Chesapeake Bay toxics reduction strategy:
    Chesapeake Bay Agreement Report. Annapolis MD: Chesapeake Bay Program.

[USEPA] U.S. Environmental Protection Agency. 1991. Chesapeake Bay toxics of concern list
    information sheets. Annapolis MD: Chesapeake Bay Program.

[USEPA] U.S. Environmental Protection Agency. 1996. Chesapeake Bay toxics of concern list.
    Annapolis MD: Chesapeake Bay Program.

Van den Brink PJ, Ter Braak CJF. 1999. Principal response curves: analysis of time-dependent
    multivariate responses of biological community to stress. *Environ Toxicol Chem* 18:149–157.

Walters CW. 1986. Adaptive management of renewable resources. New York: MacMillan.

Young-Dubovsky C, Shepard GR, Smith DR, Field J. 1996. Striped Bass Research Study final report.
    Washington DC: U.S. Department of the Interior and Department of Commerce.

CHAPTER 2

Effects-driven Assessment of Multiple Stressors Using Fish Populations

Kelly R. Munkittrick and Mark E. McMaster

The past several decades have seen a number of trends that reflect a decrease in the level of anthropogenic stress on aquatic systems associated with individual developments. There has been a decrease in the acute toxicity of many industrial and municipal effluents as waste treatment has become more common and the discharge, release, or application of persistent, lipophilic compounds has decreased. As a result, some level of recovery has been seen in many North American systems that previously had been affected dramatically. However, there is clear evidence that the density of development is increasing, and, despite improved treatment of some stressors, there is a recognized need to try to deal with cumulative impacts in a more systematic manner. To this end, the Canadian government has included a requirement for addressing cumulative environmental effects under the Canadian Environmental Assessment Act. The regulation requires that development proponents identify any potential cumulative environmental effects, analyze them, determine their significance, and identify possible mitigation measures. The requirement extends cumulative effects assessment (CEA) to include both existing and probable activities over the lifetime of a project.

Although this requirement has been in place since 1995, only a few CEAs have been conducted. These assessments involve a traditional environmental impact assessment conducted on a large geographic scale (CEAWG 1997). Traditional impact assessments typically utilize stressor-based predictive methods, which have been designed to deal with single stressors, such as a single chemical within a discharge or a single effluent discharge.

CHAPTER PREVIEW

Multiple Stressors in Ecological Risk and Impact Assessment: Approaches to Risk Estimation. Susan A. Ferenc and Jeffery A. Foran, editors.
©2000 Society of Environmental Toxicology and Chemistry (SETAC). ISBN 1-880611-40-6

Stressor-based approaches work to develop a conceptual model of how stressors interact with a system to prioritize issues to be considered during risk assessment or environmental impact assessment (Figure 2-1). The assessment works toward developing a consensus on the interactions of stressors, potential responses, and potential interactions of responses. These approaches may have few requirements for collecting new data specific to the system, and, if any new data are collected, the

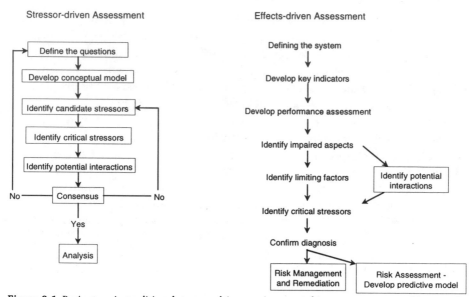

Figure 2-1 Basic steps in traditional stressor-driven environmental impact assessments (Foran and Ferenc 1999) versus those of effects-driven assessments

absence of methods for developing an effects-driven assessment limits the utility of the data for evaluating or assessing potential impacts.

Stressor-based approaches, and the risk assessments conducted from them, are also limited by their lack of sensitivity. Recent aquatic studies have identified numerous subtle responses to chemical stressors that were previously unsuspected and would not have been considered during risk assessments or environmental impact assessments. For example, during the past 5 years, previously unsuspected changes have been seen in aquatic environments exposed to effluents from pulp mills (Munkittrick et al. 1998), sewage effluents (Jobling et al. 1998; Servos, Bennie et al. 1998), agricultural discharges (Servos, Brown et al. 1998), and other industrial sources (Matthiessen et al. 1998) including textile effluents (Servos 1999). These changes include the occurrence of changes in fish maturity (Munkittrick et al. 1991), appearance of intersex fish (Jobling et al. 1998), and alterations in reproductive function (Colborn et al. 1996; Matthiessen 1998; Tattersfield et al. 1998) as a consequence of exposure to environmental endocrine disruptors. Similar subtle changes can also be associated with nonchemical stressors, which were not known or were previously unsuspected to be hazardous. Lack of sensitivity in stressor-based or risk-based approaches may result in "inappropriate, inefficient, and potentially expensive analyses, and may delay the identification of cause beyond the time frame in which appropriate remedial action could reasonably have been taken" (Fairbrother et al. 1997). In fact, the time frame of development usually demands a rapid assessment of environmental conditions and, in most cases, there is little commitment to follow-up monitoring. In the case of new, large developments occurring in previously developed areas, assessments commonly examine new stressors associated with development, but not the potential interactions with existing stressors. Furthermore, existing baseline data may be unsuitable for developing post-operational monitoring programs to cost-effectively evaluate the effectiveness of the risk assessment decisions.

The purpose of CEA is initially to determine whether there is an impact of the accumulated existing development and subsequently to determine or predict the extent of impact associated with the addition of any future developments. Although it is important to be able to examine the potential for known impacts of new stressors, it is difficult to estimate the impact of future development on a system when the existing status and sensitivity of the system are unknown. The consequences of a suite of anthropogenic and natural stressors can be buffered or synergized by preexisting environmental conditions or by site-specific factors. For example, the potential impacts of stressors can be buffered in systems where there is the potential for immigration and exacerbated in systems that are closed to movement. Additionally, there is the potential for synergistic impacts of stressors in a system that is food-limited or in which the reproduction of species is constrained by competition. Increased predation pressure, intra- or interspecific competition for food and habitat resources, and increased parasitism can synergistically contribute to and possibly confound the identification and assessment of anthropogenic stressors such as increased nutrient loading (Power 1997). The identification of environmental factors limiting performance is necessary for predicting and preventing the site-specific integration and possible consequences of new development.

Tools that were commonly used to look for single effects in the past were not designed to detect the subtle sublethal responses being detected today, nor are they suitable for CEAs. While there have been recent attempts to adapt the existing ecological risk assessment framework to deal with multiple stressors (Foran and Ferenc 1999), there may be other ways to deal with the issue of multiple stressors, including the use of effects-driven assessments.

Effects-driven assessments attempt to define the accumulated environmental state of a system. For example, fish populations integrate the site-specific factors affecting performance, and act as an indicator of the "accumulated" environmental state. In most situations, the effectiveness of predictions can be increased by measuring the accumulated environmental state before evaluating the risk of new developments altering those factors most likely to have placed current limitations on the system.

An effects-based assessment system can be used in two situations: 1) when an impact assessment is required of an existing development or 2) when an assessment needs to be undertaken to evaluate the possible consequences of an additional development. These approaches will drive the collection of better baseline data and encourage the adoption of post-development monitoring programs. The collection of better baseline data should make prediction and risk assessments more accurate. The collection of better post-operational data recognizes that decisions will have to be made before a complete understanding of the system is possible. A commitment to continued monitoring makes it possible to manage the system in an adaptive manner, rather than by prediction and extrapolation. In this chapter, we describe methods to conduct effects-driven assessments that have all of these characteristics and that can be used for both retrospective and prospective assessments.

Advantages of Effects-driven Assessment

The major advantages of effects-driven assessments are that they provide 1) a site-specific focus for ecological risk or cumulative effects assessments, 2) a basis for post-development assessment, and 3) a site-specific basis to understand assimilative capacity.

Effects-driven assessments as a site-specific focus for risk and cumulative effects assessment

An effects-driven assessment does not require an exhaustive identification or documentation of stressors prior to evaluation. While there may be a large number of stressors involved, the "accumulated environmental state" is the summation of the impacts of all stressors. If organisms are growing, reproducing, and surviving at rates comparable to reference sites, it can be assumed that existing conditions are not limiting the performance of resident organisms. If sentinel species are limited in their performance—in terms of growth, reproduction, or survival—the environmental factors limiting performance can be used to focus the risk analysis. Further study can provide detailed knowledge of the site-specific factors involved; the risk or effects assessment would focus on how those limiting factors would interrelate with the proposed development. This approach is also amenable to retrospective examinations of an existing set of stressors. The focus of the assessment would be to determine whether mitigation is needed and to determine which factors should be modified or emphasized during mitigation to ensure the most benefit. This approach ensures that each assessment is focused on a site-specific basis.

Effects-driven assessment as a basis for post-development monitoring and assessment

There are a number of approaches and management frameworks designed to address environmental impacts. Recent frameworks tend to have greater stakeholder involvement, decreasing emphasis on quantitative characterization of risk and uncertainty, and the development of iterative, decision-based analysis cycles (Power and McCarty 1998). It is becoming more common for developments to require an ongoing assessment in the receiving environment. Programs for environmental effects monitoring (EEM) have been developed in Canada (Environment Canada 1997a–1997c, 2000), Sweden (Thoresson 1993; Swedish EPA 1997), and Australia (Keough and Mapstone 1995, 1997; Mapstone 1995; Terrens et al. 1998). Effects-driven assessments can provide the reference base for assessing cumulative changes and for focusing the post-development monitoring and assessment programs. Because it is difficult to develop a complete understanding before making a decision, there is a need to continue to evaluate predictions after development. This information can be used to adapt management strategies based on this new information. Impact and risk assessment should not be seen as a substitute for research that is needed to increase our understanding (Larkin 1984). The post-developmental information is critical for groundtruthing risk estimates and improving the risk-assessment process.

Effects-driven assessment as a site-specific basis to understand assimilative capacity

As development occurs within a system, there is increasing interest in being able to estimate the capacity that a system has for tolerating or assimilating waste without adversely affecting its performance. Estimates of assimilative capacities of receiving environments need indicators of the limits of "acceptable" change within a system. Evaluations of performance prior to and after significant development on the system will provide estimates of the consequences of change within the system. In an undeveloped system, an understanding of the environmental factors limiting the performance of the system will allow a better understanding of the capability of that specific system to tolerate changes in those limiting factors and will provide a basis for site-specifically beginning to address the issue of assimilative capacity. If existing development is associated with decreases in performance, limiting factors must be monitored, and new development must not result in further loading related to the limiting factors. Quantifying the level of existing stress and its consequences for performance can provide loading goals for future development. Additional research would be required to determine whether a further increase in loading would be possible, but, on an interim basis, the existing level of stress can be used as a maximum target for future development if existing development is associated with no changes in performance.

Proposed Decision-making Process

The main output of the performance assessment is to provide information that will feed into a decision-making process. The purpose of this section is to outline a proposed decision-making process for effects-driven CEAs using fish populations. Environmental regulation historically has been based on a command-and-control philosophy, with loading targets based on extrapolations from laboratory-based data. These programs traditionally have not enjoyed public scrutiny, have had limited stakeholder involvement, and have had only limited scientific peer review (Stern and Fineberg 1996).

Many existing decision-making processes are based on weight-of-evidence approaches that attempt to establish the relationship between putative stressors and effects observed or predicted to occur in the environment. In the case where response measures give conflicting evidence, lines of evidence can be linked with predetermined weighting or placed into a decision framework that has been developed a priori. One of the major limitations seen with existing assessment programs is that they do not feed easily into a decision-making process. The absence of a predefined decision-making process has led to a variety of attempts to develop decisions based on a weight-of-evidence approach. Weight-of-evidence approaches commonly lack scientific rigor and do not always yield decisions that are clear or that are relevant to the needs of the stakeholders.

These factors have led to confusion surrounding some of the foundations of effects-based assessment, including determining what is an effect, determining when a response is an impact, and determining when an impact becomes damage. For example, after 12 years of studies conducted on the potential impacts of pulp-mill effluents at Jackfish Bay, Lake Superior (Munkittrick, McMaster et al. 1999), there is no consensus about whether impacts exist. A large pulp mill discharges effluent into a creek that drains into an isolated, unpopulated bay on Lake Superior (see McMaster et al. 1991). Studies of the system have documented delayed sexual maturity, reduced gonadal size, altered secondary sexual characteristics, and altered physiology of fish (reviewed in Munkittrick et al. 1997, 1998). However, the fish community is intact, and consistent improvements have been seen as the mill has undergone process and waste-treatment modifications. The controversy rests on whether the delayed maturity and altered gonadal sizes represent impacts. There are concerns that the reference sites may not be valid and that there may be year-to-year and site-to-site variability that can explain the changes (Kovacs et al. 1997).

Some of the problems have been related to deficiencies inherent in traditional ecological assessment. Ecological assessments can be affected dramatically by interpretation difficulties and personal biases related to reference sites, site specificity, and natural variability. For example, the following are differences in the interpretation of changes observed in Jackfish Bay effluent studies (Munkittrick and Sandström 1999):

- Biochemical differences would have to be persistent year-round and under all conditions in order to be important and must be linked to higher levels of organization to be useful.
- Organismal and suborganismal changes that do not impact the population and community are not ecologically relevant.
- Population-level changes that do not impact abundance are not important.
- Abundance changes are not important if populations do not become rare or extirpated.

These concerns would be common to any effects-based assessment program and relate to stakeholders' differing interpretations, biases, and perspectives. In general, researchers have been reluctant to conclude that there has been an impact because of the perception that it will trigger the need for some further response, either in terms of further studies or in terms of some process change (Munkittrick and Sandström 1999). Obviously, individual organisms can survive numerous bio-chemical impacts, and populations can survive numerous organismal-level impacts. One of the major factors limiting progress is the misconception that all impacts are adverse and therefore are unacceptable. While these issues have a long history, efforts to conduct impact assessments have not made progress in dealing with them. Rather, there is the tendency to accept that we have reached the site-specific goal once obvious signs of impacts and short-term toxicity are reduced. The issue for CEAs is whether an existing system can assimilate additional develop-ment without affecting the carrying capacity or thresholds for the receiver.

The decision-making process may not always be a scientific process, but it can use scientifically based decision rules. It is the responsibility of the scientific process to quantify and provide information objectively about the types of changes, the distribution of changes, the frequency and duration of changes, and the relevance of changes to other levels of organization so that decisions can be made. In Sweden, decisions about environmental quality objectives may be based on ethical concerns and public perceptions and not strictly on ecological relevance (Swedish EPA 1997), and decisions commonly take economic, sociological, and technological factors into consideration, as well as the scientific information.

As risk management frameworks move toward increasing stakeholder involvement (Power and McCarty 1998), the questions facing the assessment process need to change. The question of ecological relevance may not always be directly pertinent to the question of defining unacceptable changes. In risk assessment, stakeholders have a strong role in helping to focus the problem formulation; in effects-driven assessments, the role of stakeholders is to help evaluate the question of acceptability. In some cases, changes that are not ecologically relevant, such as tainting or undesirable external lesions, may be deemed unacceptable by stakeholder negotiation. In other cases, changes in sexual maturity or fecundity, which are ecologically relevant, may be deemed acceptable when examined within the context of sociological and economic factors that play a role in management decisions. These issues are crucial for defining the extent of ecological "dysfunction" or for evaluating how "adverse" the impacts are when there are demonstrable environmental impacts occurring as a result of multiple stressors.

For effects-based CEAs to proceed, the questions are not related to the ecological relevance of the existing impacts and the relationship of these changes to natural variability. Rather, the following questions need to be addressed for effects-based assessment:

- Do the measurements indicate a real change?
- Is the current environmental situation sustainable?
- Is the current situation acceptable?
- Would additional development or climatic changes affect the response?

The first question requires a clear confirmation process. The second question is spatially and temporally limited. Additional ongoing monitoring would be required to ensure that environmental conditions that affect the response do not change the sustainability (e.g., drought, global warming, or large-scale eutrophication). A subcomponent of this issue relates to whether there is evidence that the changes are getting better or worse. Given that there are real changes present, the third question requires the input of stakeholders and their various perspectives and interests. The fourth question requires a determination of whether additional development should take place in light of determinations of the impact of additional development. For this determination, it is more important and more relevant to interpret the ecological data in terms of the impacts on self-sustaining populations and to include the data in subsequent decisions related to additional development or changing environmental conditions. Ultimately, any change in the load of environmental stressors would have to be monitored and modeled closely to ensure that sustainability was not affected.

The role of science must be limited to defining the magnitude and extent of changes. Once changes have been documented, the first important decision is to define whether the changes will result in loss of the populations, i.e., Is the situation sustainable?[1] (Figure 2-2). The priority has to be to ensure that populations

---

[1] The following definition of sustainable development is offered by the World Commission on Environment and Development (also known as the Brundtland Commission): "Development that meets the needs of the present without compromising the ability of future generations to meet their own needs." (Environment Canada. 1995 Report of Canada to the United Nations Commission on Sustainable Development).

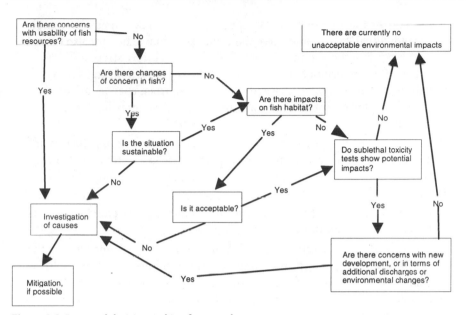

Figure 2-2 Proposed decision-making framework

and communities are preserved within a discharge or development area. Developing the answer to the question of sustainability will involve a number of factors other than the impact assessment and will include knowledge of the operational history and some judgment about the short-term future implications of discharges. A new development that is associated with rapid responses at the population or community level may need mitigation to ensure persistence of the system. Obviously, if fish are food-limited and the discharge has been present for a considerable period of time, the situation has been sustained and is relatively stable. The relevant question is whether it will continue to be stable and sustainable under new circumstances.

If a situation is sustainable, and the changes that are present are acceptable, the remaining relevant decision relates to the possibility that future development of environmental changes may alter the situation. The focus of studies has to change from the unnecessary emphasis on defining "adverse" changes to dealing with the questions of sustainability, acceptability, and the consequences of additional future changes or developments on the system. There are several key points for determining impact, evaluating sustainability, and predicting the consequences of cumulative changes (Munkittrick and Sandström 1999):

1) Fish represent the highest trophic level for most aquatic systems. The issues of acceptability and potential future cumulative effects require information on more than the traditional assessment indices based on community

diversity or the abundance of key species. There can be impacts detectable at the individual level that are acceptable and sustainable but are also key to understanding the potential impacts of additional future stressors on a system. It is important to protect the growth, reproduction, and survival of fish, as well as the abundance and health of fish; when changes are present, the geographic extent and the magnitude of the changes will affect decision-making.

2) Evaluations have to include ecologically important or relevant species of fish and not just commercially important species. The key factors are that the fish must be abundant and exposed and must provide interpretable data.

3) Indicators cannot be selected generically. The best indicators for monitoring purposes will vary between sites and will be directly related site-specifically to the stressors and the mechanism of impact.

4) Determination of "acceptability" of changes is not the responsibility of the scientific process, and the perception of acceptability or unacceptability may change with a number of nonscientific factors, including economic status, sociological factors, technological capabilities, and the level of environmental awareness (Swedish EPA 1997).

5) Assessments will be temporally and spatially limited. The absence of impact in one system does not guarantee absence of response in another; study design, habitat characteristics, species habitat preferences, and fish mobility may play important, unidentified roles in contributing to the degree of impact evident at some sites.

The failure of existing studies to focus on delineating impacts and evaluating sustainability on a site-specific basis means that there is a tendency to see impact assessment as a black or white issue. Consequently, there is a tendency to dismiss results as not being relevant when such a decision may have consequences. Ignoring evidence of sublethal changes that are within the assimilative capacity of resident biota also ignores the potential for interaction of potential new stressors with existing stressors. There is a need to understand the extent and magnitude of all existing responses, regardless of their magnitude, so that potential future stressors can be adequately managed.

Effects-driven Assessment of Cumulative Effects Using Fish Populations

We have been developing an iterative, cyclical framework for an assessment of cumulative aquatic effects since the early 1990s (Munkittrick and Dixon 1989a, 1989b; Munkittrick 1992; Gibbons and Munkittrick 1994; Hodson et al. 1996; Munkittrick et al. 2000). This effects-driven assessment approach involves measuring the "accumulated environmental state" of the system and trying to identify

1) whether performance is below the level expected at comparable sites and 2) what factors are preventing the performance from being "normal." The analysis depends on fish populations and communities integrating the existing suite of environmental conditions and stressors. Prediction can be possible only after a basic understanding of the system exists, and extrapolation to other watersheds will require a basic understanding of the processes that structure those systems. The assessment should provide sufficient evidence for evaluating the performance of the system and must provide a description of the responses in the system to a decision-making process that will determine the acceptability of the changes. The responses already present in the system can focus the risk-assessment process. The key steps in conducting an effects-driven assessment are to define the system, select key indicators, develop the performance assessment, identify the impaired aspects, and then try to predict how new developments will alter the situation (Figure 2-1).

Defining the system

Because the assessment involves determining the "accumulated" environmental status, it is essential to understand the basics of the ecology and performance of the system. In the Canadian Environmental Effects Monitoring Program (Environment Canada 1997a–c, 2000), this understanding is equivalent to a predesign or site-characterization phase. The purpose of the system definition is to provide sufficient background information so that the study design can be site-specifically tailored. Basic requirements include an understanding of hydrogeology; local climate influences; industrial development, both existing and proposed; water chemistry; physical structure; and resident biota (Table 2-1). The basic structure of the system needs to be understood to develop the key indicators to be used in monitoring and assessment.

Developing key indicators or measurement endpoints

There are three main uses for measurements: 1) to define ecological impacts; 2) to measure the progress of restoration or reconstruction; or 3) to make predictions. Stressor-based approaches commonly use multi-stakeholder workshops to develop a list of the valued ecosystem components early in the process of selecting assessment endpoints. These assessment endpoints are usually statements about the aspects of the ecological system that are valued for protection but that are rarely directly measurable. An effects-driven assessment needs to evaluate the indicators that are most suitable to understanding the performance of the system. Selection of the most appropriate species and monitoring level should focus on the ecological characteristics of the system and the site-specific nature of the assessment requirements. There are several steps involved in selecting the monitoring endpoints for the system, including the selection of monitoring level and the selection of the measurements to be used as indicators.

Table 2-1 Baseline information requirements for defining the system to be studied

Component	Information requirements	Rationale
Bedrock geology	Geologic history Mineralization in the headwaters Surficial geology	Affects baseline water chemistry
Hydrogeology	Channel form Turbidity Soils Substrate Discharge Gradient	Major influence on fish habitat
Climate	Temperature Precipitation Rare event history	Seasonal and annual patterns and variability, extremes and rare events can affect variability, interpretation and extrapolation
Industry	Industrial footprints	Define potential concerns
Development	Recent process changes Water intakes and discharges Dilution zones Historical contamination and atmospheric deposition Potential future development	
Water chemistry	Broad characterization of general characteristics should be reflective of the geology, with developments superimposed on the background Nutrient chemistry	Relevant to understanding potential impacts Understanding of the energy flow and productivity are important
Physical structure	Tributaries Dams, barriers Bathymetry Zones of plant growth	Impact on mobility, energy sources and energy flow
Biota	Fish species present Rare, threatened and endangered species Fisheries exploitation - sports, subsistence or commercial Other predesign biota knowledge (benthic community data) Historical data available for the system	Helps with indicator selection

Selecting a monitoring level

The selection of monitoring level will be largely philosophical, based on the purpose of the assessment to be undertaken and the frequency, extent, and magnitude of monitoring. The selection encompasses two facets: the level of organization within the food web (algal, bacterial, benthic invertebrate, fish, or other) and the level of biological organization to be surveyed for endpoints (biochemical, cellular, organ, individual, population, or community). All organisms integrate the stressors and all levels of organization may have measurable changes, but the monitoring level selected must have relevance to the decision-making process.

While some monitoring programs prefer a balanced, weight-of-evidence approach where all aspects are considered, there are efficiencies to be gained by focusing the assessment through a tiered approach. Within Canada, there are requirements under the Fisheries Act that developments must not affect fish, fish habitat, or man's use of fish. While there have been a variety of taxonomic levels that are available for assessment, decisions relating to acceptability and sustainability focus the assessments towards benthic invertebrates and fisheries resources. There has been considerable effort invested towards the development of assessment methods using benthic invertebrates, and community-based indices are widely available (Environment Canada 1995a; Taylor and Bailey 1997). Within the context of the fisheries-based CEA framework presented here, benthic data play a key supporting role in the determination of acceptability and thresholds of effects.

Changes at lower levels of the ecosystem, such as in bacteria or algae, may occur without consequence to higher levels of organization. In terms of retrospective assessments, if existing changes were relevant to higher levels of organization, they would be translated to higher levels of organization. It is difficult enough to convince stakeholders about the importance of changes in maturity or growth rates of fish, but it is much more difficult to establish the relevance or importance of a change in algal or bacterial populations that are unrelated to changes at higher levels of organization. Changes in lower levels of organization that are large enough to have relevance for fish or benthos will be reflected at those levels. Changes below this level are useful for understanding thresholds, assimilative capacity, and for predicting potential future impacts. Thresholds and assimilative capacity should be important only in systems that are sustainable and that have acceptable changes present.

In terms of prospective assessments, indirect, food-related effects are the aspects that have been most often ignored in environmental impact assessments. However, in terms of post-operational monitoring, fish and benthos-related monitoring programs can be designed that will be responsive enough and cost-effective enough to detect damage early enough to prevent loss of sustainability. The relevance of information needs to the decision-making process can be illustrated best with a hypothetical example.

If a development were to proceed within an undeveloped watershed, baseline studies would be required to understand both the benthic invertebrate community and the fisheries resources. The focus of these studies would be to determine factors limiting the performance of the fish. It should be obvious prior to development that there will be some impact zone associated with development and effluent discharge, although the magnitude and geographic extent would be speculative. The traditional risk-assessment process would attempt to minimize this impact zone. Traditional post-operational monitoring would focus on determining changes within the system in response to discharges.

If the performance of key species within the fish community is unaffected after development, it can be assumed that the development is sustainable, at least within a relatively short time frame. An understanding of the size and extent of changes in benthic communities would provide key information about the amount of change in benthic communities that can be tolerated without a resulting change in fish performance in that system. Such information would be critical for understanding how close the existing situation may be to a threshold for change, what post-operational monitoring requirements should be increased, and what the assimilative capacity of the system may be for tolerating changes associated with future developments.

The second facet involves determining the level of biological organization to survey; this selection also should be geared toward the decision-making process. Again, some key decisions should be made prior to initiating the study about what level of impact may be considered unacceptable within the system. The purpose of the effects-driven assessment is only to determine the magnitude and extent of impacts and what factors are limiting performance. Changes in performance can be evident at a variety of levels of organization, including the level of the individual, population, or community. Furthermore, within a level, changes can have a variety of consequences. While it is widely recognized that individuals can respond to stress at several levels of organization, populations and communities usually are interpreted to have a simple stress response. It is important to understand that populations can show responses other than in terms of total abundance. Table 2-2 summarizes stress responses at different levels of organization within different levels of organization.

Determining the level for monitoring will depend on which components provide the information required to make a decision. Decisions can involve several scenarios, including determining impact assessment, evaluating the possible consequences of future development, or determining sustainability. Physical, chemical, and biological stressors can affect performance only through changes in food and habitat availability, through direct impacts on physiological processes, or through indirect impacts mediated through physiological changes. There are clear discontinuities in which our current understanding and tools are insufficient to allow extrapolation and prediction, e.g., how do wild animal responses correlate

Table 2-2 Comparison of stress responses at different levels of organization

Monitoring level	Primary	Secondary	Tertiary	Specificity	Impact at ecosystem level
Time lag	Short	Medium	Long		
Individual	Neuroendocrine responses (i.e., ACTH, sex steroids)	Physiological responses (glucose, heart rate, etc.)	Whole organism changes (growth, reproduction, disease resistance)	High	Low
Population	Integrators of individuals (growth rates, maturity rates)	Dynamics (recruitment, survival, etc.)	Production (abundance of individual populations)	Medium	Medium
Community	Production	Dynamics/Diversity	Ecosystem function	Low	High

with laboratory toxicity tests or how do physiological responses and individual performance relate to community structure (Figure 2-3; modified from Munkittrick and McCarty 1995)? There are research activities underway to try to link individual and population outputs to the community level (Wrona and Cash 1996), but there needs to be a compromise between fast and slow indicators and between specific and nonspecific indicators.

At higher levels of organization, there is a time delay before detection of impacts and a decrease in the ability to trace causality (Table 2-2). If the focus of the assessment is to determine the sustainability of the system and the acceptability of the changes, then a community-based assessment would have a time delay that could be inadequate for predicting changes in time to remediate the system. The disappearance of species would be neither sustainable nor acceptable in most assessments, and monitoring the system at this level lacks the level of predictability offered by other levels. Community-level monitoring also can be intensive and requires historical information. In a large country like Canada, where much of the country is sparsely populated and poorly studied, background information of this detail usually is unavailable.

At the other end of biological organization, biochemical assessments are too sensitive, with many changes occurring without whole organism consequences. While this level of monitoring may be suitable for defining responses and exposure, the inability to extrapolate changes to whole-organism and population-level consequences limits its usefulness for determining the significance of changes and the consequences for determining acceptability. The main disadvantage of the biochemical indicators is that there is a need to know how big a change is important and what it is important for (Munkittrick and Van Der Kraak 1999).

Clearly, there are complicated relationships between closely related levels, and factors other than the stressors of interest play a key role in producing the variability seen in responses. There has to be a decision about the minimal level of environmental damage that can be tolerated to allow sustainability of industry,

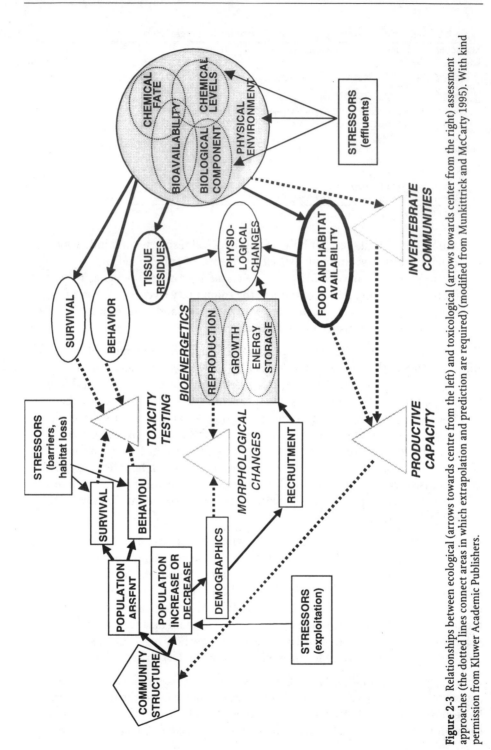

Figure 2-3 Relationships between ecological (arrows towards centre from the left) and toxicological (arrows towards center from the right) assessment approaches (the dotted lines connect areas in which extrapolation and prediction are required) (modified from Munkittrick and McCarty 1995). With kind permission from Kluwer Academic Publishers.

communities, and the environment. Our decision has been to focus on individual integrators of responses, such as growth, reproduction, and age distribution. There are certainly other approaches under development, including those based on fish-community structure (Ohio EPA 1987; Minns et al. 1994) and habitat productive capacity (Minns 1997). The approach outlined here involves the determination of impacts in fish populations and ways in which to use them in order to develop an assessment of the cumulative effects within the system.

Selecting measurements

If fish are to be monitored at the individual level, some decisions have to be made about which measurements should be selected to determine whether the performance of fish is limited and, if so, how? The objective of the approach is to try to understand what aspects of the performance are limited and to try to define what factors are associated with that limitation.

A series of iterative snapshots provides a useful temporal component for interpretation and will be more cost-effective than a large single collection if the sampling and analyses are tiered. It makes little sense to set out to conduct an exhaustive study of the reproductive implications of a proposed development if the particular system under study is food-limited or if reproduction is unaffected as a result of site-specific habitat qualities that offer some level of protection for the species at risk. Biological measurements can be affected by a wide variety of factors, and it is important that conclusions be cautious. It should be no easier to conclude that no effect exists than to conclude that there are responses present. Either the presence or absence of responses should be confirmed in an independent sample before proceeding to the next step. For the Canadian Environmental Effects Monitoring Program, the extent and magnitude of responses are important components of follow-up studies.

Let us return to the previous example of developing baseline studies in undeveloped regions. The purpose of the baseline studies would be to determine the performance of key fish species within the community. It is assumed that fish populations that are growing, reproducing, and surviving within ranges comparable to those seen at reference sites would be "normal" (Munkittrick and Dixon 1989a, 1989b). Important performance aspects to define during baseline studies would be growth rates, reproductive investments, and the age distribution of fish. The focus of the studies should be to detect large changes from a reference condition (i.e., > 20%), since there will always be debate about the relevance of smaller changes, especially if the changes are within the range of normal variability for the species.

If changes from baseline conditions are seen, it would be important to develop an understanding of why these populations did not fulfill their performance potential. Post-development monitoring would focus on the same performance parameters to monitor changes. Risk estimates and predictive modeling should focus on how development interacts with the limiting factors, as well as with other stressors.

In an ideal system, an understanding could be developed with respect to the size and age distribution of fish when they reach sexual maturity. Any change in food or habitat availability or in the efficiency of utilizing energy would result in a change in the size and/or age of fish reaching maturity. Post-developmental monitoring could pick up changes very rapidly, allowing time for mitigation to be initiated prior to the changes becoming irreversible or being translated to higher levels of organization.

Over the last decade, we have been developing an effects-based approach to identifying the responses of fish populations to stress (Munkittrick and Dixon 1989a, 1989b; Munkittrick 1992; Gibbons and Munkittrick 1994; Munkittrick et al. 2000). While the approach will be explained in more detail in the sections under interpretation, the analysis uses indicators of energy utilization, energy storage, and age distributions. In order to understand the factors limiting the performance of the fish population, information is collected about whether the fish have enough food, whether they are utilizing it properly, and whether the population has an altered age structure. Later sections will discuss which species to monitor, how to collect them and how many individuals have to be examined for this assessment.

Developing performance assessment

The performance assessment involves developing a database on indicators of energy utilization, energy storage, and age distributions, collected on relevant fish species within the study area. Aspects to be considered include selection of the most appropriate species, sampling time, capture techniques, reference sites, sample size, and minimum data requirements. While these issues will not be discussed in detail here, an overview will be presented with reference to sources of further information. The Environmental Effects Monitoring Program developed in Canada offers technical guidance documents (Environment Canada 1997b, 2000) and interpretation documents (Environment Canada 1995a, 1995b) that contain information on a program that has a similar design. Guidance is also available in relation to EEM programs developed in Sweden (Thoresson 1993; Swedish EPA 1997) and Australia (Keough and Mapstone 1995, 1997; Mapstone 1995; Terrens et al. 1998). Guidance on the statistical analysis can be found in Chapter 3.

Interpretation will always be affected by sample sizes, data quality, and sampling problems. These will not be dealt with here other than to state that interpretation should be cautious and that any conclusions must be verified. It is essential that any changes detected by monitoring programs be confirmed prior to initiation of larger or more detailed follow-up studies (Hodson et al. 1996). Major problems encountered during application of the sampling protocols by inexperienced personnel relate to poor capture success, poor reference-site selection, and poor success at separating mature and immature fish during analysis (Environment Canada 1997a). The guidance provided here does not substitute for common sense and experience.

Selecting sentinel species

Studies designed to examine the potential impacts of the construction of a pulp mill on the Lesser Slave River, Alberta, used three benthic species during baseline and post-operational monitoring (Munkittrick et al. 1990; EVS Consultants 1992). The current requirements for EEM are that two species be examined. While information on a single species can be valuable, the quality of the information used for assessment increases with the number of species that are examined.

Selection of the sentinel species will have to balance stakeholder views, political agendas, and scientific needs. There also may be conflicts between the confounding influences of sport fishing, commercial fishing, and subsistence fishing, as well as possible conflicts with public and aboriginal concerns versus science issues. The purpose of the effects-driven assessment is to define the factors limiting the performance of the system, and it is important that the species chosen as sentinels be suitable. The priority factors for species selection should be exposure, abundance, and relevance to the study area and the study objectives. Characteristics and species suitability may be altered by whether the dominant stressors are point-source or diffuse (i.e., agricultural). In many cases, the issues of the potential impacts of chemical stressors on human health are confused with the potential impact on aquatic environmental health (Table 2-3).

Basic general and site-specific information is needed on life-history traits, feeding behavior, etc. In most cases, exhaustive databases are not required to consider these issues, but a number of factors do need to be considered using common sense and professional judgment. It is important to consider the residency patterns of fish species in attempting to evaluate the exposure to stressors, especially for point-source discharges. Choosing a relatively abundant species will be important for ensuring that there are sufficient individuals present to allow monitoring. It also is important to ensure that the selected species are not rare and have life-history characteristics that are easy to measure. Fish that are difficult to age will make interpretation difficult. The role of the species within the food web should also be examined. Some species depend almost entirely on terrestrial drift for their food and therefore would be of little relevance to a study examining most aquatic impacts.

Many of the other characteristics to consider are more flexible and will be site- and issue-specific. These factors include fish energetic requirements, longevity, food preference, and spawning time. The energetic requirements of a fish will be related to their growth rate, maturity, and reproductive rates. Species that have high energetic demands generally show changes more rapidly. Although longevity will

Table 2-3 Sentinel species characteristics for optimizing effects-driven assessment of aquatic environmental health using fish populations

Characteristics	Fisheries health		Human health	Comments
	Point source	Nonpoint source		
Residency (in absence of barriers)	Local	Wide ranging	Issue-specific	For non-point source impacts, need a species that will integrate the signals from the area
Abundance	High	High	Issue-specific	For human health - there may be local concerns associated with food preferences and consumption that outweigh all other factors
Longevity	Short–Medium	Short–Medium	Long	For fisheries health issues – long-lived species will decrease the likelihood of detecting changes. For human health, long-lived species increase the body burdens and possible consequences of exposure
Food preference	Benthic	Issue-specific	Piscivorous	For human health - want a species that is at the top of the food chain. For other issues, this would be associated with (usually) increased mobility
Fecundity and growth rate	High	High	Low	High energetic requirements are preferred, so that changes in food availability or quality will be detected quickest. For human health, species with slow growth and reduced reproduction would be preferred since they will retain higher body burdens
Age to maturation	Short	Short	Long	For impacts on fisheries health, species that need energy for initiation of spawning, while retaining needs for fast growth will show impacts sooner; for human health, delayed maturity reduces the clearance of contaminants in females associated with spawning
Spawning time	Site-specific	Site-specific	Site-specific	The relationship between exposure and spawning time will vary with the issue. In prairie systems, spring spawning fish develop eggs over-winter, during maximum exposure from point-sources. In other systems, maximum exposure occurs during the late summer or fall
Food-chain involvement	Yes	Yes	Yes	Always want a species with an aquatic-based diet, and not one depending predominantly on terrestrial-based foods

influence the lag time for detecting responses, in the case of lipophilic contaminants and food-chain biomagnification, a species with a prolonged life span would be preferred to maximize bioaccumulation. Low reproductive rates also would increase the body burdens of lipophilic compounds. Similarly, predatory fish would be preferred for biomagnification concerns, but they would be a disadvantage for point-source discharges because of their higher mobility.

Spawning time is also a site-specific issue. In the case of prairie river systems in Canada, maximum exposure to most point-source discharges can occur during overwinter periods as a result of low flow and ice cover. A species that spawns in the fall in the near-field area would have maximum exposure to their eggs and early life stages during the period of maximum effluent concentrations. However, a spring-spawning species would have maximum exposure during ovarian develop-ment at this same period. The relative importance of habitat preferences, residency, and spawning should be evaluated to ensure that the sentinel species exhibit the best characteristics for the specific issue under investigation. The relative benefits and disadvantages of the species should be weighed when selecting the monitoring species (Table 2-4). The list may be reduced by the availability of species that are abundant and common in all sampling areas (Table 2-5).

One of the concerns expressed during studies on large river systems in the Cana-dian prairies was that larger fish showed the potential to be extremely mobile (RLL 1993; Swanson 1994; Swanson et al. 1994; Environment Canada 1995b). There has been considerable success in Canada using smaller species with small home ranges as monitor species for point-source discharges (Gibbons, Munkittrick, Taylor 1998; Gibbons, Munkittrick, McMaster et al. 1998; Frank et al. 1999). Many of these species have reduced mobility relative to larger species (Hill and Grossman 1987; Minns 1995). For stressors that are more diverse, such as non-point impacts or stressors that affect habitat on a large scale, a species with broader mobility may be more advantageous. The key is to understand the specifics of the study site, look at the available species, and decide on a scientific basis what makes the most sense to examine. A lack of background knowledge is not sufficient reason to ignore the species that makes the most sense to monitor.

In some cases, the habitat may not be suitable for a large number of species or for all life stages of some species. This is especially true for some coastal rivers, estuarine areas, and marine sites. If the study area is utilized primarily as a rearing area, and adults do not frequent the area or are present only as transients or for spawning, the examination should emphasize the life stages that are relevant for the receiving area. There are also some concerns about monitoring marine discharge areas, where issues related to the monitoring of fish populations are still poorly defined (Environment Canada 1997a). In Canada, the development of EEM require-ments for pulp mills (Environment Canada 1997c) met with poor success in marine areas (Environment Canada 1997a). The requirements for EEM at metal-mining sites considered the marine issues but recognized the problems associated with developing an environmental assessment program (Environment Canada 2000). Several alternatives have been considered for use in marine systems, but the issue of how to adapt an effects-driven assessment for marine ecosystems requires further research (Courtenay et al. 1998).

Table 2-4 Life-history characteristics for species reported in the Lesser Slave River, Alberta[1]

Species	Food	Spawning time	Fecundity	Growth rate[2]	Longevity	Age to maturation	Relative abundance	Ranking[3]
Rating guide	In this system, a benthic feeder was preferred (+1)	Due to sampling difficulties at this site, a spring spawner was preferred (+1)	A high reproductive output was preferred	A fast growth rate during the time of maturation was preferred	An average life span was preferred (long [>20] or short [10] was considered a negative)	A relatively early age to maturation (< 6y) was preferred (+1)	Rare or seasonal migrants were negative	+7
White sucker	Benthos	Spring	>20,000	50%	<15y	4–8y	High	+7
Longnose sucker	Benthos	Spring	>20,000	100%	<15y	5–7y	High	+7
Northern pike	Fish	Spring	>30,000	100%	>20y	4–6y	High	+5
Walleye	Fish	Spring	>50,000	65%	<20y	>4y	Low	+3
Mountain whitefish	Benthos	Fall	<10,000	55%	<10y	3y	High	+1
Lake whitefish	Benthos/plankton	Fall	<10,000	55%	>20y	7y	High	+1
Perch	Benthos/fish	Late spring/summer	>30,000	85%	<10y	3 to 4y	High	+1
Burbot	Fish	Mid-winter	>50,000	55%	>10y	3 to 4y	Low	+1
Cisco	Benthos	Fall	>20,000	40%	<10y	2–4y	Low	–1
Arctic grayling	Terrestrial insects	Spring	<7,000	40%	<9y	4y	Low	–3
Goldeye	Fish/Insects	Late spring/summer	>20,000	25%	<15y	6–10y	Low	–3

[1]The study design was for baseline studies (preoperational) for a potential prairie river-based pulp-mill discharge. Rankings were based on assigning a value of +1 for a preferred characteristic and –1 for a characteristic that reduced the suitability of the species. [2]Relative changes in growth rate were calculated as the relative change in fish size from ages 3 to 7 (the time period during sexual maturity). [3]The rating will vary with the design parameters for each river system and each study design. These ratings are meant only as an example of how to view the characteristics; maximum rating in this example is +7. Source: Munkittrick et al. 1990

Table 2-5 Large fish species reported from four tributaries of the Moose River[1]

Common name	Scientific name	Missinaibi	Mattagami	Groundhog	Kapuskasing
Lake sturgeon	Acipenser fulvescens	P[2]	P	A	P
Northern pike	Esox lucius	A	A	A	A
Walleye	Stizostedion vitreum	A	A	A	A
White sucker	Catostomus commersoni	A	A	A	A
Longnose sucker	Catostomus catostomus	P	P	P	P
Yellow perch	Perca flavescens	P	P	P	P
Lake whitefish	Coregonus clupeaformis	R	R	R	R
Goldeye	Hiodon alosoides		R		
Burbot	Lota lota		R	R	R
Mooneye	Hiodon tergisus	R			
Redhorse suckers	Moxostoma sp.	R			
Fall fish	Semotilus corporalis	P	R		
Smallmouth bass	Micropterus dolomieui	P			
Pumkinseed	Lepomis gibbosus		R		

[1] Only species thought to be present in the rivers proper are included.
[2] Species were rated as A - abundant, P -present in our surveys, R- reported but appear to be rare.
Reprinted with permission from Munkittrick et al. 2000. ©2000 CRC Press, Boca Raton, FL.

Schedule of sampling

The selection of sample timing will depend on site-specific habitats, the species selected, and the nature of the questions being asked. Most species show seasonal differences in habitat preferences and mobility. In extreme cases, a species may move seasonally from a feeding area, to a spawning area, to an overwintering area, which can be very different habitats (McKinley et al. 1998). In situations where there are no natural barriers to prevent movement in and out of the exposure areas, a basic understanding of the species' habitat preferences is needed to ensure that residency in the area of interest is maximized. The understanding required may be limited to ensuring that fish are sampled during the period of maximum residency. If there are doubts as to the duration of residency, alternative species should be investigated as to their suitability. If the most abundant and relevant species do not fully utilize the habitat, then within the concept of sustainability, impacts on that habitat could be tolerated by the species without affecting their performance.

The main concern with scheduling of sampling time relates to the ability to define residency within the study area. Although spawning usually results in a congregation of large numbers of individuals and facilitates sampling, spawning migrations also result in the mixing of groups of fish from different areas. In situations where barriers restrict fish movement into or out of the study area, sampling at spawning time allows optimization of sampling effort. Sampling must be conducted prior to the initiation of spawning to allow information on gonad size and fecundity to be utilized.

Capture techniques

Capture techniques must be appropriate for the species of interest. In many cases, sampling will have to be designed to avoid the unintentional killing of non target species, especially when sampling must be conducted in an area where there are limited numbers of sport fish, migratory species, or rare, threatened, or endangered species.

A multidisciplinary working group developed a number of research recommendations while reviewing data from the first cycle of the Canadian Environmental Effects Monitoring Program for pulp mills (Environment Canada 1997a). They divided the knowledge gaps into those related to capture, exposure, and interpretation. In terms of fish capture, the main concerns were related to defining mobility and migratory species (Environment Canada 1997a). The main problem encountered by consultants collecting fish were associated with not capturing sufficient numbers of fish, and, in many cases, variances for fish characteristics were high because of the capture techniques, reducing the power of comparisons. Less than 10% of the 118 studies developed were successful in capturing the targeted 20 adult male and 20 adult female fish of 2 sentinel species at a reference site and an exposed site. Reduced capture success was associated in some cases with the lack of familiarity with the sampling sites, an absence of predesign sampling, poor selection of the timing of sampling, and improper sampling gear for collections.

While there is no strict guidance to provide on capture techniques, priority must be given to reducing measurement variability in order to increase the power of comparisons (Environment Canada 1997a). In many cases, daylight electroshocking has been used in large rivers (Environment Canada 1997a), sometimes resulting in inflated variability; electroshocking is effective only in near-shore shallow water areas, which are not highly utilized by many fish species during daylight hours. There are conflicting philosophies of trying to capture all variability by selecting a wide variety of fish sizes, and trying to restrict the variability to increase the power of sampling.

Capture success commonly increases as a sampling crew becomes more familiar with the study area. An iterative sampling program has several advantages, including that fewer numbers of individuals have to be captured at each collection period and capture success will increase as familiarity with the study site increases. Guidance on sampling gear is available from the technical guidance documents prepared for the EEM programs in Canada (Environment Canada 1997c, 2000) and Sweden (Thorreson 1993; Swedish EPA 1997). The Swedish environmental effects program is highly standardized, including the size ranges of fish to be sampled and the timing of the sampling. The variability in North American receiving environments prohibits the development of this level of standardization.

Selecting reference sites

Poorly selected reference sites are the most common criticism of ecological studies and are often used as a scapegoat for avoiding interpretation of differences (Munkittrick, Sandström et al. 1999). Differences between study sites are often dismissed as being related to habitat, food availability, or genetic differences without any supporting evidence, and reference sites are often dismissed as irrelevant without sufficient justification. It is common to declare a specific point source as the causative factor when multiple factors are present. The existence of differences between populations should drive subsequent studies to isolate the responsible factors. In some cases, the conclusion will be that the reference site used was not valid for the comparison. In this case, follow-up studies should add new reference sites and attempt to determine the factors that reduced the effectiveness of the original reference sites. In many cases, problems related to reference-site selection can be related to a lack of a priori appreciation of which statistical analyses need to be performed. An improved understanding of the study design clarifies issues related to replication and sample size.

Local reference sites are essential for interpreting differences, and interpretation can be strengthened by the use of gradient designs and the use of multiple reference sites. While there is agreement that there are no perfect reference sites, factors associated with site selection have to include similarity of sites, confounding factors that may affect interpretation, and the biology of the monitoring species (Environment Canada 1997a). Because it can be very difficult to pick a good reference site, it is becoming more common to use multiple reference sites to get an indication of the variability between reference sites. There are several approaches to using reference sites (Foran and Ferenc 1999):

- utilizing baseline historical data;
- development of information on local reference sites;
- a reference population approach, where larger numbers of sites are sampled using either predefined reference criteria using historical data or undefined reference criteria, where biological reference criteria are defined from the maximum values of the indicators at the least stressed sites; and
- gradient designs.

The scientific process also has to play a role in educating stakeholders about the importance and the relevance of the changes. Differences that are outside of the range of values seen at a number of reference sites are accepted to have more ecological relevance. The Moose River studies have used more than 10 reference sites for comparisons, but interpretation is not different than using a simple upstream and downstream gradient design (Munkittrick et al. 2000; Chapter 3, this volume). There needs to be caution before interpreting any change as real or important, but there also has to be acceptance that evidence of any depression in the performance of fish must be fully assessed and that the reasons for differences between sites must be understood.

Sample size requirements

The statistical power of a comparison is a function of the sample size and the variability and difference observed between sites. To determine the sample size required for detecting a specific difference, some knowledge is required about the variability of the sample and the statistical power that is acceptable for the decision-making process. It is essential for studies to examine the implications and consequences of effect sizes early in development of the program (Keough and Mapstone 1995, 1997; Mapstone 1995; Terrens et al. 1998).

It is also essential that some discussion occur about the magnitude of difference between sites that is required for decision-making; this difference is called the "effect size." Determination of effect size and sample size requirements has been difficult. A detailed discussion on effect sizes as they relate to parameters examined in this approach can be found in Environment Canada (1997a), but the options for defining effect sizes and determining sample sizes include

- using a predetermined difference, based on previous experience, that constitutes a change of sufficient magnitude that will be a concern (Environment Canada 1997a);
- selecting an arbitrary difference that is assumed to be of sufficient size to be ecologically significant (Kilgour et al. 1998); and
- attempting to define statistically significant differences of smaller magnitude.

It is important to establish up front what will constitute a significant impact and what will be done if a significant impact is found. It is more common for comparisons to be conducted, and the power level to be calculated, a posteriori so that a level of confidence in the detection of the difference between sites can be stated. It is more valuable to establish the power levels and decision criteria a priori. Without a basic understanding of how a decision will be made, it is virtually impossible to design the studies properly. The Australian EEM program has attempted to move the discussion of effect size and power levels to the beginning of the program, early in the design process (Mapstone 1995; Keough and Mapstone

1997). If power levels arc insufficient to meet the needs of the study, either the study has to be redesigned, or the decision-making criteria has to be adjusted.

Because of the complexity and site-specificity of ecological assessments, hypotheses and sample collections must be tiered and steps should be sequential (Hodson et al. 1996). The results of initial studies should be used to drive subsequent studies. Tiered designs are much more cost-effective, but they have not been employed successfully for a variety of reasons (Munkittrick and Sandström 1999).

1) The interest in finding the answer quickly leads to a search for shortcuts and the tendency to jump on preliminary results and make broad conclusions or to use an untested follow-up hypothesis as a scientific fact.

2) Scientific inertia leads to the tendency to accept traditional explanations for initial results and to ignore new facts and theories without sufficient testing.

3) The traditional focus on chemistry leads to tendencies to formulate an early conclusion using preliminary evidence that either ignores or emphasizes the role of possible contributing factors, including habitat issues, confounding discharges, and historical impacts.

4) Because both process changes and regulatory decisions carry enormous costs, there is the tendency to look for the exception and retain it, ignoring the weight-of-evidence approach and avoiding the use of standard statistical testing to drive hypotheses and conclusions.

Much of the balance of this manuscript will be devoted to describing a process for tiering analyses and collections in order to effectively identify the impaired aspects in a system and to define the causative factors. If the emphasis is placed on determining the magnitude and geographic extent of statistically significant differences, it becomes the objective of stakeholder discussions to decide what the implications of the observed changes are and whether the situation is sustainable and acceptable.

Identifying impaired aspects and limiting factors

A CEA program has to be tiered to be economical, with successive phases determining whether responses exist within the system, whether they can be confirmed, what the geographic extent of the impacts is, and whether that impact zone is getting larger or smaller (Hodson et al. 1996). Initial examination of the data should include a comparison of obvious differences in abundance, catchability, and community composition. Data from a regional collection can be used to develop a knowledge of the geographic extent and magnitude of changes, detect sites where there are serious concerns, monitor performance over time as remediation and process changes occur, define baseline-data requirements for future developments, and detect undeveloped sites where there are unexpected low levels of performance in the absence of development.

The approach is based on a predefined maximum amount of change that will be tolerated as evidence of no damage. The position of this line can be adjusted either up or down. The effects-directed assessment approach does not assume that growth, reproduction, and survival must be protected. The approach does assume that a subsample of "n" males and females showing normal growth, reproduction, and age distribution is sufficient to demonstrate acceptable fish populations.

Collections following this approach have been conducted on the Moose River Basin in Northern Ontario, Canada, between 1991 and 1998. Information was collected on energy utilization, energy storage, and age distribution, as well as various biochemical parameters (Munkittrick et al. 2000). During the study period, fish were sampled from 50 different collections, demonstrating significant differences between sites (Munkittrick et al. 2000). Sites that received industrial wastes were altered by hydroelectric facilities demonstrated clear differences in comparison to upstream sites and in gradient designs. There were also some undeveloped sites where fish showed performance levels below those seen at some developed sites (Figure 2-4).

The integrated response of fish should be evaluated to define the characteristics of the receiving environment that are limiting the performance of fish. This involves examining the integrated responses of the individuals. Sites where fish are thinner and show reduced condition, smaller livers, and poor reproductive development are all consistent with an initial hypothesis of food limitation (Munkittrick and Dixon 1989a, 1989b; Gibbons and Munkittrick 1994). Follow-up studies, in a tiered fashion, should be focused on determining the geographic extent of the change, as well as whether the food limitation is real and whether there are obvious ecological differences that support this conclusion (Table 2-6).

In the example given here, the main objective of follow-up studies is to define why the fish are food-limited in that system. If the purpose of the study is to evaluate the potential impacts of existing development, the knowledge that there is a stress of food limitation will focus subsequent studies and allow hypotheses to focus on what factors are associated with the food limitation. In the case of pre-development baseline studies, the knowledge that there is a preexisting potential food limitation in the system prior to development will aid in the design of subsequent monitoring programs. Any valid risk assessment of the consequences of new developments will need to know that, prior to discharge, the resident fish are already stressed in terms of food availability. The risk assessment can then evaluate the potential additional risks associated with development in terms of how they may interact with the factors already limiting performance within the system.

Similar integrated changes can be seen in fish in cases where there is increased competition, recruitment failure, or exploitation (Table 2-6). The performance-based assessment focuses on the classification and interpretation of fish responses, as well as the identification of possible causative agents, using a framework

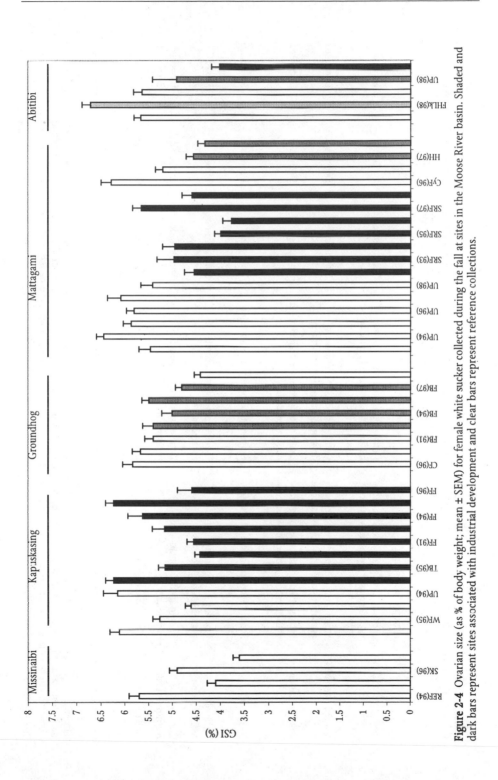

Figure 2-4 Ovarian size (as % of body weight; mean ± SEM) for female white sucker collected during the fall at sites in the Moose River basin. Shaded and dark bars represent sites associated with industrial development and clear bars represent reference collections.

Table 2-6 Generalized response patterns of fish populations to changes in populations

Generalized pattern	Cause of changes[1]	Follow-up study	Age distribution[2]	Energy utilization[3]	Energy storage[4]
Exploitation	Decreased competition between adults associated with mortality or eutrophication	Examine food resource availability and population density	Shift to younger	Increased	Increased
Recruitment failure	Shift to older age classes associated with decreased reproductive success	Detailed examination of spawning habitat, utilization and reproductive development	Shift to older	No change	No change
Multiple stressors	Simultaneous impacts on food availability and reproductive success	Detailed studies of reproductive development and food resources	Shift to older	Decreased	Decreased
Food limitation	Increased competition associated with increased reproductive success or decreased food availability	Examine food resource availability and population density	No change	Decreased	Decreased
Niche shift	Modest increase in competition for forage base	Examine food base and competition aspects	No change	Decreased	No change
Metabolic redistribution	Inability to maximally utilize available food resources	Detailed physiological studies of energetics	Shift to younger	Mixed	Mixed
Chronic recruitment failure	Shift to small population of older individuals	Detailed study of reproductive performance	Shift to older	Increased	Increased or decreased
Null response	No obvious changes	Check population size data to see if carrying capacity of the system has changed	No change	No change	No change

[1]The stressors could be chemical- or habitat-related, and the surviving populations integrate the conditions in the receiving environment (both chemical and habitat). [2]A shift in age distribution can be indicated by mean age or larger samples for ages of the population. [3]Energy utilization can be reflected in growth rate, reproductive rates or age at maturity. [4]Energy storage can be reflected in condition factors or in lipid storage levels. Sources: Munkittrick and Dixon 1989a, 1989b; Gibbons and Munkittrick 1994

designed to interpret the responses of fish populations (Munkittrick and Dixon 1989a, 1989b; Munkittrick 1992; Gibbons and Munkittrick 1994). The framework is used iteratively to design hypotheses to focus follow-up studies on the aspects of performance that are responding to the stressors within the system. The original framework separated impacted populations into five specific response patterns, but it had several limitations and deficiencies, including the subsequent description of additional patterns and the absence of a pattern reflecting no detectable response of the population. In light of new information and response patterns described in the published literature, the framework has been further revised and reorganized by Gibbons and Munkittrick (1994), with additional modifications by Gibbons (1997).

Gibbons and Munkittrick (1994) categorized fish responses according to the impacts of stressors on the ability to use or process food, availability and use of food and habitat; and mortality of adults, juveniles, and larvae and/or eggs. Because the absence of fish cannot be easily monitored, it is the changes in the fish that remain in the study area that are used to drive the assessment. Each of these effects was found to result in identifiable changes in the surviving or remaining fish, and, to date, there have been at least eight response patterns documented in the literature. Although there may be additional response patterns, the documented patterns could be linked conceptually in a progression of responses to a stressor. The response represents an indication of how the population may have arrived at its current status and not necessarily of the future trends. Specifically, the framework outlines the progression and direction of fish responses to alterations in food/habitat availability, rates of mortality, and physiological impairment. Some of the patterns may be very stable.

There are limitations to using these response pathways, and the analysis is designed to direct follow-up studies. Responses can be masked by compensatory mechanisms (i.e., van den Huevel et al. 1999), and interpretation must be cautious. The response pathways form the basis for interpretation of the results of initial sampling and facilitate the identification of the response pattern and pathway, the probable mode of action in the fish population, and the strategy for future follow-up studies.

A fish population that is limited by food availability would show a reduced growth rate, reduced reproductive rate, and delayed sexual maturity and would be thinner with reduced lipid stores. Under situations where food limitation is prolonged, the age distribution would start to climb. For presentation purposes, whole-organism parameters were grouped into summary categories describing age structure, energy expenditure, and energy storage. For example, the population that is faced with food limitation would initially show no difference in age structure; however, it would have decreased energy expenditures and then decreased energy storage. A continued decrease in energy expenditure and reproductive output would result in an increased age distribution.

The interconnection among the response patterns provides a more comprehensive theoretical linkage, describing how fish respond to direct and indirect stresses, including decreased habitat availability, increased habitat availability, increased mortality, and metabolic disruption (Figure 2-5). Although the relationships between response patterns may be conceptual, the framework developed from these patterns represents a useful model for interpreting results of monitoring data. The pathways of the framework were developed to help the researcher understand the likely progression leading to a particular response. The response pathways share some common elements, and a summary of all the response pathways integrated through the common relationships is presented in Figure 2-5.

When significant changes are seen, data should be examined for evidence that supports the direction of the change, and follow-up studies should be designed specifically to offer insight into the changes. Information on two or more species within the system will provide insight into the consistency and magnitude of responses. The responses do not have to be consistent between the species to be interpretable. In some cases, the differences between species may relate to the magnitude of impact, but in others, they may relate to differences in life-history characteristics (Gibbons, Munkittrick, McMaster et al. 1998).

The proposed interpretation framework is meant only to guide follow-up studies that will determine the magnitude and extent of changes and the possible causative factors. Without understanding the existing system, the consequences of further development cannot be fully evaluated.

Identifying causative factors

The importance of identifying causal factors varies with the scope of the proposed development, the extent and magnitude of the observed differences, and the ecological significance of the observed changes. When examining existing development, it may be necessary to define the acceptability of the changes prior to investing effort in defining the causative agents, especially if the causes may not be obvious. In the case of proposed developments, it will be critical to define the factors associated with decrease in performance in order to be able to evaluate the possible change in limiting factors associated with development. There are numerous papers that deal with the principles of using ecoepidemiological techniques to define causality in more detail (see Fox 1991; McMaster et al. 1996).

The main difference between the directed assessment approach and other approaches is that the emphasis is on defining the ecological factors associated with the change in fish performance. If growth is affected, the effort is on defining what factors have caused those changes in food availability or utilization (Table 2-3). In the case of a proposed development, the key effort in risk assessment and CEA is to define how the development may affect those factors currently limiting perfor-

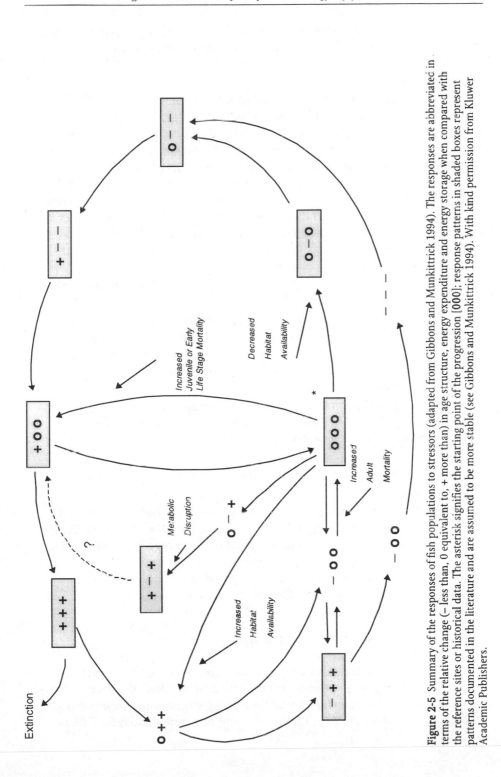

Figure 2-5 Summary of the responses of fish populations to stressors (adapted from Gibbons and Munkittrick 1994). The responses are abbreviated in terms of the relative change (− less than, 0 equivalent to, + more than) in age structure, energy expenditure and energy storage when compared with the reference sites or historical data. The asterisk signifies the starting point of the progression [000]; response patterns in shaded boxes represent patterns documented in the literature and are assumed to be more stable (see Gibbons and Munkittrick 1994). With kind permission from Kluwer Academic Publishers.

mance of the fish in the system. This is a significant difference from the present, largely chemical-by-chemical focus of the risk-assessment process.

Research needs

The EEM Programs designed for pulp and paper (Environment Canada 1997a–1997c) and mining (Environment Canada 2000) are cyclical or tiered programs relating to assessments of the potential impacts of effluent discharges on fish and benthic invertebrates, using a combination of field assessments and toxicity tests. These programs are based on the same philosophy as this effects-driven CEA program. The implementation issues and deficiencies in the initial stages of the EEM program would be similar to those experienced for CEA. Those deficiencies are worth highlighting here. At the end of the first cycle of the pulp and paper EEM, expert working groups were established to review the data collected and to make research recommendations to better improve the monitoring programs. For fish, the following were the main concerns:

- Timing of sampling: How to optimize sampling to achieve maximal relevance, residency period, and minimal variability and sampling costs;
- Range in natural variability versus potential responses to effluent exposure: Because of cost limitations, most studies utilized the minimal number of reference sites (one); additional information is needed to interpret the ranges in variability that are seen, relative to the differences seen between exposed and reference sites;
- Multiple discharge environments: Confounding discharges were common in the first cycle, and research is needed on how to discriminate between impacts from different effluents when they are discharged in close proximity;
- Timing or frequency of sampling for forage species that are multiple spawners; and
- Link between physiological/morphological changes and responses at the population or community level: It is a research need outside of the EEM program to develop the information that could tie together suborganismal, organismal, population, and community-level responses. A joint government/industry research program is required to evaluate the relative strengths, weaknesses, and effectiveness of the various approaches.

Summary

There are a variety of methods that can be used to develop a CEA related to potential or existing developments on an aquatic system. Most of the methods currently used are based on identifying the existing stressors and their potential impacts. This chapter describes the development of a methodology for CEA based

on defining the existing effects in a system. The effects-based program described is
a retrospective assessment to define the accumulated environmental state and to
identify the limiting factors so that a risk assessment can be conducted for development (see Chapter 4). Such a method is dependent on a post-operational monitoring system that would provide the information needed to validate the risk
assessment predictions and to provide the information necessary to manage the
system adaptively.

The failure of existing studies to focus on delineating impacts and evaluating
sustainability on a site-specific basis means that there is a tendency to see impact
assessment as a black or white issue. Consequently there is a tendency to dismiss
results as not being relevant. For example, if the decision is made that impacts on
sexual maturity and gonad size in fish in a receiving water are not relevant, the
conclusion would be that there are no impacts. This decision would have significant adverse consequences in the face of additional development or additional
stressors. If additional industrial development were to occur, the conclusion that
there are no existing impacts in that area would ignore evidence that fish populations may be sustaining themselves by a combination of immigration and clean
water refugia.

Any decision on additional discharges could affect populations adversely far
beyond the level predicted from a single discharge. An assessment of the potential
cumulative environmental effects would ignore important information from the
biochemical and individual levels. It is more important and more relevant to
interpret the ecological data in terms of impacts on self-sustaining populations and
to include the data in subsequent decisions related to additional development or
changing environmental conditions (Munkittrick and Sandström 1999).

Some regulatory authorities already have reached the point where discharge
licences are being allocated between dischargers to distribute the assimilative
capacity for biological oxygen demand. In the near future, similar calculations
could be done for biological performance. Understanding the capability of a
system to assimilate natural and anthropogenic wastes would be much easier once
the factors limiting ecological performance for a particular system are known and
the existing mechanisms of impact are understood. As industrial processes become
better and environmental impacts are reduced, continued application of Best
Available Technology will become a very expensive principle in the absence of a
better understanding of ecosystem health. Optimal management of environmental
protection will require understanding the relative roles of the various stressors in
the integrated response of the ecosystem. The priorities for ecological assessment
must be to define impacts, to understand the mechanisms of impacts, and to define
the factors limiting the performance of a particular system (Munkittrick and
Sandström 1999).

Acknowledgments—The authors would like to thank Dwayne Moore (Cadmus Group), Anne Fairbrother (Parametrix), Fred Wrona, Roy Parker, Sherry Walker (Environment Canada), Wayne Landis (Western Washington University), and Mike Power (University of Manitoba) for helpful comments on early drafts of this manuscript.

References

[CEAWG] Cumulative Effects Assessment Working Group. 1997. Practical approaches to cumulative effects assessment: a practitioner's guide. Hull Quebec: Axys Environmental Consulting for the Canadian Environmental Assessment Agency. Discussion draft, December 1997.

Colborn T, Dumanoski D, Myers JP. 1996. Our stolen future: are we threatening our fertility, intelligence and survival? A scientific detective story. New York: Penguin Books USA. 306 p.

Courtenay SC, Parker WR, Rawn GP. 1998. Proceedings of a workshop to assess alternatives to the fish survey component of the environmental effects monitoring program for Canadian pulp and paper mills. *Can Tech Rep Fish Aquat Sci* 2233:viii–108.

Environment Canada. 1995a. Further guidance for the invertebrate community survey for aquatic environmental effects monitoring related to Federal Fisheries Act Requirements. Ottawa , ON, Canada. EEM 2.

Environment Canada. 1995b. Further guidance for the adult fish survey for aquatic environmental effects monitoring related to Federal Fisheries Act Requirements. Ottawa, ON, Canada. EEM 1.

Environment Canada. 1997a. Fish survey expert working group: recommendations from Cycle 1 review. Ottawa, ON, Canada. EEM/1997/6.

Environment Canada. 1997b. Fish monitoring, fish survey section 5.1 in Technical Guidance Document for Pulp and Paper Environmental Effects Monitoring. Ottawa, ON, Canada. EEM/ 1997/7.

Environment Canada. 1997c. Aquatic environmental effects monitoring requirements (revised EPS 1/RM/18). Ottawa, ON, Canada. EEM/1997/1.

Environment Canada. 2000. Technical guidance documents for metal mining EEM Program. Ottawa ON: Environment Canada.

EVS Consultants. 1992. 1991 operational monitoring of the Lesser Slave River. Prepared for Ranger Slave Lake Pulp Corporation. North Vancouver BC: EVS Consultants. EVS Project 3/405-04.

Fairbrother A, Kapustka LA, Williams BA, Bennett RS. 1997. Perspective: effects-initiated assessments are not risk assessments. *Hum Ecol Risk Assess* 3(2):119–124.

Foran JA, Ferenc SA, editors. 1999. Multiple stressors in ecological assessments. Pensacola FL: SETAC. 100 p.

Fox GA. 1991. Practical causal inference for ecoepidemiologists. *J Toxicol Environ Health* 33:359–373.

Frank M, McMaster M, Munkittrick KR, Savoie MC, Wood C. 1999. Effects of sulphite and bleached kraft pulp and paper mill effluents on yellow perch and johnnie darters. *Can Tech Rep Fish Aquat Sci* 2260:53.

Gibbons WN. 1997. Suitability of small fish species for monitoring the effects of pulp mill effluent on fish populations [Ph.D. Thesis]. Waterloo ON: University of Waterloo.

Gibbons WN, Munkittrick KR. 1994. A sentinel monitoring framework for identifying fish population responses to industrial discharges. *J Aquat Ecosyst Health* 3:227–237.

Gibbons WN, Munkittrick KR, Taylor WD. 1998. Monitoring aquatic environments receiving industrial effluents using small fish species. 1. Response of spoonhead sculpin (*Cottus ricei*) downstream of a bleached kraft pulp mill. *Environ Toxicol Chem* 17:2227–2237.

Gibbons WN, Munkittrick KR, McMaster ME, Taylor WD. 1998. Monitoring aquatic environments receiving industrial effluents using small fish species. 2. Comparison between responses of trout-perch (*Percopsis omiscomaycus*) and white sucker (*Catostomus commersoni*) downstream of a pulp mill. *Environ Toxicol Chem* 17:2238–2245.

Hill J, Grossman GD. 1987. Home range estimates for three North American stream fishes. *Copeia* 1987:376–380.

Hodson PV, Munkittrick KR, Stevens R, Colodey A. 1996. A tier-testing strategy for managing programs of environmental effects monitoring. *Water Pollut Res J Can* 31:215–224.

Jobling S, Nolan M, Tyler CR, Brighty G, Sumpter JP. 1998. Widespread sexual disruption in wild fish. *Environ Sci Technol* 32:2498–2506.

Keough MJ, Mapstone B. 1995. Protocols for designing marine ecological monitoring programs associated with BEKM operations. National Pulp Mills Research Program, Technical Report 11. CSIRO, Canberra. 177 p.

Keough MJ, Mapstone BD. 1997. Designing environmental monitoring for pulp mills in Australia. *Water Sci Technol* 35:397–404.

Kilgour BW, Somers KM, Matthews DE. 1998. Using the normal range as an ecological criterion for ecological significance in environmental monitoring and assessment. *Ecoscience* 5(4):542–550.

Kovacs TG, Gibbons JS, Martel PH, Voss RH. 1997. Perspective on the potential of pulp and paper effluents to affect the reproductive capacity of fish: a review of Canadian field studies. *J Toxicol Environ Health* 51:305–352.

Larkin PA. 1984. A commentary on environmental impact assessment for large projects affecting lakes and streams. *Can J Fish Aquat Sci* 41:1121–1127.

Mapstone BD. 1995. Scalable decision rules for environmental impact studies: effect size, Type I, and Type II errors. *Ecol Appl* 4:401–410.

Matthiessen P. 1998. Effects on fish of estrogenic substances in English rivers. In: Kendall RJ, Dickerson RL, Giesy JP, Suk WA, editors. Principles and processes for evaluating endocrine disruption in wildlife. Pensacola FL: SETAC. p 239–247.

Matthiessen P, Allen YT, Allchin CR, Feist SW, Kirby MF, Law RJ, Scott AP, Thain JE, Thomas KV. 1998. Oestrogenic endocrine disruption in flounder (*Platichthys flesus* L.) from United Kingdom estuarine and marine waters: science series technical report 107. Essex, UK: Centre for Environment, Fisheries and Aquaculture Science, Lowestoft.

McKinley S, Van Der Kraak GJ, Power G. 1998. Seasonal migrations and reproductive patterns in the lake sturgeon, *Acipenser fluvescens*, in the vicinity of hydroelectric stations in Northern Ontario. *Environ Biol Fish* 51:245–256.

McMaster ME, Van Der Kraak GJ, Portt CB, Munkittrick KR, Sibley PK, Smith IR, Dixon DG. 1991. Changes in hepatic mixed function oxygenase (MFO) activity, plasma steroid levels and age at maturity of a white sucker (*Catostomus commersoni*) population exposed to bleached kraft pulp mill effluent. *Aquat Toxicol* 21:199–218.

McMaster ME, Van Der Kraak GJ, Munkittrick KR. 1996. An epidemiological evaluation of the biochemical basis for steroid hormonal depressions in fish exposed to industrial wastes. *J Great Lakes Res* 22:153–171.

Minns CK. 1995. Allometry of home range size in lake and river fishes. *Can J Fish Aquat Sci* 52:1499–1508.

Minns CK. 1997. Quantifying "no net loss" of productivity of fish habitats. *Can J Fish Aquat Sci* 54:2463–2473.

Minns CK, Cairns VW, Randall RG, Moore JE. 1994. An index of biotic integrity (IBI) for fish assemblages in the littoral zone of Great Lakes areas of concern. *Can J Fish Aquat Sci* 51:1804–1822.

Munkittrick KR. 1992. A review and evaluation of study design considerations for site-specifically assessing the health of fish populations. *J Aquat Ecosyst Health* 1:283–293.

Munkittrick KR, Dixon DG. 1989a. An holistic approach to ecosystem health assessment using fish population characteristics. *Hydrobiologia* 188/189:122–135.

Munkittrick KR, Dixon DG. 1989b. Use of white sucker (*Catostomus commersoni*) populations to assess the health of aquatic ecosystems exposed to low-level contaminant stress. *Can J Fish Aquat Sci* 46:1455–1462.

Munkittrick KR, Kilgour BW, Gibbons WN, Gibson WM. 1990. Baseline studies of the Lesser Slave River. Prepared by E.V.S. Consultants, North Vancouver, B.C., August 1990 for Slave Lake Pulp Corporation under E.V.S. Project No. 3/405-01. Volume 1: 129 p. + appendices.

Munkittrick KR, McCarty LS. 1995. An integrated approach to ecosystem health management: top-down, bottom-up or middle-out? *J Aquat Ecosyst Health*. 4:77–90.

Munkittrick, KR, McMaster ME, McCarthy LH, Servos MR, Van Der Kraak GJ. 1998. An overview of recent studies on the potential of pulp mill effluents to impact reproductive function in fish. *J Toxicol Environ Health* Part B 1:101–125.

Munkittrick, KR, McMaster ME, Portt C, Gibbons WN, Farwell A, Ruemper L, Servos MR, Nickle J, Van Der Kraak GJ. 2000. The development of cumulative effects assessment tools using fish populations. In: Scow K, Fogg GE, Hinton DE, Johnson ML, editors. Integrated assessment of ecosystem health. Boca Raton FL: Lewis. p 149–174.

Munkittrick KR, McMaster ME, Servos MR, Van Der Kraak GJ. 1999. Changes in the reproductive performance of fish in Jackfish Bay over the period of mill modernization. Third International Conference Environmental Fate and Effects of Pulp and Paper Mill Effluents; 9–13 November 1997; Rotorua, New Zealand.

Munkittrick KR, Portt CB, Van Der Kraak GJ, Smith IR, Rokosh DA. 1991. Impact of bleached kraft mill effluent on population characteristics, liver MFO activity and serum steroid levels of a Lake Superior white sucker (*Catostomus commersoni*) population. *Can J Fish Aquat Sci* 48:1371–1380.

Munkittrick KR, Sandström O. 1999. Ecological assessments of pulp mill impacts: issues, concerns, myths and research needs. Third International Conference Environmental Fate and Effects of Pulp and Paper Mill Effluents; 9–13 November 1997; Rotorua New Zealand.

Munkittrick KR, Sandström O, Larsson Å, Van Der Kraak GJ, Förlin L, Lindesjöö E, McMaster ME, Servos MR. 1999. A reassessment of the original reviews of Norrsundet and Jackfish Bay field studies. Third International Conference Environmental Fate and Effects of Pulp and Paper Mill Effluents; 9–13 November 1997; Rotorua, New Zealand.

Munkittrick KR, Servos MR, Carey JH, Van Der Kraak GJ. 1997. Environmental impacts of pulp and paper wastewater: evidence for a reduction in environmental effects at North American pulp mills since 1992. *Water Sci Technol* 35:329–338.

Munkittrick KR, Van Der Kraak G. 1999. Appropriate uses of physiological techniques for endocrine studies. In: Henshel D, Black MC, Harras MC, editors. Standardization of biomarkers for endocrine disruption and environmental assessment. Environmental Toxicology and Risk Assessment, 8th Volume. West Conshohocken PA: American Society for Testing and Materials. ASTM 1364. p 95–118.

[Ohio EPA] Ohio Environmental Protection Agency. 1987. Biological criteria for the protection of aquatic life: Volume 2. Users manual for biological field assessment of Ohio surface waters. Columbus OH: Division of Water Quality Monitoring and Assessment, Surface Water Section.

Power M. 1997. Assessing the effects of environmental stressors on fish populations. *Aquat Toxicol* 39:151–169.

Power M, McCarty LS. 1998. A comparative analysis of environmental risk assessment/risk management frameworks. *Environ Sci Technol News* 1 May 1998;224 A–231A.

[RLL] RL&L Environmental Services Ltd. 1993. Fish radiotelemetry demonstration project Upper Athabasca River, May to August 1992. Northern Rivers Basin Study Report 11. Ottawa ON: Environment Canada.

Servos MR, Bennie D, Brown S, Burnison K, Sherry J, Gamble A, Hewitt M, McInnis R, Toito J, Jurkovic A. 1998a. Impacts of alkylphenols, natural and synthetic estrogens in municipal effluents in Canada. 19th Annual Meeting of the Society of Environmental Toxicology and Chemistry (SETAC), Charlotte, NC; 15–19 November 1998. Pensacola FL: SETAC. p 247.

Servos MR, Brown S, Burnison K, Mayer T, Parrott J, Sherry J, McInnis R, Toito J, Jurkovic A. 1998. Runoff of estrogens into small streams after the application of hog manure to agricultural fields in Southern Ontario. 19th Annual Meeting of the Society of Environmental Toxicology and Chemistry (SETAC); 15–19 November 1998; Charlotte, NC. Pensacola FL: SETAC. p 247.

Servos MR. 1999. Review of the aquatic toxicity, estrogenic responses and bioaccumulation of alkylphenols and alkylphenol polyethoxylates. *Water Qual Res J Can* 34:123–177.

Stern PC, Fineberg HV, editors. 1996. Understanding risk: informing decisions in a democratic society. Washington DC: National Academy Press.

Swanson SM, editor. 1994. Wapiti- Smokey River Ecosystem Study. Final Report, Weyerhauser Canada, Grande Prairie, AL.

Swanson SM, Schryer R, Shelast R, Kloepper-Sams PJ, Owens JW. 1994. Exposure of fish to biologically treated bleached-kraft mill effluent. 3. Fish habitat and population assessment. *Environ Toxicol Chem* 13:1497–1507.

[Swedish EPA] Swedish Environmental Protection Agency. 1997. Environmental impacts of pulp and paper mill effluents: a strategy for future environmental risk assessments. Stockholm, Sweden: Swedish EPA. Report 4785.

Tattersfield L, Matthiessen P, Campbell P, Grandy N, Lange R, editors. 1998. SETAC-Europe/ OECD/EC Expert Workshop on Endocrine Modulators and Wildlife: Assessment and Testing; 10–13 April 1997; Veldhoven The Netherlands. Brussels, Belgium: SETAC Europe.

Taylor BR, Bailey RC. 1997. Technical evaluation on methods for benthic invertebrate data analysis and interpretation. AETE Report #2.1.3 CANMET (Natural Resources Canada).

Terrens GW, Gwyther D, Keough MJ. 1998. Environmental assessment of synthetic-based drilling mud discharges to Bass Strait. *APPEA J* 1998:610–625.

Thoresson G. 1993. Guidelines for coastal monitoring: fishery biology. Fiskeriverket Kustlaboratoriet, Kustrapport 1993:1. Öregrund, Sweden: National Board of Fisheries.

Van de Heuvel MR, Power M, Mackinnon MD, Van Meer T, Dobson EP, Dixon DG. 1999. Effects of oil sands related aquatic reclamation on yellow perch. I. Water quality characteristics and perch physiological and population responses. *Can J Fish Aquat Sci* 56:1213-1225.

Wrona FJ, Cash KJ. 1996. The ecosystem approach to environmental assessment: moving from theory to practice. *J Aquat Ecosyst Health* 5:89–97.

CHAPTER 3

Multivariate Statistical Applications for Addressing Multiple Stresses in Ecological Risk Assessments

Anne Fairbrother and Richard S. Bennett

Ecological risk managers more and more frequently are asking how specific risk factors act in the environment within the context of the large number of natural stressors and amount of variability that always have occurred. They wish to manage for ecologically relevant solutions that will incorporate anthropogenic stress into what is now perceived as a highly complex, even chaotic, natural system. Fortunately, multivariate statistical methods are available that allow risk assessors to explore complex datasets and mine information in ways that enable these types of interpretations to be made. As Geographic Information Systems (GIS) continue to advance, multivariate statistics will become available within a spatially explicit context. This exciting new field will allow long-term predictions to be made on the watershed or landscape scale, such as investigating consequences of land-use changes, pollution reduction, or different farming and harvesting programs.

Techniques for statistical analysis of multiple variables have been available for many years, although they have not been included routinely in ecological risk assessments or environmental impact assessments. Generally, they have been taught in "advanced" statistics courses at the postgraduate level, building on the simple case of univariate statistics. Certainly, the more variables that are added to the discussion, the more complex becomes the underlying mathematics for solving the problem. It is easy to visualize relationships among two or three variables using two- or three-dimensional graphics, but it becomes much more difficult to visualize relationships in 4, 5, 6....n dimensions. Similarly, equations with one or two unknowns are

CHAPTER PREVIEW

Multiple Stressors in Ecological Risk and Impact Assessment: Approaches to Risk Estimation. Susan A. Ferenc and Jeffery A. Foran, editors.
©2000 Society of Environmental Toxicology and Chemistry (SETAC). ISBN 1-880611-40-6

solvable with simple arithmetic approaches, but multivariate analyses require solving simultaneous equations that can be very intimidating. Thus, classical statistics courses that aimed to teach students not only methods for selection among various analytical tools, but also the underlying mathematical theories, were viewed with alarm and avoided by many environmental scientists. However, with today's desktop computing power and the availability of powerful statistical software packages such as Statistica® (StatSoft Inc., Tulsa, OK) and SAS® (SAS Institute Inc., Cary, NC) for personal computers, it has become less important to understand the mechanics of the computations. What remains is the need to know the kinds of questions that can be asked and which methods are most appropriate for answering such questions.

Knowing which methods are available and appropriate for answering which types of questions will allow environmental scientists to conduct risk assessments within the context of the complexity of natural systems. Those who manage environmental-assessment projects need to understand that these methods are available and, therefore, must require that studies are directed in this manner. Those who do the work should know how to design the appropriate study for the questions being asked, how to select the most appropriate methods, how to operate the software, and, most importantly, how to interpret and explain the results in a risk-management context.

Statistical and mathematical manipulations of data return information only about the mathematical relationships among the pieces of input information. They say nothing about the underlying biology or the ecological associations. Therefore, the second step in the assessment process is to place the statistical relationships into an ecological context. Do the statistical relationships make sense ecologically? Do they adequately and appropriately explain observed phenomena? Do the predictions appear reasonable in light of what is known about the system? Risk managers are not interested in the complexities of the numerical analysis; rather, they need to understand how a proposed action will change the environment for which they are responsible. While the underlying statistical and ecological theory may or may not be of interest to the technician conducting the assessment, it generally is of little concern to the manager using the information. Therefore, it is incumbent upon the risk assessor to communicate effectively the ecological context and meaning of the mathematically derived statistical relationships.

This paper will review available multivariate statistical methods from the viewpoint of an ecologist who is asking questions about how anthropogenic changes interact with natural stresses to modify biotic responses. Statistical theory will be studiously avoided except where it is needed to explain why a particular method is appropriate for specific questions or to understand the limitations of an approach. The goal is to acquaint the potential user with the various methods and how to select among them. It is hoped that managers will become comfortable with designing projects that take advantage of the readily available methods and commercially available software. Questions then can be structured within the more appropriate ecological context, rather than artificially simplified to include only two or three variables with which project managers are most comfortable. Ultimately, this will result in risk-assessment results that are much more useful to environmental managers, as they will be interpretable within an ecological context.

Overview of Methods

Statistical methods can be separated into several broad categories. The first division is between inferential and descriptive methods. Inferential methods are used in classical hypothesis testing. For example, during the late 1970s, it was hypothesized that acid rain was harmful to aquatic life because it lowered the pH of lakes, which, in turn, increased the availability of metals and resulted in toxicity. Ecosystem-manipulation studies were conducted where the pH of lakes (Schindler et al. 1985; Brezonik et al. 1986; Watras and Frost 1989) and streams (Hall and Likens 1980) were lowered and changes in various physical and biological responses were measured. The data from these lakes and streams were compared to co-located water bodies that had not been manipulated. The null hypothesis that lake acidification had no effect on other lake properties was tested and rejected. Inferential, or hypothesis testing, multivariate statistical methods include the Multivariate Analysis of Variance (MANOVA) or Covariance (MANCOVA) and time-series analysis (a subset of the Analysis of Variance [ANOVA]).

However, most ecotoxicological studies conducted outside the laboratory or mesocosms are observational in nature rather than manipulative. Current conditions are assessed to determine whether they have changed from the expected condition as a result of prior anthropogenic inputs or to predict what might happen if additional anthropogenic stresses are applied to the system. There are many different approaches to data analysis for these types of studies. Correlation, regression, or classification methods may be used initially as data-exploration tools or applied later as predictors. Cluster Analysis and Factor Analysis are used to look for fundamental, explainable ecological processes that are responsible for relating variables to each other or for causing an observed effect.

Where there are multiple techniques for doing essentially the same thing, selection of which one to use is primarily dependent upon whether the variables are discrete, categorical, or continuous. Discrete data are those that can take only particular values, such as counts of organisms in an area. Categorical observations place effects into different categories, such as the presence or absence of a species or whether water levels are high, medium, or low. Continuous measurements can take on any value, such as measurement of body weights or water temperature. Other criteria for the selection of appropriate statistical methods depend upon assumptions about how the data are distributed within the population that is being sampled (i.e., the shape and variance of the data distribution) (Figure 3-1). Regardless of which tests are eventually selected, all data should first be examined for outliers because these can significantly affect the outcome of nearly all the methods. Outliers are measured values that are obviously different from the majority of the other measurements, either much higher or much lower. It is good practice to generate scatter plots of data prior to any analysis in order to examine them for outliers or severe excursions from other assumptions about their distribution.

Additionally, it is recommended that relationships among data be explored using several different statistical methods prior to settling on a final "best" approach to analysis. Many of the multivariate techniques have no statistically "correct" answer; rather, they are designed to maximize separation among groups or relationships among variables regardless of their underlying ecological relevance. Thus, if a statistician is conducting the analyses, the ecologist must be consulted at each iteration to determine if the statistical result has any relevance to the project at hand. The primary purpose of multivariate analyses in environmental assessments is to provide a means for weighting the ability of undesirable stressors to change a valued ecosystem component or function, relative to the power of other stressors that are known to change that component. The ecologist, therefore, should have knowledge about the underlying relationships among the variables being tested even before beginning the analysis. If the results of the analysis are contrary to this a priori knowledge, it is likely that a meaningful statistical solution has no relevance to the system at hand. The question should be rephrased and approached using a different analytical tool or an alternate set of measurements.

Terminology

One of the greatest impediments to communication in the risk assessment process is the ambiguous use of terminology and the jargon of each discipline. These miscommunications sometimes create an unnecessary wall between statisticians and environmental scientists working on the same problem. The area of potentially greatest ambiguity is in terminology used to describe things that are measured (indiscriminately called variables, stressors, or measures) and the environmental attributes that are affected (also known as effects, assessment endpoints, or environmental attributes). The Guidelines for Ecological Risk Assessment (USEPA 1998) defines assessment endpoints as "explicit expressions of the actual environmental value that is to be protected, operationally defined by an ecological entity and its attributes." An example of an assessment endpoint is "the reproduction rate of bald eagles," which incorporates a valued ecological entity (i.e., eagles) and the attribute of concern (i.e., reproduction rate). Although many assessment endpoints meet the principal criteria of ecological relevance, susceptibility to stressors, and relevance to management goals, they may not be directly measurable. In such cases, other measures of effect (formerly known as measurement endpoints) are used to estimate or infer changes to the assessment endpoints. Measures of effects as defined in risk assessments will be used in this paper as synonymous with the statistical terms "dependent variables" or "response variables."

Measures of effects vary in response to natural and anthropogenic environmental factors that may be characterized as "stressors." The U.S. Environmental Protection Agency (USEPA) (1998) defines a stressor as "any physical, chemical, or biological entity that can induce an adverse response." In a risk assessment, only a subset of all the natural and anthropogenic entities generally is identified as stressors of concern. Quantifications of these variables are termed "measures of exposure" (USEPA 1998). In many assessments, and as used in this paper, the measures of exposure are synonymous with the statistical term "independent variables." In experimental or manipulative studies, measures of exposure are referred to as "treatments," as the goal is to determine how application of these stressors changes the measures of effect.

However, many other environmental variables that are not identified as stressors of concern also may cause the measured effects to change. These variables are termed "measures of ecosystem and receptor characteristics" (USEPA 1998) and help put the relationship between the stressor and its effects into context. These characteristics describe attributes of systems and the organisms of concern that may affect the relationship between the measures of effects and exposure. Included in this category are life-history characteristics of the species of concern, ecosystem characteristics that affect the behavior and location of these species, and attributes of the system that affect the movement, intensity, and availability of the stressors. Measures of ecosystem and receptor characteristics also are synonymous with the statistical terms "independent variable" or "covariate."

Differences between a measure of effect, a measure of exposure, and measures of ecosystem and receptor characteristics generally are a matter of perspective and the way the environmental manager frames the particular question. What may be perceived as an attribute of concern and defined as a measure of effect in one system may become a measure of exposure in another system if it also affects another attribute of greater concern. Moreover, many of the methods described in this paper do not require an explicit delineation among the types of variables that are measured. It is more important to state clearly the questions that are being addressed: What environmental attributes are of concern, what potential stressors are being considered, and what additional environmental variables are present and may change the impact of the stressors?

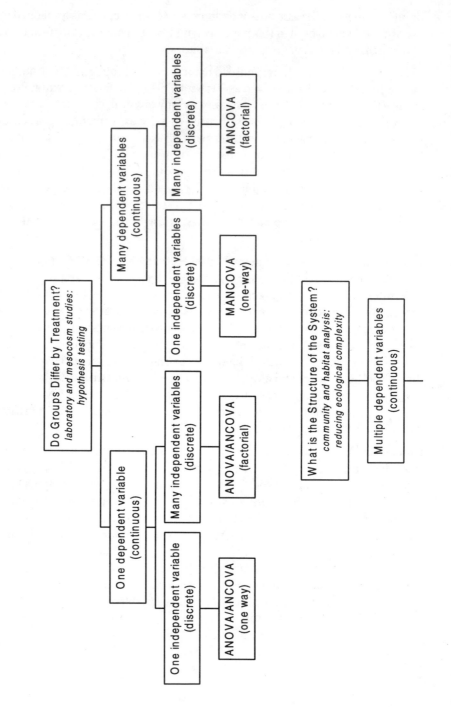

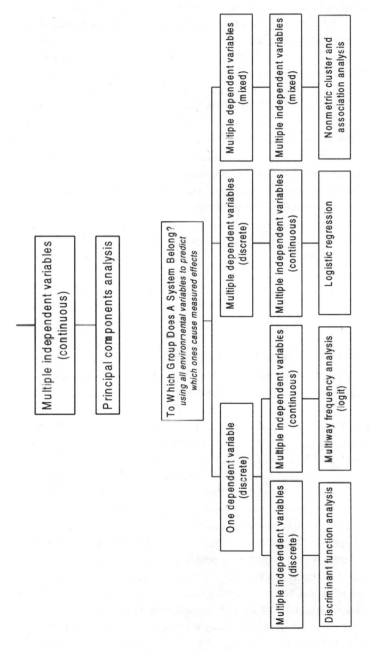

Figure 3-1 Choosing among statistical methods

Differences Among Groups (Hypothesis Testing)

In some cases, environmental assessments are conducted as experiments in which hypotheses about potential impacts of various stressors are tested. This experiment can be done through the use of mesocosms, treatment plots or fields, or manipulations of whole ecosystems (such as the lake-acidification project described above). These projects tend to be costly and frequently are time-consuming, but they have the advantage of being able to assign causality to treatments in a more rigorous manner than is available from observational studies. Examples of analyses to which these types of studies have been applied include pesticide risk assessments and the lake studies described above. In these types of studies, stressors (often referred to as "treatments") are applied to some plots or fields and not to others. Measurements of environmental variables that may interact with the treatment are made (such as water temperature, pH, and hardness), as are measurements of the desired ecosystem components or functions (such as species composition, nitrification, primary production, or organism growth rate). These measurements may be made before, during, and/or after stressor application. The statistical methods discussed in this section then are applied to determine if the ecosystem responses differ as a result of treatment with the stressors or if the variability within the systems is so large that the differences between the various treatments are to be expected as a result of natural fluctuations. Thus, the basis for these methods is to analyze the variance due to the treatment and to see if it is greater than the expected variance due to all the other environmental factors.

Multivariate Analysis of Variance and Covariance

It is important to understand that all forms of MANOVA are most appropriately applied to situations in which test subjects can be randomly assigned to treatment groups on an a priori basis. That is, they are most suitable for controlled experimental conditions. Sometimes observational data may be made to fit into this definition by setting up rules for placement of observations into groups prior to collecting the data. For example, one of the "treatments" in a study may be gender, which is difficult to randomly assign to test subjects. Ecological risk assessment field studies may use the MANOVA approach by assigning treatments (e.g., pesticide application) to fields or plots for comparison with control plots or different chemical applications. Additionally, retrospective assessments will attempt to use this approach by assigning areas to "highly contaminated," "moderately contaminated," or "uncontaminated" categories. However, this post hoc assignment of treatment groups violates the intent of the MANOVA approach. Discriminant Function Analysis (DFA) is more appropriate for use with nonexperimental (observational) studies in order to determine which anthropogenic and natural variables best describe the observed groups. Furthermore, many computer programs require MANOVA groups to be of equal size, a stipulation that often is not met in observational studies; DFA does not have such a requirement.

MANOVA is the generalized case of the more familiar ANOVA. In the particular case of the ANOVA, the potential consequences of several different treatments on a single measure of effect are analyzed. The MANOVA, on the other hand, is able to look simultaneously for differences of several treatments on several measures of effect (Figure 3-2). Analysis of covariance (ANCOVA) is a modification of MANOVA, such that the effects of various treatments on a single measure of effect are evaluated while controlling for the potential influences of other coincident measures.

Multivariate Analysis of Variance

MANOVA is conducted by artificially combining all the measured effects into a new effects variable. Simple ANOVA methods are then employed to determine which treatments or environmental variables significantly affect the desired environmental endpoint. As with single-variable ANOVA, the method asks the question, "Is the difference among treatment means greater than the difference in the variability within the treatment groups?" Factorial MANOVAs can be run as well to look for interactions among the various measured effects and among the treatments and environmental variables. In this method, various combinations of the effects variables are formed and the analysis is run for each combination.

Often, researchers will run a series of ANOVAs for each environmental endpoint or measurement variable, rather than combining them into a single MANOVA. This approach has the disadvantage of increased potential for concluding that there is a significant effect of the treatment when there really is not (known as a Type I error). In other words, repeated runs of an ANOVA, testing the response of the assessment endpoint against each measurement variable separately, has an increased probability of returning a significant result merely by chance. The most serious drawback to a series of ANOVAs is the inability to look for potential interactive effects of the treatments and environmental variables or for interactions among the desired environmental responses. MANOVA was designed specifically to look for such interactive effects. Furthermore, the MANOVA is a more sensitive test than is a series of ANOVAs. By explicitly including potential interactions of the treatments in the MANOVA analytical model, the ability of the test to detect effects increases (i.e., the error term is reduced through the explicit incorporation of variability into the model).

For example, the current guidelines for conducting avian reproduction studies require the measurement of a number of reproductive variables that can be intercorrelated. The traditional statistical testing procedure (i.e., univariate ANOVA on all variables) may not be an appropriate design when comparing many closely related and intercorrelated variables (Lacher and Willig 1994). When variables are independent and $\alpha = 0.05$, statistical tests may identify significant differences among treatment groups 5% of the time, based on chance alone, even though there is no real treatment effect. When variables are intercorrelated, the overall error rate cannot be assessed, and interpreting statistical significance becomes problematic.

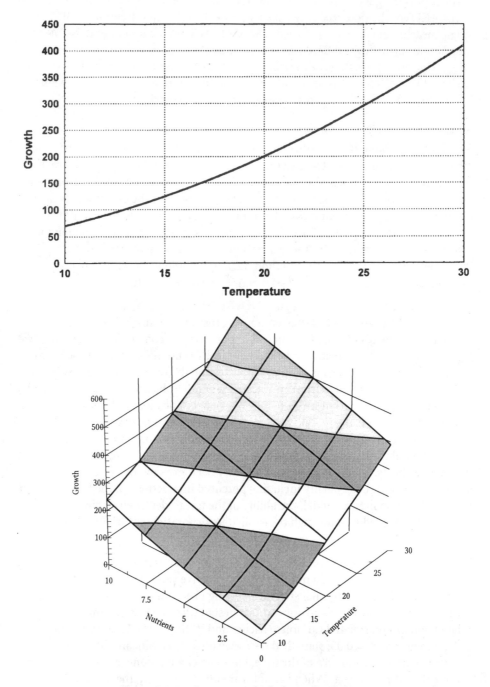

Figure 3-2 Single- versus multiple-factor distributions

Consequently, the MANOVA is a better choice when variables are intercorrelated and no single variable is of particular concern. In the avian reproduction study, the number of eggs laid per cage may be related to the number of eggs that are fertile and that hatch and survive to 14 days of age. In the study, we ask if there is evidence that the treatment produced a significant effect on avian reproduction as measured by this suite of variables. The finding that there is a significant treatment difference on the number of fertile eggs may be of importance to the overall question only if the effect on fertility translates into subsequent effects on reduced numbers of hatchlings and surviving juveniles. ANOVAs on each variable may indicate that one or more have significant differences among the treatments, but MANOVA may show that when using a composite of many intercorrelated variables there may not be an overall effect on avian reproduction. Conversely, ANOVAs on each variable may not find any significant treatment effect, whereas the MANOVA may identify an overall significant treatment effect even if none was observed in the individual variables.

Analysis of Covariance

Another way of assessing the effect that each treatment has on the desired assessment endpoint, irrespective of the influence of competing treatments, is through the Analysis of Covariance (ANCOVA). This method removes the influence of environmental variables that may be causing the assessment endpoint to change and then runs an ANOVA to see if any of the remaining changes in the environmental response are due to the treatment of interest. The primary advantage of an ANCOVA is that the ability to detect a change due to the variable of interest (in this case, the stressor of concern) is increased, as the confounding influences of the other variables are removed (i.e., as before, the size of the error term in the mathematical model is reduced). The disadvantage of this method is that interactions between the stressor and other environmental variables cannot be examined.

For example, in an avian reproduction study, variation in some of the measured variables is characteristic of individual birds (e.g., body weight may vary by ± 10% of the mean). Treatment of birds with a chemical may result in a loss of weight that might be difficult to ascertain if birds normally are quite variable in how much they weigh. The treatment effects are confounded by the increased variability in the model that results from natural differences among individuals. However, if birds are weighed at both the beginning and end of treatment, then initial weight can be used as a covariate and the confounding effect of the large amount of variance in weights prior to treatment would be removed. Remaining differences in weights could then be attributed to the chemical treatment. However, use of the ANCOVA would be inappropriate in this example if it were possible for weights to interact with treatment effects. For instance, smaller birds may be more sensitive to the chemical effect and may experience a greater percentage of weight loss than do larger birds. Basing the analysis on differences in weight after correcting for starting weights would lose the ability to determine if this type of interaction were occurring. Ideally, ANCOVA should be used only if there is a prior reason to believe that one particular stressor is of more significance than the others and that interactive effects are likely to be insignificant.

MANOVA and follow-up analyses (including ANOVA, but also encompassing many other methods) also can ascertain whether there are interactions among the various treatments as well as among the measured effects. As with ANOVA, if there are treatment effects, specific comparisons and trend analyses can be done to determine which of the treatments are responsible for the significant difference. Additionally, procedures are available to determine how much of an effect the treatments have on one or more of the assessment endpoints. For example, the proportion of the variance in the diversity of benthic taxa due to degree of salinity can be assessed.

MANOVA tests can be run in a stepwise fashion, similar to what is done in stepwise multiple regression. Each variable is entered in turn, controlling for all other variables that were previously entered and ignoring those that have not yet been entered (known as a Type I sums of squares test). Thus, you could say that, after controlling for all other variables or treatments that have been entered and ignoring those that were not, the variable or treatment of interest causes significant variation in the measured environmental endpoints. An extension of this approach controls for interactions of some effects, as well as for their direct effects, in order to look at the potential significance of the interactions of other variables (known as the Type II sums of squares). Fortunately, MANOVA designs can be used even when there is incomplete data; that is, one treatment may not have all the same environmental variables measured as do the other treatments (known as Type IV sums of squares).

MANOVA, like ANOVA, makes several assumptions about the underlying shape, or distribution, of the data. However, these tests are very robust to deviations from these assumptions particularly for studies with large sample sizes (e.g., greater than 30). The primary concern for the acceptability of the data for use in a MANOVA is whether the mean is correlated with the variance i.e., whether the variability in the data increases, or decreases, whenever the mean increases. This correlation frequently is a result of outliers in the data that occur in one of the treatment groups, particularly when large means are associated with large variances. ANCOVA is particularly sensitive to this type of deviation and often returns an incorrect result of significant differences when such data are used. Therefore, all data should be examined for outliers prior to conducting a MANOVA or an ANCOVA. Adjustments such as transformation of data to logarithms or cosines should be considered in cases where this assumption is violated.

Repeated measures analysis and time series

MANOVA may be used for analysis of time-series data, in which each time of data collection is assumed to be a measurement of a separate effect. Repeated Measures Analyses cannot be conducted using simple ANOVAs because measurements on the same subject made at successive time intervals generally are correlated with each other. This correlation violates the assumption of independence of measurements that is required for the ANOVA test to run properly. For example, if you measure the weight of a growing bird at several time intervals, it is highly likely that the measurements all will be positively correlated. That is, larger birds remain the larger birds in the population on subsequent measurements, and smaller birds remain the smaller birds; therefore each additional measurement shows that a bird's weight is a function of its previous weight. This violation of the assumption of independence of measurements from the same subject is known as "sphericity" and has severe consequences on the validity of the ANOVA. By conducting the analysis as a MANOVA, where interactions among measurements (e.g., the repeated weight measures) are allowed, the effect of autocorrelation of the data becomes inconsequential.

For example, if an avian reproduction study evaluated the changes in treatment response during the course of the study, the suite of reproductive endpoints could be measured for a series of discrete time intervals (e.g., biweekly) and used as repeated measures. Consequently, not only are the reproductive variables intercorrelated, but also the repeated measures of each variable are not independent of each other. MANOVA can be used to examine the interaction of treatment with duration of exposure where ANOVA would be inappropriate.

The major shortcoming of the MANOVA design for Repeated Measures Analysis is that it requires that there be no empty cells. Therefore, measurements for all the individual objects must be taken at each and every time interval, or that object is dropped from the analysis entirely, as if it were never a part of the study. In environmental or biological studies, it often is difficult to ensure that the measurement object will be available or accessible at each measurement interval. Because MANOVA also requires that there be a relatively large number of measured objects compared to the number of treatments and the number of time intervals in which the measurements are taken, the required number of objects may be unrealistically large. To ensure that enough objects are measured at every time interval, an environmental study should begin by including more objects than will eventually be used in the analysis.

Relationship Assessment

Relationship assessment methods look for correlations between stressor variables and measures of effect. They partition the variability of the observed effects among the various stressors to see which stressors, either alone or in various combinations, can explain the observed changes. It is important to remember that these methods do not establish causality. That is, they do not state that the stressors are causing the observed changes, only that they are correlated in a certain way. For example, population densities of chickadees may increase whenever the use of pesticides increases. This is not to say that pesticides are good for chickadees, but rather that both pesticide use and chickadee densities are responding to increased numbers of insects. By suggesting which stressors and responses are correlated, relationship assessments allow for the development of directed hypothesis testing studies or, as in the case of the above example, for investigating additional environmental variables that may be the causal factor for simultaneously changing the correlated variables and effects. Management decisions that are based on correlational relationships also should include some knowledge of the possible ecological processes that establish plausible cause-and-effect relationships among the correlated variables. Otherwise, actions taken may not result in the desired effect.

Regression analysis

Regression analysis is the most familiar and frequently used multivariate statistical technique. It allows the investigator to look at the relationship between one measure of ecological effect and multiple potential stressors. For example, the density of aquatic invertebrates might be a function of the water pH, salinity, and temperature. None of the variables alone are sufficient to explain the changes in invertebrate density, but taken together they may explain a high percentage of the observed variation in density. Moreover, regression analysis may allow an investigator to determine which variable is the best predictor of the observed effect.

Regression analysis also provides a method for determining if an apparent correlation between a single environmental variable and the measure of effect really is due to the interactions of several environmental variables. This sometimes is referred to as a "partial correlation," or the expression of effects as a consequence of one environmental stressor after controlling for the effects of all other variables. As an example, suppose there is a positive relationship between water pH and number of fish in a lake. Further suppose that the lake is contaminated with metals. As metals increase in bioavailability as pH decreases, and the fish in this example are tolerant to the range of pH present, the fish actually are responding to increased metal toxicity rather than to decreasing pH. Thus, after controlling for the variable metal concentration, the effect of pH on fish densities disappears. Therefore, its partial correlation is zero.

However, partial correlations may not always be zero. It may be that each variable contributes some information towards explaining the observed changes in the assessment endpoint. Regression analysis can be used even if the variables are correlated and, therefore, are not independent of each other. If metal toxicity were partially controlled by pH, for instance, regression analysis would still be a valid statistic for examining the relationship of both these variables on fish density. When they are highly intercorrelated, however, the analysis becomes invalid. For example, measuring the depth of water in centimeters and then in inches and asking questions about the relationship of both of the measures on water temperature would be invalid. Many of the computer statistics packages automatically will disallow inclusion of highly intercorrelated variables. There are, however, various data modifications that can be made to reduce the intercorrelation artificially and allow estimates of the pattern of their relationships to be computed. This makes regression analysis a very robust technique for exploring environmental relationships, as independence of variables cannot be assumed in many instances.

Note that the relationship between the environmental stressors and the measured effect need not be linear. While linear multiple regression (or variations such as transformation of data to logarithms and analyses of loglinear relationships) is the most commonly applied method, second- or third-order functions often better explain environmental relationships (Figure 3-3). Therefore, it is important to investigate possible alternatives before assuming which relationship provides the best explanation. Analyses can be conducted to investigate how much of the total variability is accounted for by each variable (known as the semi-partial correlation) or how much of the residual variability is accounted for by one variable after all the other variables have been accounted for (the partial correlation). If the semi-partial correlation is very small but the partial correlation is large, then the variable provides predictor information that no other variable can provide, even though it does not predict a large percent of the total variability. On the other hand, if the two values are similar, then the variable does not add to the predictive power provided by the other variables.

Many researchers are confused about the different meaning of "R" and "R-squared" in regression analysis. The term "R" refers to the multiple correlation coefficient and is a measure of the degree to which two or more predictors are related to the response variable. Each of the variables has its own "r" value (its partial correlation coefficient) as described above. The final "R" value for the entire equation is an expression of the predictive power of all the variables taken together. "R" can vary between 0 and 1.0, with larger numbers indicating greater predictive power of the model equation. The "R-squared" value is an indication of how well the model fits the data. That is, how far from the predicted equation do the actual observations lie? In other words, if the R-squared is 0.4, then the derived equation explains 40% of the variability in the data. The predictive power of the equation ("R") in this example is 0.63 (the square root of 0.4), indicating that the portion of the variability explained by the measured environmental variables has a reasonable chance of predicting the response about which questions were being asked. Note that "R" will always be larger than "R-squared" because both numbers are less than 1. Thus, it may not be necessary to explain all the variability in the system if the portion that has been accounted for has good predictive power for the response of interest.

Most statistical computer packages allow for stepwise multiple regression, either forward or backward. Forward regression analyzes each variable one at a time, including them in the order relative to their strength of association. Backward regression analysis puts all the variables into the model initially and then removes them one at a time to determine how much the model changes without each

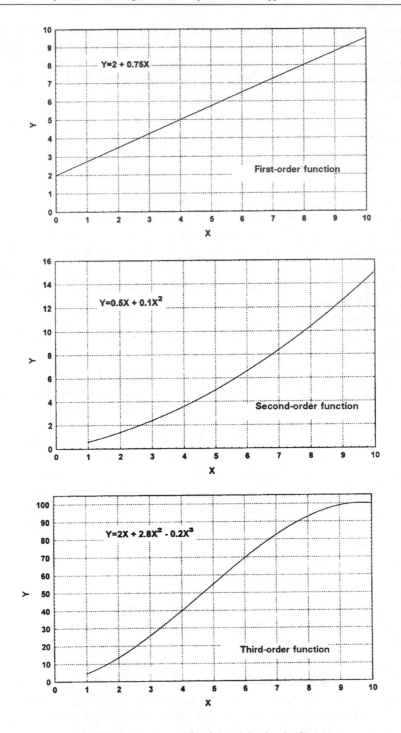

Figure 3-3 Linear, second-order, and third-order functions

variable. Neither of these regression analysis techniques examines directly the relative strength that the interaction among variables might have on influencing the observed effect. That is, variables are added to or deleted from the model based entirely on the correlation of that variable alone with the measured effect. However, interactions of variables can be incorporated into the exercise by creating an artificial variable that is the interactive term. This variable is then included in the analysis along with the original parent variables and its strength of association is determined. It is reasonable to do this if prior knowledge suggests that two environmental variables may interact with each other, resulting in a different effect on the stressor variable. For example, two variables (e.g., pH and temperature) may be known to affect the toxicity of a chemical to *Daphnia*. It also may be known that they are not independent of each other, but tend to act synergistically. A variable can be created that combines pH and temperature (e.g., product of values) and included in the list of variables for conducting the regression analysis. If a forward or backward regression keeps such a created variable, it may be in addition to one or both of the original variables or in place of them. While created variables may help to explain variation in regression analysis, their relationship to the response may be more difficult to visualize since they have lost recognizable units.

Information about how large a change in the effect will occur as a result of an incremental change in the environmental variable can be determined by looking at the regression coefficients for each variable. Also, looking at the sign of the correlation between the environmental variable and the measured effect will provide information about the direction of the relationship. However, if there are many variables, it is likely that at least one will be correlated to the measured effects simply due to chance. Furthermore, if the number of variables is much greater than the number of observations, the model is considered to be "overspecified" and the procedure will not work. It has been suggested that one should have at least 10 times as many observations as variables. Note that R is sensitive to the number of observations of effects; smaller datasets generally result in a larger R value.

Canonical Correlation Analysis

Canonical Correlation is analogous to multiple regression and is used to investigate the relationship between two sets of continuous variables. Rather than having a single measure of effect expressed as a function of multiple environmental stressors, Canonical Correlation Analysis simultaneously analyzes the relationship of several measures of effects to the suite of environmental stressors.

Note that Canonical Correlation Analysis is applicable only to continuous data. If categorical data have been collected, then DFA should be used instead. Another limitation of Canonical Correlation Analysis is that it often describes complex relationships that are difficult to interpret ecologically. In addition, if the relationship between the two sets of variables is nonlinear, the correlation will be underestimated; a log transformation of the data may reduce this source of error. Only the uncorrelated solution is available; therefore, interactions among either the stressors or the measures of effect cannot be assessed. This absence is a significant failing of this method because the strength of association between the two sets of variables often depends upon the relationships of the variables within each set, as well as between the two sets. Because the intraset relationships cannot be assessed, the association between the stressor and measures of effects generally is interpreted as if all variables were independent with no interactive effects, resulting in overemphasis of the contribution of single stressors to the observed effects. Missing data cannot be tolerated in this approach, and outliers can dramatically change the solution.

A simplifying approach to Canonical Correlation Analysis that has been used is the development of indices of environmental effects. In brief, the scores of all the measures of effects are combined (e.g., by addition, multiplication, or some other simple arithmetic function) and then analyzed using multiple regression analysis as if there were only a single measured effect. However, a significant amount of information is lost about interactions of environmental stressors with the multiple effects measures or potential interactions among the effects themselves. For example, suppose that benthic invertebrate species diversity, species density, and size of individuals are a function of sediment pH, percent organic matter, and grain size. Suppose further that the three response variables diversity, density, and size are collapsed into a single index called "benthic invertebrate condition." It would be impossible to determine whether pH, organic matter, or grain size are correlated with changes in diversity or density of the invertebrate community or if they perhaps had no direct effect on the invertebrates at all. By explicitly comparing all variables with each other through the use of canonical correlation, the relationships of all the variables, whether designated as a stress or a response variable, can be assessed.

One must be careful not to over-interpret the results of the Canonical Correlation Analysis. Although the method is based on the overall correlation matrix of all the variables, generally only the first two or three groups contribute significant amounts of information towards explaining the relationships observed. Nevertheless, most computer packages will provide correlation values for all possible groupings of variables defined by the model.

Predicting Group Membership

The methods in the following two sections have similar goals: to ascertain which variables (in which combination) are required to accurately predict in which group each datum (measure of effect) belongs. For example, if six physiological variables are measured in mice that were exposed to three levels of a pesticide treatment on 24 different field plots, these methods should be able to determine which physiological variables will be needed to correctly place each mouse within a pesticide treatment group or a particular field plot (Fairbrother et al. 1998). The methods differ primarily in their requirements for discrete versus continuous data, independence of the variables, and assumptions about how the data are distributed.

Multiway Frequency Analysis

Relationships among three or more discrete variables are examined using Multiway Frequency Analysis or its more general extension called Loglinear Analysis. This is a multivariate extension of the familiar chi-square analysis of the relationship between two discrete variables. Here it is unimportant which variables are designated as measures of effect and which as measures of exposure or ecosystem characteristics. Rather, the interest lies in determining the relationship among all the variables to predict to which group a new case would belong. In brief, tables are formed containing the one-way, two-way, and higher-order interactions. The model then develops the expected cell frequencies, using either a linear model or a loglinear model. The model starts by containing all the associations and testing for goodness of fit. It then eliminates as many of the variables as possible, while still maintaining an adequate fit between the expected and observed cell frequencies. If all are eliminated, such that only a single variable remains, it is tested against the expected probability of equal frequencies in all cells.

This method can be used to address the following kinds of questions:
- What is the expected frequency of occurrence of a particular combination of categories? For example, out of all the potential combinations, what percentage of the time is the combination of high bird density, moderate plant cover, and high occurrence of off-road-vehicle use likely to occur?
- Given the level of one or more variables, what is the probability of being at a particular level of another variable? In the above example, what is the probability of high bird density given high off-road-vehicle use?
- What is the relative importance of each of the variables towards predicting to which group a particular case would belong? How important is off-road-vehicle use toward determining whether bird density in a particular area will be high, medium, or low? How important is the relative amount of plant cover or other measured ecosystem characteristic?

This method can be applied to a large number of study designs because it does not require that the measurements have a uniform underlying distribution (i.e., it applies to nonparametric distributions). However, the measured variables must be independent of each other, although they may interact with one another. Furthermore, the sample size should be adequate so that all the cells are filled. There should be at least five times as many observations as cells in the design. For example, if there are three levels of off-road-vehicle use (high, medium, and low) and five bird species with presence/absence scores, then a complete design would need $3 \times 5 \times 5$ = 75 observations as a minimum for conducting this analysis. Independence means that each case (e.g., each area measured for bird-species presence and for off-road vehicle use) contributes values to only one cell.

Logistic Regression Analysis

Logistic regression is used to predict a discrete outcome (e.g., disease/no-disease) based on input from multiple variables. The variables may be continuous, discrete, dichotomous, or a mix. For example, can presence or absence of deer be predicted from knowledge of geographic area, season, degree of contamination, and number of forage shrubs? Logistic regression answers essentially the same questions as DFA or MANOVA. It first ascertains whether there is a relationship between any of the measures of exposure either alone or in some combination with each other or with measured environmental attributes, and the measured effects. The goal is to use as few of the measures of exposure or environmental attributes as possible, while still maintaining a strong predictive capability. Once the relationship between the stressor variables and the measured effects has been established, the model can be used to predict the outcomes for new cases on a probabilistic basis. For the above example once the geographic area, season, number of forage shrubs, and degree of contamination are specified, the probability of deer being present could be computed.

Logistic regression is much more flexible than are multiple regression or MANOVA. Logistic regression makes no assumptions about the underlying distributions of variability of the measures of exposure or other predictor variables. The measurements can be any mix of variable types (discrete, continuous, etc.). As discussed with previous methods, the number of variables should not exceed the number of cases measured, and outliers significantly influence results. For example, logistic regression may evaluate the probability that a given area has no deer, few deer, or many deer, based on the pattern of responses to questions about geographic area, contaminant load, season, or amount of forage. Logistic regression can be used for experimental data or for observational data. However, logistic regression cannot produce negative correlation coefficients; a stressor or environmental attribute must always be positively correlated with the measured effect.

Logistic regression is particularly useful when the relationship between the effect and one or more of the environmental variables or stressors is nonlinear. This is important in environmental assessments where variables often are related logarithmically rather than linearly. Measured values are transformed to natural logarithms and the usual linear regression equation is derived. The goal is to obtain the best combination of measured exposure and environmental attribute variables to maximize the likelihood of obtaining the observed outcome in the measure of effect. As with multiple regression, this is done by using none, some, or all of the stressors and environmental attributes and a goodness-of-fit test to see which combination maximizes the predictive power of the model.

The most straightforward approach to testing the predictability of the measured effect based on the measures of exposure or environmental attributes is to compare a loglinear model that contains only a constant (or only one of the stressor variables), with a model that contains some of the measured attributes. If these are significantly different, then the measured attributes have the effect of increasing the predictability of the occurrence of the measured effect. These comparisons are made, adding variables one at a time, until the full model (containing all the measures of exposure and environmental attributes) has been compared to the model containing only the constant or single variable. Alternatively, models containing only some of the measures of exposure or attributes can be tested against the full model to see if any significant improvement in predictability occurs as variables are added. The model also can include interactions among the measures of exposure and environmental attributes variables. As with multiple regression, covariates may be added to develop a model given that the variability from a particular environmental attribute or stressor of concern has been removed.

Multiple regression is a more powerful tool than logistic regression if the measure of effect is a continuous variable and other assumptions are met. Also, if these assumptions are met, DFA generally is a more powerful and efficient method, even with dichotomous outcome data. Therefore, logistic regression is used in the special cases where the data do not meet the above assumptions, most generally when there is a mix of types of environmental attributes and stressor variables (i.e., both discrete and continuous variables). Because this is not uncommon in environmental measurements, logistic regression should remain under consideration as an appropriate data analysis tool.

Discriminant Function Analysis

Discriminant Function Analysis can be thought of as the inverse of the MANOVA approach. In MANOVA, the measures of exposure define groups and the question is whether the measured effects can be placed into the appropriate treatment group. In DFA, the measures of effect define the groups and the measures of exposure are used to explain the processes underlying the grouping. The DFA procedure develops the groups, but the ecologist must explain why the particular effects are grouped together. If there is no logical explanation for the groupings, either an important exposure variable was not measured or there is insufficient ecological knowledge to explain what was observed.

Discriminant Function Analysis is applicable to categorical effects information. If data are continuous variables, canonical correlation may be a better approach. The DFA procedure follows up its group determination by a classification routine, to see how many data are placed into the "correct" grouping and which ones are not. With multiple variables, there may be multiple answers. That is, there may be more than one way to group the measures of effect to accurately predict the groups. It is very important that the selection among the possible combinations be based on a priori knowledge of the ecology of the system. For example, if nesting bird species in a forest in southeastern Alaska were counted (the measure of effect) and the species, height, and mean breast diameter of trees were measured along with the number of sunny days in Florida (measures of exposure and environmental attributes), there is no reason to believe that sunny Florida days would have any effect on the number of bird species that nest in Alaska. Species groups may be defined by heights of nests and mean breast diameter in trees, but any grouping that appears to rely on the number of sunny days in Florida for explanation should be deemed irrelevant and be ignored. Thus, using the DFA approach requires a considerable knowledge of the ecological system prior to data collection and analysis.

Standard DFA puts all the variables in the analysis at once and considers all measures of effect simultaneously. However, stepwise DFA, analogous to stepwise regression or MANOVA, is a more common approach. This can be done forward (at each step, review all variables and select the one that contributes the most to explaining the variance) or backward (include all variables initially and then eliminate one at a time those that do not contribute information significantly to group assignment). The researcher determines the order in which the variables are added or subtracted. A priori knowledge of the most likely discriminators is very helpful in this situation. Alternatively, if a researcher has no preferences among the variables, programs are available in SPSS™, SAS™, or Statistica™ that utilize various statistical approaches for assigning priority. These statistics packages also provide methods for determining a posteriori whether or not the groups of measured effects are significantly different from each other.

DFA generates information on the predictive power (known as "functional axes") of either all or many of the environmental attributes and measures of exposure. Frequently, however, it is the case that only the first two, or at most three, stressor variables or environmental attributes contain most of the discriminating power for separating the groups, with the remainder adding little additional information. The predictive power of each variable generally is provided as part of the program output. However, to interpret correctly the results of a DFA, the data should be plotted against the primary discriminating functions and examined visually. Generally, no more than two or three variables contribute significantly to the explanation of between-group variability, and plots therefore can be visualized in two or three dimensions. The final interpretation of why certain variables contribute the most information to discrimination between measured effects, and why the effects sort themselves into groups in a particular manner, is a matter of ecological understanding rather of than statistical inference.

The requirements of equal sample sizes, normally distributed data, and independence of variables (known as "orthogonality") are relaxed in DFA and other classification methods. However, if sample sizes are highly unequal among treatment groups, logistic regression may be a better approach than DFA. The size of the smallest group should be larger than the number of measures of exposure and environmental attributes. Otherwise, the model overfits the data, i.e., it predicts exactly the current situation but cannot be generalized to other situations. Discriminant Function Analysis is robust to violations of the underlying assumptions when sample sizes are large, but not when they are small, although the method is always highly sensitive to outliers.

Classification

Once a DFA model has been developed and the discriminant functions have been derived, one may ask "How well do the variables predict to which group a particular case should belong?" Of course, using the same dataset to answer this question that was used to develop the discriminant functions in the first place will give a very high predictive capability. Therefore, it is best to generate new data from which the classification predictions can be made. Each observation is given a classification score for each potential group, and the observation is then assigned to the group for which it has the highest score. Classification scores are based on the mean values for each of the measures of exposure and the variance within all the measured exposure or environmental variables.

Most computer programs that run DFA automatically compute the classification functions for the initial dataset. These functions can then be specified in a spreadsheet as the formulas for computing new classification scores as new observations are added. Observations are then assigned to the group for which they have the highest classification score.

The probability that an observation will be classified in a particular group is known as the "posterior probability." This probability is determined by calculating the distance within the two- or three-dimensional space in the DFA plot from the location of the observation of interest to the location of the center of the group to which it has been assigned (known as the group "centroid"). If the measures of effect and the measures of exposure and environmental attributes are truly independent of each other, then the axes on the graphs will be at right angles, and the distances could, in theory, be measured with a ruler. If the assumption of independence is violated, then the axes are not at right angles and the distances cannot be measured but must be calculated. The probability of correctly assigning a measure of effect to the correct group is proportional to the distance of the measured effect from the centroid of a group. Thus, assignment is made by choosing the group whose center is closest to the graphical location of the measured effect.

Sometimes there is a prior reason to believe that more of the measures of effect will be assigned to one group than to others. If so, this information can be entered into the program prior to generating the classification scores. However, one must be cautious because specification of different a priori probabilities can greatly affect the accuracy of the prediction. Most programs return a classification matrix that shows the number of observations correctly classified and those that were misclassified.

Again, the classification of the new data should be examined to see if it makes ecological sense to put the measured effects into the various groups.

Nonmetric Cluster and Association Analysis

Discriminant Function Analysis is relatively robust in regards to the type of data it can analyze. However, DFA is most suited for datasets comprised of similar types of variables (e.g., species numbers or habitat designations). It often is difficult to interpret results if disparate parameters are included, such as pH (which varies on a log scale and is bounded between 1 and 14), species numbers (discrete but un-bounded variable), and water hardness. Nonmetric Cluster and Association Analysis (NCAA) (Matthews and Hearne 1991) broadens the application of DFA to all types of datasets, including those with unequal sample sizes and abnormality of data. Moreover, NCAA produces clusters of variables and statistical strengths of clustering that are more intuitively obvious than are the vector distances and hypothetical "factors" of DFA and do not require conceptualizing multidimensional space. Conceptual clustering, such as NCAA, attempts to distinguish groups using as few variables as possible through the use of simple "yes/no" comparisons. For example, NCAA would ask if the number of individuals of species A is greater than 5, if water hardness is less than 100, and if pH is between 2 and 6. In DFA, by contrast, the linear distance between variables is calculated and groups are formed based on rules about these linear functions rather than on the variables themselves. In NCAA, data first are clustered independent of any knowledge about the treatment group to which they belong. The associations between clusters and treatments then are measured in a standard chi-square contingency table. The application of NCAA in ecology and environmental toxicology has been extensively documented (Fairbrother et al. 1998; Landis, Matthews, Markiewicz, Slough et al. 1993, Landis, Matthews, Markiewicz, Matthews 1993, Landis et al. 1994, 1996; Matthews and Matthews 1990; Matthews and Hearne 1991; Matthews et al. 1995).

A major advantage of this approach is that the unit of analysis is the description of the environmental component of concern. This may be an animal described by a suite of biomarkers, an aquatic community described by species composition, or a terrestrial ecosystem described by rates of decomposition and primary production. The question is simply, "Can I place this animal, community, or ecosystem into a cluster of similar animals, communities, or ecosystems, and is this cluster associated with some particular stressor about which I am concerned?" Several iterations of the Cluster Analysis are conducted, followed by an Association Analysis to determine whether the clusters are associated with identified stressors. Note that the stressors do not have to be quantified or quantifiable, but could be qualitative descriptions arbitrarily assigned to numeric classes for purposes of the Association Analysis.

The NCAA is a post hoc method for determining stressor effects. In fact, once the clusters are formed, a large number of Association Analyses between the clusters and potential driving variables can be performed. If none of the originally identified variables can be associated with confidence with the clusters, additional variables should be sought that might explain the clustering results. Many of the more conventional multivariate statistical methods described above are applicable only to data in which all the variables have been measured simultaneously. Thus, one of the strengths of the NCAA is that it provides a cost-effective means of expanding the analysis as information becomes known. Not all of the potential driving variables need to be measured initially. However, after clusters are formed and associations are tested, new knowledge has been gained that may point toward other environmental variables that may reduce uncertainty further. Nonmetric Cluster and Association Analysis and other similar methods of pattern analysis that use all the information about the system of interest simultaneously are very powerful methods and can detect subtle changes in responses that have great influence in causing long-term changes in the system of interest.

Structure Analysis

Principal Components Analysis and Factor Analysis

Principal Components Analysis (PCA) and Factor Analysis (FA) are techniques used when the researcher is interested in knowing which variables cause the observed effects to form independent groups. Measures of exposure or environmental attributes that are correlated with each other form the components or factors, and are assumed to have some underlying ecological processes that explain the reasons that they have acted together to form the observed clusters of measures of effects. The goal of the these analyses is to reduce a large number of variables to a few components or factors that can be used to explain underlying processes. They also will group or classify environmental attributes and stressors, as underlying structure is identified. Thus, these are data reduction or structure detection methods.

Factors, or components, are derived by plotting the effects data and then rotating the axes of the plot in order to form new variables that are made up of groups of measured environmental attributes and stressor variables. In statistical language, these are generated by maximizing the variance along the axis of the newly formed variable while minimizing the variability around this new axis. Once the first new variable is formed, another new variable is derived and the data are again rotated to form the next factor. There are many different methods for rotating the data, some of which require independence of the environmental attributes, stressors, and measures of effects, while others are more robust from deviations of this assumption.

It is useful to begin by measuring a large number of measures of exposure and environmental attributes, some of which may or may not prove useful in explaining the observed effects. Principle Components Analysis and FA will group the measurements, some of which will be shown to not add significantly to the ability to predict the observed effects. During the analysis, measured variables are added sequentially to the model until they are found to not add significantly to its ability to separate groups of measured variables. These tests are most useful in an iterative design in which environmental attributes and stressors can be measured, tested, and eliminated. A new set of variables that contains those significant from the first round plus new environmental measurements that were suggested as a result of the first analysis are then tested. Once again, those that do not contribute significantly to the predictive power of the model are eliminated, new environmental measurements are added, and the process is repeated.

There is no objective test for goodness of fit of the PCA or FA model. There is no means to measure how well the predicted effect matches with observed effects or the accuracy of assignment of measures of effects to groups. In reality, these models do not predict how the environmental attributes will change the measured effect; rather, they reduce the dimensionality of the problem into something that is simpler to conceptualize. In PCA and FA, the best way to evaluate the goodness of the model is to see whether the results are interpretable, i.e., do the groupings of variables into PCA or FA axes make ecological sense? In a good analysis, a high proportion of the variability is accounted for by only a few factors (i.e., the new variable formed by grouping selected environmental attributes or stressors), with the first factor being of the greatest magnitude. How many of the factors are needed to explain the structure of the data is fairly subjective, although some objective guides are available. The computer programs provide information about the degree of separation of the groups. Values greater than 1 mean that the factor contains at least as much information as one of the original variables. Therefore, all those factors with values greater than 1 likely contribute to the explanation of the structure of the dataset and the separation of the groups.

An ecologically based evaluation of significance is particularly important for PCA or FA for two reasons. First, there are many mathematical solutions that give similar levels of fit to the data. Selection of the "correct" solution can be made only through assessment of the ecological realism of the model, which is, of course, open to argument depending upon particular scientific viewpoints. Second, even very chaotic datasets can be reduced in complexity by this process, even if there are no true underlying processes that explain the observed groupings (i.e., a statistical artifact that has no biological meaning). Thus, PCA and FA often have been applied a posteriori to datasets that turn out to be too complex or "noisy" or violate too many assumptions for other statistical methods to be applied.

There are two major types of FA: exploratory and confirmatory. In exploratory FA, a large number of variables may be examined without really knowing which ones will be grouped or without understanding the potential underlying processes. Once knowledge has been gained and hypotheses are formulated about the ecological drivers, the study can be run again with data collected on variables that are known to be important forcing functions for the observed effects. The confirmatory FA is then run on these fewer, but carefully selected, variables.

Principle Components Analysis and FA study designs require that a large number of environmental attributes and stressors be analyzed (preferably 10 or greater). When setting up the study design, it is important to hypothesize which ecological processes might be the underlying cause of any measured change in the effect variables. Then, several environmental attributes that are representations of these processes should be measured. Since there likely will be more than one process that theoretically could cause the measures of effect to change, and since each process should have several environmental attributes associated with it, there will be a large number of environmental attribute variables for each measure of effect of interest.

The difference between PCA and FA is in the type of variance that is analyzed. Principal Components Analysis analyzes all the variance in the measured environmental attributes and stressors, while FA analyzes only the variance that is shared among these variables. In practice, PCA is used for data reduction (i.e., reducing the dataset to those groups of environmental attributes and stressors that are important to explain the observed or predicted effects). Factor Analysis is preferred when the goal is to detect structural relationships among the environmental attributes often as an alternative to the hierarchical Cluster Analysis described in the following section. However, they both return very similar results and frequently are used interchangeably.

Cluster Analysis

Cluster Analysis is another method for examining structure in a multivariate dataset. It is a hierarchical method that looks at the relative closeness of relationships among attributes of variables. This method puts like objects closest together and unlike objects farthest apart. Generally, Cluster Analysis is used to explore data, but it may be used to explain or discern patterns in observations. Examples of the usefulness of Cluster Analysis in ecological research include grouping of subsets of larger areas by variables such as species presence, physical factors (e.g., pH, organic matter, temperature of soil or water, percent moisture), and contaminant concentrations. This grouping would allow an exploration of whether one or more contaminants cause areas to cluster together or whether all similarities are explainable by physical factors only.

A typical result of Cluster Analysis is the hierarchical tree, which begins with each object in a class by itself. In very small steps, the criterion for what is or is not unique is relaxed, so objects can be grouped together as "like" objects. As the differentiating criteria are relaxed, larger and larger groups are formed or aggregated into clusters of increasingly dissimilar elements. In the last step, all objects are joined together. For each node, where a new cluster is formed, the criterion distance is calculated. Selection of which one to use may be based on personal preference or whether or not the data are categorical rather than continuous. Objects are then linked following one of various rules based on the calculated distances. They can be chained together by groupings based on nearest neighbor distances or grouped using complete linkages or through the use of many other methods.

If there is more than one measure of effect, both may be clustered simultaneously by "two-way joining." This is used when it is likely to expect that both the effects and the measures of exposure of environmental attributes will contribute simultaneously to the uncovering of meaningful patterns of clusters. For example, different measures of fitness may be measured, such as litter size, age structure, pregnancy rates, and sex ratios, for several populations of mice located in areas containing low, moderate, or high contaminant levels. Cluster Analysis can address the question of whether those populations that cluster together, based on fitness attributes, are all from an area of high contaminant levels, while those that are in other clusters have moderate, low, or no exposure.

Another cluster approach is the K-means clustering method, where there is prior knowledge of the number of clusters that should be formed. The program is instructed on how many clusters to make, and it finds the best combination of the variables to maximize the separation of that number of clusters. The difference in the means of the clusters is then examined to see if the clusters are significantly distinct. This method may force clusters to be formed that are inappropriate and should be used with caution.

Spatially Explicit Approaches

A relatively new approach to ecological assessment is the use of spatially explicit analyses. The increased computing power of desktop computers has made it possible to store and analyze very large sets of data, a requirement for the use of GIS. In these systems, all environmental variables are georeferenced, i.e., they are related to a particular point in space. Such information can then be used to make maps of the locations of each of the measured variables. All measurements of a single variable are plotted together and form what is known as a single data layer. For example, the presence or absence of various plant types can be entered into the database, with reference to a particular geographical location for each of the data entries. A vegetation map would then be produced showing where the various plant types exist. If the elevation at each of the geographical points also is known, an elevation map could be produced and layered on top of the vegetation map, similar to layering maps printed on clear sheets of acetate over each other. The correlation of vegetation type with elevation can then be made both visually and with more rigorous statistical methods incorporated into such GIS programs as ARC/INFO® (ESRI, Redlands, CA). It is easy to imagine how this process can be extended to multiple layers of variables, looking for the multivariate interactions among them.

Maps of ecological attributes may be made in various ways. Physical and vegetation attributes generally are recorded from fixed-wing aircraft aerial photography or from satellite imagery. These methods, while conceptually simple, are labor intensive because they must rely on fairly extensive groundtruthing (i.e., some effort must be made to ascertain that the photographs and the locations to which the attributes are described are correct as observed from the ground). Incorporation of biological information may be theoretical or may employ some level of empirical data. For example, assumptions can be made that associate animal species with particular combinations of vegetation type, elevation, or other physical attributes. Conversely, empirical data from censuses may be used to input biological information.

Once the various data layers are established and the correct correlations among them are defined, it becomes possible to construct "what if" scenarios. For example, if changes in vegetation type occur, then all other parameters associated with vegetation will change accordingly. Again, this analysis can be done through qualitative measures, by means of quantitative measures of how much habitat remains and then a semi-quantitative association with known species needs, or through more rigorous models that interconnect data layers.

For example, a model is available that integrates socioeconomic and ecological information with remotely sensed data to predict land-use change in the tropics under various agricultural scenarios (Dale et al. 1993; Southworth et al. 1991). This model is called the Dynamic Ecological Land Use Tenure Analysis (DELTA) and is a stochastic, dynamic computer simulation model developed to simulate patterns of human colonization and deforestation (Dale et al. 1994). It can, for example, predict areas of forest clearing under typical, worst-case, and innovative agricultural scenarios over a 40-year period. It was used by Dale et al. (1994) to examine the effects that such practices would have on faunal biodiversity in the tropical, moist lowland forests. Input parameters included the ability of species to cross open areas, the use of edge by species, and specialized habitat requirements such as use of fruits present at only particular seasons. It is easy to see how other specialized habitat requirements, such as the level of tolerance to application of forest pesticides, could be incorporated into the analysis as well. In this case, Dale et al. (1994) identified "suitable habitat" for their selected species (as defined by vegetation type and other parameters) and measured the size of habitat clusters. Habitats did not need to be adjacent to each other on the grid, but they needed to be within the maximum distance that a species would cross in order to be included in a particular cluster. Other anthropogenic environmental stressors were not included in this analysis. However, if habitat suitability had included a maximum pesticide concentration, or maximum number of applications, then it would have been possible to include these additional stresses in the analysis (e.g., a piece of habitat could be considered part of the cluster only if it met the pesticide-acceptability criteria).

In another example, contours of air pollution, such as SO_2 mission, developed from air dispersion models can be mapped at various scales (Carruthers 1998). This information could then be used as a data layer with thematic mapping of habitat types and species diversity. Areas where SO_2 are sufficiently high to cause known effects to vegetation can be identified and appropriate changes can be made in the vegetation layer. This would, in turn, result in changes in the animal biodiversity layer, allowing predictions to be made about how alterations in SO_2 emissions will affect biodiversity. Similarly, Sauget and Balent (1993) used spatially explicit information to map the relationships of agricultural practices including chemical use (e.g., nitrogen fertilizer inputs, herbicide inputs) with total number of birds and species diversity in France. They conducted a qualitative assessment of the interrelationship of agricultural practices with biodiversity, but it also would be possible to utilize more rigorous statistical methods.

Other similar hypothetical examples can be posed for how spatially explicit statistical analyses can be used to determine current or future risks from multiple environmental stressors, whether human-induced or naturally occurring changes. Because all data are necessarily georeferenced, the resulting information also is applicable only to the geographical area for which the data were gathered. Generally, these efforts are conducted over relatively large scales and may incorporate long time intervals in the analysis. These tools are still in their infancy with regard to use for predicting ecological consequences of human activity. To date, they have primarily been directed toward studying impacts of biodiversity as a result of land-use changes (e.g., the U.S. Fish and Wildlife Service Gap Analysis). However, the application to other environmental assessments including ecotoxicological concerns is a simple extrapolation of the same basic underlying principles.

Summary

The intent of this document is to provide the reader with a sense of what can be done to assess effects of multiple variables on single or multiple responses of ecosystem structure or function, using conventional multivariate statistical techniques. Hopefully, one is left with the sense that there currently are tools available that can be used to answer complex, large-scale environmental management questions. There certainly are limitations to each of these methods, and there are many pitfalls for the unwary. It is advisable that an experienced statistician be consulted during the design phase of any study to ensure that the various assumptions and requirements of a particular method are not be violated. Nevertheless, it is hoped that the reader is left with at least a basic understanding of multivariate statistical methods and can now more readily follow discussions in a general statistics text (e.g., Tabachnick and Fidell 1996).

The most important concept that was presented is that although there are various approaches that might be applicable in any given situation, the question being asked is the primary determinant of which type of method should be used. Inferential methods are used in classical hypothesis testing. These include the MANOVA or MANCOVA and time-series analysis (a subset of the ANOVA). These studies generally involve the use of mesocosms, treatment plots or fields, and, occasionally, manipulations of whole ecosystems. This approach has the advantage of being able to assign causality to observed responses to applied stressors in a more rigorous manner than is available from observational studies.

Observational ecotoxicological studies use various approaches to data analysis. Relationship assessment methods such as Regression Analysis and Canonical Correlation Analysis look for correlations between stressor variables and measures of effect. Management decisions that are based on correlational relationships should also include some knowledge of the possible ecological processes that establish plausible cause-and-effect relationships among the correlated variables. Otherwise, actions taken may not result in the desired effect. Thus, these types of studies add greatly to the "weight of evidence" but are not definitive cause-and-effect analyses. Cluster Analysis and Factor Analysis are used to look for fundamental, explainable ecological processes that are responsible for relating variables to each other or for causing an observed effect. They strive to ascertain which variables (in which combination) are required to accurately predict in which group each measure of effect belongs.

Given the complexity of ecological systems, it is not unusual to explore relationships among data using several different statistical methods prior to settling on a final "best" approach to analysis.

Examples of multivariate approaches

All of the examples presented in this appendix, except one, were run using a software program known as STATISTICA® by StatSoft, Inc., 2325 East 13th Street, Tulsa, OK 74104. It is a Windows-based statistical package with a variety of multivariate program modules and graphics capabilities. The STATISTICA manuals also provide examples of all of these approaches. This appendix is not an endorsement for STATISTICA, but it explains the origin of some of the results.

Multivariate Analyses of Variance Example

Avian reproduction studies involve several measurements of reproductive performance in birds exposed for several months to a test substance through the diet. Many of these measurements are intercorrelated, especially the series of count variables such as number of eggs laid, number set, number fertile, and number hatched. All the variables are considered important indicators of potential impacts on productivity. However, when variables are intercorrelated, the overall error rate cannot be assessed, leading to interference with the statistical decision-making. Multivariate procedures are more appropriate because the algorithms incorporate intercorrelation in the analysis.

Consider a dataset from an avian reproduction study with a control group and two dietary treatment groups (see Table A-1). There were 15 or 16 pairs per treatment. The study measured the number of eggs laid per pair during the course of the study (EGGSLAID), eggshell thickness (EGGSHELL), number of eggs set in the incubator (EGGS_SET), number of eggs viable on days 11 (VIA_D11) and 18 (VIA_D18) of incubation, number of live hatchlings (HATCH), and number of 14-day-old surviving hatchlings (SURVIVOR).

Table A-1 Dataset from avian reproduction study

TRT	EGGSLAID	EGGSHELL	EGGS_SET	VIA_D11	VIA_D18	HATCH	SURVIVOR
0	58	0.409	53	49	48	8	5
0	80	0.395	80	78	76	30	25
0	53	0.406	49	49	48	24	21
0	49	0.376	45	45	45	24	22
0	31	0.413	30	28	28	13	13
0	72	0.405	68	68	68	35	33
0	66	0.416	61	56	56	50	31
0	49	0.400	44	36	36	25	22
0	84	0.393	78	73	71	28	25

Multiple Stressors in Ecological Risk and Impact Assessment: Approaches to Risk Estimation. Susan A. Ferenc and Jeffery A. Foran, editors. ©2000 Society of Environmental Toxicology and Chemistry (SETAC). ISBN 1-880611-40-6

Table A-1 continued

TRT	EGGSLAID	EGGSHELL	EGGS_SET	VIA_D11	VIA_D18	HATCH	SURVIVOR
0	78	0.424	72	63	63	31	29
0	58	0.358	53	45	43	36	30
0	66	0.385	59	57	56	29	29
0	49	0.342	45	45	45	30	30
0	49	0.397	46	46	46	35	30
0	44	0.391	39	39	38	30	26
1	38	0.382	34	26	26	22	18
1	84	0.385	79	77	77	39	31
1	73	0.400	69	57	57	26	22
1	36	0.379	32	30	29	13	11
1	50	0.314	47	43	43	12	11
1	42	0.399	38	36	36	20	13
1	85	0.374	80	79	79	20	18
1	72	0.391	66	64	64	48	37
1	84	0.401	78	77	77	38	32
1	52	0.401	48	46	46	18	18
1	32	0.414	28	28	28	7	5
1	52	0.387	48	38	37	22	17
1	60	0.375	55	51	51	25	23
1	86	0.365	80	76	75	37	37
1	36	0.373	34	28	27	12	9
1	42	0.405	39	38	38	21	19
2	54	0.380	49	46	45	20	16
2	75	0.368	67	57	57	21	16
2	75	0.397	70	63	61	35	30
2	67	0.382	61	61	61	23	15
2	22	0.370	21	20	20	11	9
2	86	0.365	80	54	54	30	28
2	87	0.372	79	78	78	36	32
2	51	0.375	47	44	44	32	27
2	92	0.386	85	79	79	20	17
2	71	0.390	65	51	51	18	14
2	86	0.375	78	76	76	43	37
2	68	0.374	63	57	57	21	18
2	19	0.402	18	9	9	7	6
2	39	0.360	34	32	32	10	5
2	45	0.385	41	24	24	6	6
2	32	0.375	30	22	22	12	10

When a one-way ANOVA is conducted on each variable independently, none produces a statistically significant overall p value. However, the multivariate Wilks' Lambda Rao test applied to the same suite of variables indicates that there is a statistically significant difference (p = 0.047). This discrepancy indicates that there is a significant pattern of treatment effect in one or more of the variables measured, even though this pattern is not identified by viewing each variable in isolation.

After obtaining a significant multivariate test for a particular main effect or interaction, customarily one would examine the univariate F test for each variable to interpret the respective effect and to determine which of the dependent variables contributed to the overall effect, as the following example illustrates:

Variable	Mean square effect	Mean square error	F(df 2,44)	p-level
EGGSLAID	31.68	399.95	0.079	0.924
EGGSHELL	0.0010	0.0004	2.528	0.091
EGGS_SET	17.58	353.46	0.050	0.952
VIA_D11	47.82	352.85	0.136	0.874
VIA_D18	35.26	350.12	0.101	0.904
HATCH	195.52	116.42	1.679	0.198
SURVIVOR	188.83	84.95	2.223	0.120

			Treatment group means				
TRT	EGGSLAID	EGGSHELL	EGGS_SET	VIA_D11	VIA_D18	HATCH	SURVIVOR
0	59.1	0.394	54.8	51.8	51.1	28.5	24.7
10	57.8	0.384	53.4	49.6	49.4	23.8	20.1
20	60.6	0.378	55.5	48.3	48.1	21.6	17.9

Multivariate Analyses of Covariance Example

Consider an avian reproduction test with a control group and three treatment groups having 10 pairs each in which there is a concern that the response to chemical treatment may be delayed in the test population. The study was designed to measure response at discrete periods before and after treatment to examine the changes in response over time. Measurements of an endpoint, such as number of eggs laid or number of hatchlings, were made during a two-week pretreatment (PRE) period and during two-week intervals of the six-week treatment period (Time 1, Time 2, and Time 3). The column MEAN in the following example represents the mean of the three treatment time periods, but could just as easily represent the sum.

TRT	PRE	TIME 1	TIME 2	TIME 3	MEAN	TRT	PRE	TIME 1	TIME 2	TIME 3	MEAN
0	14	13	13	14	13.3	2	8	9	9	9	9.0
0	13	14	12	12	12.7	2	13	10	11	11	10.7
0	10	10	9	9	9.3	2	12	10	12	11	11.0
0	12	11	13	11	11.7	2	9	10	9	9	9.3
0	9	8	11	10	9.7	2	13	12	12	11	11.7
0	11	14	12	12	12.7	2	9	9	10	8	9.0
0	8	9	9	7	8.3	2	14	13	11	13	12.3
0	11	11	11	12	11.3	2	12	11	13	12	12.0
0	13	12	12	13	12.3	2	12	10	12	10	10.7
0	14	11	11	13	11.7	2	13	14	14	11	13.0
Mean	11.5	11.3	11.3	11.3	11.3	Mean	11.5	10.8	11.3	10.5	10.9
1	13	12	13	12	12.3	3	12	12	11	8	10.3
1	12	14	13	14	13.7	3	8	7	7	6	6.7
1	9	8	9	7	8.0	3	12	13	12	12	12.3
1	13	11	11	13	11.7	3	8	10	9	7	8.7
1	10	11	11	11	11.0	3	13	12	11	10	11.0
1	14	13	12	14	13.0	3	13	12	11	9	10.7
1	8	11	10	8	9.7	3	11	8	10	9	9.0
1	14	12	13	11	12.0	3	14	14	12	10	12.0
1	9	10	8	8	8.7	3	12	13	11	9	11.0
1	13	12	12	14	12.7	3	12	13	13	11	12.3
Mean	11.5	11.4	11.2	11.2	11.3	Mean	11.5	11.4	10.7	9.1	10.4

Current practice for analyzing data from avian reproduction studies is to conduct a one-way ANOVA to response variables representing the entire treatment period, such as the MEAN values. If a one-way ANOVA is applied to the MEAN values in Table A-2, the test fails to reject the null hypothesis that all treatments are equal ($p = 0.61$). The PRE values could be used as a covariate in the analysis to adjust for individual variation among individuals in their response prior to treatment. If an

Table A-2 (a) One-way ANOVA on MEAN values representing the entire treatment period; (b) One-way ANCOVA on MEAN values representing the entire treatment period and PRE values used as a covariate; (c) MANCOVA on repeated measures of effect (T1, T2, T3) and PRE values used as a covariate

Source of variation	df	Mean square	F value	p-level
TRT	3	1.7731	0.60826	0.6140
Error	36	2.9151		

Source of variation	df	Mean square	F value	p-level
TRT	3	1.7731	2.0683	0.1222
Error	35	0.8573		

Source of variation	df	Mean square	F value	p-level
TRT	3	5.3194	2.0683	0.1222
Error	35	2.5719		
TIME	2	5.7333	5.8415	0.0045
TRT x TIME	6	3.3111	3.3735	0.0055*
Error	72	0.9815		

*Univariate test of TRT × TIME interaction. The multivariate Wilks' Lambda Roa test is significant at $p = 0.02002$

ANCOVA is applied to the MEAN values using the PRE values as covariates, the test still fails to reject the null hypothesis (p = 0.12). However, if a Multivariate ANCOVA is applied using Time 1, Time 2, and Time 3 as three repeated measures of effect in time and PRE values as covariates, then the factor time (i.e., the repeated measures) and the treatment by time interaction are statistically significant (the multivariate test of the interaction has p = 0.02). The source of the statistical difference can be identified by setting up specific contrasts within the treatment by time interaction. In this example, the response to the chemical occurred only after a few weeks of exposure (see Figure A-1). Averaging the response over the entire treatment period obscured the effects observed in the last two weeks of the study.

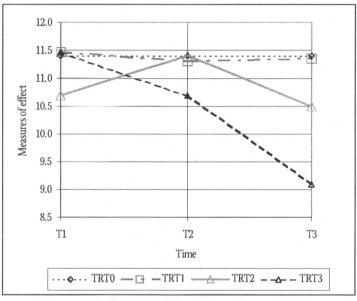

Figure A-1 Two-way interaction

Multiple Regression Analysis Example

Multiple regression is used to analyze the relationship between several independent variables (e.g., measures of stressor intensity or characterizations of habitat quality) and a dependent variable (e.g., population growth rate or density). In the following example, four independent variables (concentration of lead in soil, concentration of cadmium in the soil, density of shrubs, and number of voles present) were considered in relation to the dependent variable population of deer mice (*Peromyscus maniculatus*). The analysis results in a multiple regression equation that predicts the response based on the values of the various measures. In this example, the response variable is the population density of deer mice at 25 surveyed sites, and the environmental variables are measures of habitat quality.

In this example, the multiple regression is run using a forward stepwise procedure to bring one variable at a time into the regression. This procedure includes the variables into the model that best fit the data, while leaving out variables that do not significantly contribute to the overall regression. The forward stepwise procedure also can drop variables that were added previously if that improves the fit of the model. In this example, illustrated by Table A-3, density of shrubs was the first variable added because it explained 80% of the variation in the number of deer mice at a site (i.e., $R^2 = 0.805$). The second variable added was soil lead concentration, explaining an additional 13% of the variation in the number of mice, followed by number of voles present, explaining 3% of the variation. Soil cadmium concentration was not included in the final regression equation, since it did not improve the

Table A-3 (a) Regression summary for dependent variable: DEER MICE; (b) Summary of stepwise regression for dependent variable: DEER MICE; (c) Multiple regression example dataset

	BETA	St. Error of BETA	B	St. Error of B	t(21)	p-level
Intercept			−124.200	9.874	−12.578	0.000000
SHRUB DENSITY	0.619	0.069	1.357	0.152	8.937	0.000000
SOIL LEAD	0.310	0.046	0.296	0.044	6.784	0.000001
NO. VOLES	0.284	0.072	0.517	0.131	3.948	0.000735

	Step +in/−out	Multiple R	Multiple R^2	R^2 change	F to enter/ remove	p-level
SHRUB DENSITY	1	0.897	0.805	0.805	94.782	0.0000000
SOIL LEAD	2	0.966	0.933	0.128	42.116	0.0000019
NO. VOLES	3	0.981	0.962	0.029	15.588	0.0007353

Observation	SOIL LEAD	SOIL CADMIUM	NO. SHRUBS	NO. VOLES	DEER MICE
1	86	110	100	87	88
2	62	97	99	100	80
3	110	107	103	103	96
4	101	117	93	95	76
5	100	101	95	88	80
6	78	85	95	84	73
7	120	77	80	74	58
8	105	122	116	102	116
9	112	119	106	105	104
10	120	89	105	97	99
11	87	81	90	88	64
12	133	120	113	108	126
13	140	121	96	89	94
14	84	113	98	78	71
15	106	102	109	109	111
16	109	129	102	108	109
17	104	83	100	102	100
18	150	118	107	110	127
19	98	125	108	95	99
20	120	94	95	90	82
21	74	121	91	85	67
22	96	114	114	103	109
23	104	73	93	80	78
24	94	121	115	104	115
25	91	129	97	83	83

fit of the model. The overall regression model had an $R^2 = 0.962$ and can be presented as follows:

Number of mice $= -124.2 + 1.36 \times$ shrub density $+ 0.30 \times$ soil lead $+ 0.52 \times$ soil moisture

Principle Components Analysis Example 1

An example of Principal Component Analysis (PCA) was presented by Baril et al. (1994) to evaluate interspecies variation in acute toxicity of pesticides to birds. In one analysis involving eight species of birds and 22 pesticides, PCA was used to rank the toxicity of the pesticides and to identify species by degree of sensitivity to acute poisoning. Table A-4 illustrates the utility of PCA for ranking variables and for identifying grouping with similar loading values.

Principle Components Analysis Example 2

In the dataset used in the MANOVA example (see Table A-1), the concerns about intercorrelation of the measures of avian reproduction can be examined using PCA. For example, the associations among the seven reproduction variables could be examined for all the experimental units (i.e., bird pairs) in the study. Three principle components emerge with eigenvalues greater than 0.8. The first factor is represented

Table A-4 Results of the PCA run on 8 species and 22 chemicals

Analysis by chemical				
Loading of species components:		Loading of chemicals on components:		
Species	1st	Chemical	1st	
Pheasant	0.3069	Fensulfothion	-5.6243	Most toxic
Mallard	0.3452	Carbofuran	-3.3760	
Red-winged blackbird	0.3717	Aldicarb	-2.5979	
Starling	0.2763	Monocrotophos	-2.0906	
Japanese quail	0.3479	Dicrotophos	-2.0418	
House sparrow	0.3926	Phosphamidon	-1.3506	
Common grackle	0.3802	Mevinphos	-1.2685	
Rock dove	0.3903	Parathion	-1.2463	
		Diazinon	-0.0540	
% Variation explained	67%	EPN	-0.0100	
		Mexacarbate	0.0466	
		Ethoprop	0.1663	
		Demeton	0.2301	
		Fenthion	0.2935	
		Coumaphos	0.5708	
		Propoxur	1.8954	
		Dichlorvos	2.0665	
		Methiocarb	2.3771	
		Chlorpyrifos-ethyl	2.6250	
		Chlorfenvinphos	3.0052	
		Bufencarb	3.1138	
		Methomyl	3.2698	Least toxic

Table A-4 continued

				Analysis by species		
Loading of chemicals on components:					Loading of species components:	
Chemical	1st	2nd	3rd	Species	1st	
Aldicarb	0.2244	0.0693	-0.1035	Red-winged blackbird	-5.0319	Most sensitive
Bufencarb	0.3523	-1.1234	0.0685	Common grackle	-0.8876	
Carbofuran	0.3172	-0.1654	0.1930	House sparrow	-0.8814	
Chlorfenvinphos	0.0819	-0.0366	-0.4557	Mallard	-0.6598	
Chlorpyrifos-ethyl	0.0733	0.3716	0.1388	Rock dove	-0.0717	
Coumaphos	0.2428	0.2338	0.0662	Pheasant	2.3547	
Demeton	0.0251	0.0116	0.1657	Japanese quail	2.4248	
Diazinon	0.1720	0.1176	0.4246	Starling	2.7528	Least sensitive
Dichlorvos	0.1112	0.0683	0.2420			
Dicrotophos	0.3101	0.1493	0.0866			
EPN	0.2018	-0.3845	0.0321			
Ethoprop	0.0622	0.3692	-0.1769			
Fensulfothion	0.2952	-0.0171	-0.2723			
Fenthion	0.2278	-0.2513	-0.0052			
Methiocarb	0.1448	-0.3164	-0.1288			
Methomyl	0.1585	0.1538	-0.1154			
Mevinphos	0.1761	0.3087	-0.1202			
Mexacarbate	-0.0358	0.0284	0.4806			
Monocrotophos	0.2677	0.2362	-0.1071			
Parathion	0.2464	-0.3008	0.0693			
Phosphamidon	0.2333	0.0489	0.1372			
Propoxur	0.2576	0.0369	-0.1591			
% Variation Explained	30%	20%	18%			

by the variables EGGSLAID, EGGS_SET, VIA_D11, and VIA_D18, reflecting the high correlation among these variables (Table A-5). The second factor is represented by EGGSHELL, and the third by HATCH and SURVIVOR. Figure A-2, representing the factor loadings for the three principle components, illustrates how the seven measured variables essentially can be collapsed into three distinct variables.

Table A-5 Factor loadings (Varimax normalized)

Variable	Factor 1	Factor 2	Factor 3
EGGSLAID	0.940	-0.016	0.310
EGGSHELL	-0.005	0.999	0.033
EGGS_SET	0.942	-0.007	0.306
VIA_D11	0.923	0.012	0.356
VIA_D18	0.924	0.011	0.355
HATCH	0.372	0.059	0.916
SURVIVOR	0.391	0.000	0.910
Explained Variation	3.767	1.003	2.110
Proportion of Total	0.538	0.143	0.301

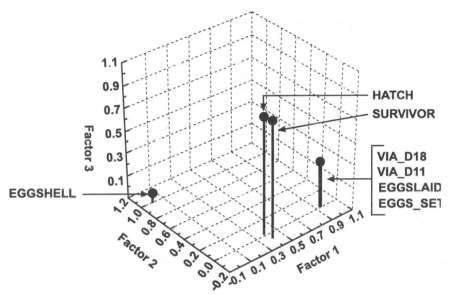

Figure A-2 Factor loadings: Factor 1 versus Factor 2 versus Factor 3

Principle Components Analysis Example 3

Consider a study of Wisconsin forests where 10 sampling units are surveyed. Measurements are taken on the relative abundance of eight tree species on each site, as well as metrics of soil texture (SOIL_TXT) and stand diversity (STAND_DY).

SAMPLE UNIT	BUR_OAK	BL_OAK	WH_OAK	RED_OAK	AM_ELM	BASSWOOD	IRONWOOD	SG_MAPLE	SOIL_TXT	STAND_DY
1	9	8	5	3	2	0	0	0	4	1
2	8	9	4	4	2	0	0	0	5	2
3	3	8	9	0	4	0	0	0	3	1
4	5	7	9	6	5	0	0	0	2	2
5	6	0	7	9	6	2	0	0	1	1
6	0	0	7	8	0	7	0	5	1	3
7	5	0	4	7	5	6	7	4	2	3
8	0	0	6	6	0	6	4	8	1	5
9	0	0	0	4	2	7	6	8	1	4
10	0	0	2	3	5	6	5	9	1	5

The associations among sampling units can be examined with PCA. Three principle components emerge with eigenvalues greater than 1.0. The first factor is represented by SU1, SU2, SU3, SU4, SU9, and SU10, with the first four sampling units characterized as the opposite of the last two units (Table A-6). The second and third factors are dominated by the remaining four sampling units. Figure A-3 represents the factor loadings for Principle Components 1 and 2 and illustrates the relative associations of the sampling units.

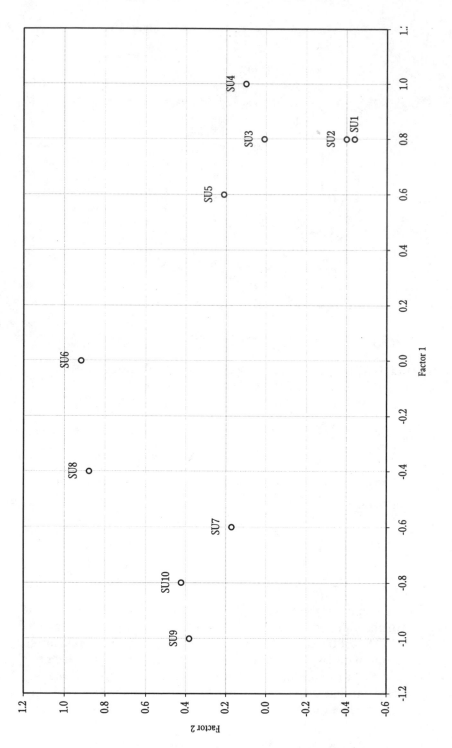

Figure A-3 Factor loadings: Factor 1 versus Factor 2

Table A-6 Factor loadings (Varimax normalized) Extraction: principal components

	Factor 1	Factor 2	Factor 3
SU1	0.861	−0.382	0.007
SU2	0.844	−0.404	−0.077
SU3	0.871	0.007	−0.278
SU4	0.934	0.111	0.218
SU5	0.469	0.204	0.833
SU6	−0.028	0.917	0.276
SU7	−0.496	0.147	0.822
SU8	−0.422	0.869	0.049
SU9	−0.901	0.370	−0.011
SU10	−0.817	0.438	−0.064
Explained Variation	5.209	2.309	1.584
Proportion of Total	0.521	0.231	0.158

Alternatively, one could examine the associations among tree species across the 10 sampling units. Three principle components emerge with eigenvalues greater than 1.0 (Table A-7). The first factor is represented by the close association BASSWOOD, IRONWOOD, and SG_MAPLE, which are opposite of WH_OAK. The second factor is defined by BL_OAK and RED_OAK at opposite ends of the spectrum. The third factor is defined by AM_ELM. BUR_OAK does not figure significantly into any of the three factors. Figure A-4 represents the factor loadings for principle components 1 and 2 and illustrates the relative associations of the tree species.

Table A-7 Factor loadings (Varimax normalized) Extraction: principal components

	Factor 1	Factor 2	Factor 3
BUR_OAK	0.562	−0.281	0.595
BL_OAK	0.638	−0.730	0.149
WH_OAK	0.842	0.199	−0.017
RED_OAK	0.103	0.933	0.065
AM_ELM	−0.043	0.091	0.910
BASSWOOD	−0.753	0.492	−0.408
IRONWOOD	−0.936	0.113	0.066
SG_MAPLE	−0.842	0.202	−0.457
Explained Variation	3.596	1.826	1.589
Proportion of Total	0.450	0.228	0.199

Cluster Analysis Example 1

Associations among variables in the MANOVA dataset also can be examined using Cluster Analysis. Using the Statistica® program for Cluster Analysis, a tree diagram

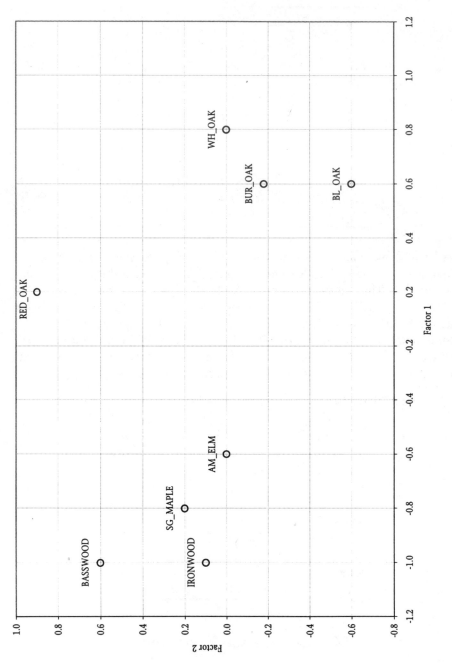

Figure A-4 Factor loadings: Factor 1 versus Factor 2

can be constructed showing the Euclidean distances among variables (Figure A-5). The smaller the linkage distance, the more similar are two variables of variable groups.

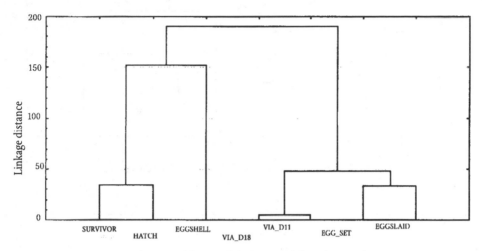

Figure A-5 Tree diagram for 7 variables (Single linkage, Euclidean distances)

Cluster Analysis Example 2

Consider a study of Wisconsin forests where 10 sampling units are surveyed. Measurements are taken on the relative abundance of eight tree species on each site, as well as metrics of soil texture (SOIL_TXT) and stand diversity (STAND_DY).

SAMPLE UNIT	BUR_OAK	BL_OAK	WH_OAK	RED_OAK	AM_ELM	BASSWOOD	IRONWOOD	SG_MAPLE	SOIL_TXT	STAND_DY
1	9	8	5	3	2	0	0	0	4	1
2	8	9	4	4	2	0	0	0	5	2
3	3	8	9	0	4	0	0	0	3	1
4	5	7	9	6	5	0	0	0	2	2
5	6	0	7	9	6	2	0	0	1	1
6	0	0	7	8	0	7	0	5	1	3
7	5	0	4	7	5	6	7	4	2	3
8	0	0	6	6	0	6	4	8	1	5
9	0	0	0	4	2	7	6	8	1	4
10	0	0	2	3	5	6	5	9	1	5

The similarity of the 10 sampling units can be examined using a tree diagram of the Euclidean distances among units (Figure A-6). The smaller the linkage distance, the more similar are the characteristics among sites. Alternatively, one may want to look at the associations among the eight tree species across the 10 sampling units (Figure A-7). In this case the smaller the linkage distances, the more likely are species or species groups to coexist.

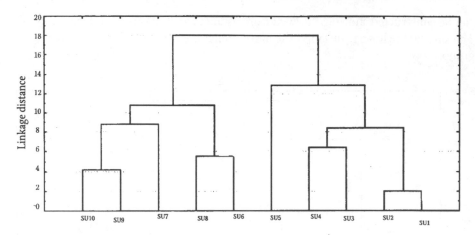

Figure A-6 Tree diagram for 10 variables (complete linkage, Euclidean distances)

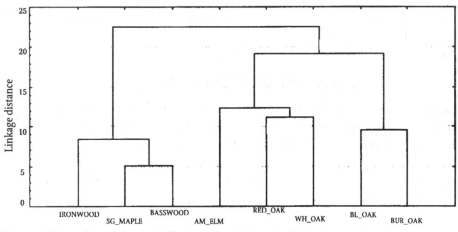

Figure A-7 Tree diagram for 8 variables (complete linkage; Euclidean distances)

Discriminant Function Analysis Example

Based on the PCA results from the Wisconsin forest example, one could use the factor loadings from the first principal component to classify the 10 sampling units into two groups consisting of SU1 through SU5 in one group and SU6 through SU10 in another. Discriminant Function Analysis considers each of the forest measurements on species abundance, soil texture, and stand diversity to test whether each sampling unit would be correctly assigned to the two groups defined by PCA. A stepwise analysis with five steps brings measurement variables into the analysis in the following order: BASSWOOD, BL_OAK, STAND_DY, IRONWOOD, and

WH_OAK. The analysis defines a functional axis with the following standardized coefficients for the five measures: 3.1, 2.5, 0.87, 1.4, and 1.3. Finally, the Discriminant Function Analysis produces a classification matrix to determine what proportion of the sampling units are correctly classified into groups. In this example, 100% of the sampling units are classified correctly (Table A-8).

Table A-8 (a) Discriminant Function Analysis summary; and (b) classification matrix

	Wilks' Lambda	Partial Lambda	F-remove (1,4)	p-level	Toler.	1-Toler. (R^2)
BASSWOOD	0.1206	0.0468	81.4642	0.0008	0.0978	0.9022
BL_OAK	0.0226	0.2495	12.0346	0.0256	0.1205	0.8795
STAND_DY	0.0106	0.5338	3.4931	0.1350	0.6125	0.3875
IRONWOOD	0.0142	0.3965	6.0885	0.0691	0.3015	0.6985
WH_OAK	0.0115	0.4909	4.1490	0.1113	0.3202	0.6798

Step 5, N of variables in model: 5; Grouping: GROUP (2 groups)
Wilks' Lambda: .00565 approx. F (5,4) = 140.91 p < .0001

	Percent Correct	Group 1 p = 0.50	Group 2 p = 0.50
Group 1	100	5	0
Group 2	100	0	5
Total	100	5	5

Rows: Observed classifications
Columns: Predicted classifications

References

Baril A, Jobin B, Mineau P, Collins BT. 1994. A consideration of inter-species variability in the use of the median lethal dose (LD_{50}) in avian risk assessment. Technical Report Series No. 216, Canadian Wildlife Service, Headquarters. Ottawa, Ontario, Canada: Environmental Canada.

Brezonik PL, Baker LA, Eaton JR, Frost TM, Garrison P, Kratz TK, Magnuson JJ, Rose WJ,. Shepard BK, Swenson WA, Watras CJ, Webster KE. 1986. Experimental acidification of Little Rock Lake, Wisconsin. *Water Air Soil Pollut* 31:157–163.

Carruthers D. 1998. Air dispersion modeling. In: Douben PET, editor. Pollution risk assessment and management. Chichester UK: Wiley. p 115–132.

Dale VH, O'Neill RV, Southworth F. 1993. Causes and effects of land-use change in central Rondônia, Brazil. *Photog Eng Remote Sensing* 59:997–1005.

Dale VH, Pearson SM, Offerman HL, O'Neill RV. 1994. Relating patterns of land-use change to faunal biodiversity in the Central Amazon. *Conserv Biol* 8:1027–1036.

Fairbrother A, Landis WG, Dominguez S, Shiroyama T, Buchholz P, Roze MJ, Matthews GB. 1998. A novel nonmetric multivariate approach to the evaluation of biomarkers in terrestrial field studies. *Ecotoxicology* 7:1–10.

Hall RJ, Likens GE. 1980. Ecological aspects of whole-stream acidification. In: Shriner DS, Raymond CR, Lindberg SE, editors. Atmospheric sulfur deposition: environmental impacts and health effects. Ann Arbor MI: Ann Arbor Science. p 443–451.

Lacher Jr TE, Willig MR. 1994. Univariate and multivariate approaches to the analysis of ecotoxicological data. In: Kendall RJ, Lacher Jr TE, editors. Wildlife toxicology and population modeling: integrated studies of agroecosystems. Boca Raton FL: Lewis. p 425–438.

Landis WG, Matthews RA, Markiewicz AJ, Slough NA, Matthews GB. 1993a. Multivariate analysis of the impacts of the turbine fuel Jet-A using a microcosm toxicity test. *J Environ Sci* 2:113–130.

Landis WG, Matthews RA, Markiewicz AJ, Matthews GB. 1993. Multivariate analysis of the impacts of the turbine fuel JP-4 in a microcosm toxicity test with implications for the evaluation of ecosystem dynamics and risk assessment. *Ecotoxicology* 2:271–300.

Landis WG, Matthews GB, Matthews RA, and Sergeant A. 1994. Application of multivariate techniques to endpoint determination, selection and evaluation in ecological risk assessment. *Environ Toxicol Chem* 13:1917–1927.

Landis WG, Matthews RA, Matthews GB. 1996. The layered and historical nature of ecological systems and the risk assessment of pesticides. *Environ Toxicol Chem* 15:432–440.

Matthews GB, Hearne J. 1991. Clustering without a metric. *IEEE Transactions on Pattern Analysis and Machine Intelligence* 13:175–184.

Matthews GB, Matthews RA. 1990. A model for describing community changes. Pesticides in natural systems: How can their effects be monitored? Proceedings of the Conference, Environ. Res. Lab./ ORD; Corvallis OR. EPA-9109/9-91/011.

Matthews GB, Matthews RA, Landis WG. 1995. Nonmetric conceptual clustering in ecology and ecotoxicology. *AI Appl* 9:41–48.

Sauget N, Balent G. 1993. The diversity of agricultural practices and landscape dynamics: the case of a Hill Region in the southwest of France. In: Bunce et al., editors. Landscape ecology and agroecosystems. Boca Raton FL: Lewis. p 113–130.

Schindler DW, Mills KH, Malley DF, Findlay DL, Shearer JA, Davies IJ, Turner MA, Linsey GA, Cruikshank DR. 1985. Long-term ecosystem stress: the effects of years of experimental acidification on a small lake. *Science* 228:1395–1399.

Southworth F, Dale VH, O'Neill RV. 1991. Contrasting patterns of land use in Rondônia, Brazil: simulating the effects of carbon release. *Int Soc Sci J* 130:681–698.

Tabachnick BG, Fidell LS. 1996. Using multivariate statistics (3rd ed.). New York: Harper Collins College Publishers Inc.

[USEPA] U.S. Environmental Protection Agency. 1998. Guidelines for ecological risk assessment. Washington DC: USEPA Risk Assessment Forum. EPA/630/R-95/002F.

Watras CJ, Frost TM. 1989. Little Rock Lake (Wisconsin): perspectives on an experimental ecosystem approach to seepage lake acidification. *Arch Environ Contam Toxicol* 18:157–165.

CHAPTER 4

Estimating Ecological Risks of Multiple Stressors: Advanced Methods and Difficult Issues

Dwayne R.J. Moore and Steven M. Bartell

The objectives of this paper are to describe some of the difficult issues confronting assessors charged with estimating risks posed to nonhuman biota by multiple stressors and some of the advanced methods that are being developed to deal with these issues. Because these methods require a great deal of expertise and are data intensive, their use should be restricted to assessments that 1) have gone through several iterations to eliminate risk scenarios of little concern or those requiring immediate risk management actions, 2) involve resources, such as commercial fisheries, for which the consequences of an incorrect decision are high, and 3) have or can obtain sufficient information to conduct a defensible analysis. This paper focuses on two subject areas—uncertainty analysis and ecological modeling. There are many sources of uncertainty in a multiple stressors assessment. These sources of uncertainty can have important consequences on decision-making, and, therefore, an uncertainty analysis should be considered an integral part of any higher-tier assessment involving multiple stressors. We view ecological modeling as critical because it may be the only means available to assessors to characterize risks to highly valued resources from multiple stressors, determine the sources of the risk, and evaluate likely risk reductions that could be achieved with various remediation options.

Estimating effects of multiple stressors to biota is a difficult problem. Stressors usually are disparate in nature and interact on differing temporal and spatial scales.

CHAPTER PREVIEW

Multiple Stressors in Ecological Risk and Impact Assessment: Approaches to Risk Estimation. Susan A. Ferenc and Jeffery A. Foran, editors.
©2000 Society of Environmental Toxicology and Chemistry (SETAC). ISBN 1-880611-40-6

For example, fisheries resources may be impacted simultaneously by local contamination, regional exploitation, and global warming. These and other factors may cause effects on one or more life stages of sensitive populations. Effects are both direct, such as increased mortality or decreased fecundity, and indirect, as in altered predator and prey dynamics (Rose et al. 1993). Effects to exposed subpopulations also can have ecologically significant effects on unexposed subpopulations, the so-called action at a distance (Landis et al. 1998; Spromberg et al. 1998). Nonlinear dynamics of populations and meta-populations (i.e., subpopulations connected by immigration and emigration) means that even small changes in, for example, population growth rate induced by multiple stressors could potentially result in chaotic behavior (May 1974; May and Oster 1976; Schaffer and Kot 1986; Allen 1990). When several stressors vary simultaneously, interactive effects are likely. The number of possible combinations of stressors and potentially affected populations, both exposed and unexposed, far outstrips our ability to obtain sufficient information from controlled field studies to confidently predict the effects of multiple stressors.

Because multiple-stressor assessments are complex, the assessment must be focused early on. It is not possible to estimate the impacts of all potential stressors on all biota at all levels of organization. Thus, the focus of the assessment must be narrowed to receptors that are highly valued, sensitive, and at greatest risk of exposure. This focusing is done during problem formulation and in the early tiers of the assessment process. The matrix approach outlined in Foran and Ferenc (1999) is one means of accomplishing this task. This approach uses a stepwise or iterative process to determine risk scenarios (*sensu* Kaplan and Garrick 1981) in need of more detailed analysis or immediate risk-management actions. In the earliest iteration, qualitative judgments of likelihood and consequence are used to eliminate risk scenarios of little or no concern (i.e., those combinations of stressors and receptors that have low likelihoods of causing even minor ecological effects). Successively more detailed, quantitative analyses are used in subsequent iterations to eliminate low-risk scenarios, to characterize the probabilities and ecological consequences of the remaining risk scenarios, and to choose among possible remediation options. The initial identification of risk scenarios and their subsequent refinements should be made in consultation with risk managers and interested parties (Moore and Biddinger 1995; PCC 1997a, 1997b; USEPA 1998; Landis et al. 1998).

Ecological risk assessments involving multiple stressors are uncertain because of the complexity of ecological systems and the economic costs of collecting the data required to predict the behavior of such systems. Most ecological risk assessments conducted to date have not been supported by an explicit uncertainty analysis. As a result, risk managers and interested parties generally are not aware of the extent of uncertainty in the risk assessment and its consequences to the decision-making process. Regulated parties often believe that excessively conservative assumptions were used, environmental advocates believe that important uncertainties were overlooked, and risk managers tend to believe that the assessment results are more precise than warranted on appeal to the available evidence. An open and explicit process of uncertainty analysis can reduce suspicion and misapprehension (Warren-Hicks and Moore 1998). Individuals and organizations aware of the uncertainties in a multiple-stressor assessment will not find point estimates credible. Given that many assessments of multiple stressors are being conducted over large regions or for entire watersheds, we can expect much public scrutiny and media attention. Gaining and maintaining credibility through an open acknowledgment and characterization of uncertainties in a multiple-stressor assessment will be crucial to the success of the decision-making process. In the next part of this chapter, we discuss the kinds of uncertainty that arise in multiple-stressor assessments and describe methods that may be used to quantify uncertainty. Simple case studies illustrating how the risks of several stressors can be combined also are provided.

To be relevant to society and decision-makers, regulatory agencies are beginning to promote assessments of effects at higher levels of organization (e.g., population, community, ecosystem) (Harwell et al. 1994; Environment Canada 1994, 1997; USEPA 1998; Landis et al. 1998), an objective that requires an understanding of current ecological theories and issues (Moore 1998). Given that controlled field studies will be impractical for most multiple-stressor risk scenarios, we believe that ecological modeling will be the tool of choice for assessing possible effects at higher levels of organization. This will be true particularly for prospective assessments. In this chapter we discuss several important ecological issues that should be considered in higher-tier, multiple-stressor assessments and briefly describe methods that may be used to explore these issues. A community-level case study will be presented to illustrate how ecological models can be used in a multiple-stressor assessment.

Quantifying Uncertainty

Uncertainties abound in multiple-stressor assessments. In addition to the usual gamut of uncertainties encountered in single-stressor assessments, we can expect uncertainties to arise because of lack of information on the way that stressors interact with each other and with biota. Multiple-stressor assessments tend to focus on larger spatial scales (e.g., watersheds, regions) and are concerned with effects at higher levels of organization (e.g., ecosystem), subject areas for which we lack experience in ecological risk assessment. Ignoring these uncertainties or treating them with mere guesses (i.e., order-of-magnitude safety factors) is not a credible approach. Quantifying uncertainty in any ecological risk assessment, let alone a multiple-stressor assessment, is, however, not a trivial exercise. In this section, we briefly discuss the different types of uncertainty and issues that may be encountered in multiple-stressor assessments and very briefly describe methods that can be used to quantify such uncertainties.

Issues

Classical probability is based on the notion that past frequencies make good predictors. If a coin has come up heads half the time in the past, then there is a 50% probability that it will come up heads on the next coin flip. Use of relative frequencies is a way to characterize uncertainties. It is not the only way, however, and ultimately may prove to be a rather impractical approach to characterizing uncertainties in ecological risk assessments that lack data on past performance of environmental parameters.

Another approach to characterizing uncertainties is to reason back from observed effects to cause, or, more precisely, from evidence to hypothesis. Consider the example of an urn filled with black and white balls. A classical or frequentist approach would ask what is the chance that the next ball will be black and base the answer on the number of black and white balls drawn previously from the urn. Bayesian or subjective probability would ask what is the ratio of black and white balls in the urn. Bayes' theorem is essentially a formula that allows probabilities to be updated as new evidence becomes available. In the complete absence of information, Laplace's principle of indifference applies: all alternatives are equally likely. That is, prior to extracting any balls from the urn, we start with the belief that the ratio of black and white balls in the urn is 1:1. This non-informative prior belief is then updated as balls are extracted. Eventually, the updated probability converges on the true ratio of black to white balls in the urn. Bayesian probabilities do not depend on a track record of past performance. As such, they are subjective and can be thought of as degrees of belief rather than relative frequencies. Intuitively, this would seem to be a more useful paradigm for ecological risk assessments in which serious data gaps exist but for which we may have much expert knowledge to draw upon. Is Bayesian probability sufficiently broad to deal with the types of uncertainties likely to be encountered in multiple-stressor assessments? The answer depends on how the assessment problem is defined and, more likely, on who you ask. Most Bayesians would argue that subjective probability is the only way to handle uncertainties in ecological risk assessments involving multiple stressors. There are, however, several types of uncertainties that probability may not be suited to describe. Consider the ambiguities inherent in our use of words to classify objects or describe systems. Suppose, for example, that interested parties state that one of their goals for a water body is to ensure that eutrophication does not occur in the future. The task for the risk assessors and managers would be to determine the probabilities of eutrophication occurring given projections about fertilizer usage in the basin, phosphate releases in wastewater effluents, and so on. Probability, however, does not capture the uncertainty that exists because the term eutrophication lacks a precise definition. It is hard to estimate the probability of an event when the event covers a range of possibilities, some closer to the implied definition than others.

Uncertainty can be classified in many ways (for examples, see Finkel 1990; Rowe 1994; Hoffman and Hammonds 1994; Smith and Shugart 1994). These typologies generally focus on sources of uncertainty (e.g., uncertainty about model structure or parameter values), but they do not consider whether these sources are best quantified using a probabilistic approach. Another typology contends that there are four basic types of uncertainty: non-specificity, fuzziness, dissonance, and confusion (Klir and Folger 1988; Klir 1989; McNeill and Freiberger 1993). Of these, probability deals only with dissonance.

Non-specificity is ambiguity. For example, a benthic survey may reveal a degraded community that could, based on knowledge of known sources, be attributed to upstream municipal wastewater discharges, industrial effluents, or dredging. As to which of these three potential causes is responsible for the observed effects, the survey indicates nothing. The evidence is nonspecific and therefore uninformative as to the cause of the observed adverse effects.

Fuzziness is vagueness. This type of uncertainty arises because terms such as degraded, acidified, sustainable, and diverse often do not have sharp definitions. While most scientists would agree that a lake with a pH of 4 is acidified, and another with a pH of 6.5 is not, we would have trouble labeling lakes with intermediate pH levels. With fuzziness, a hypothesis can be true and false at the same time. Thus, a body weight of 120 kg for an adult human male may be considered heavy, 50 kg light, and an intermediate weight of 70 kg 0.5 heavy and 0.5 light. A lake with pH 5.5 could be, for example, 0.7 acidified and 0.3 not acidified.

Dissonance is pure conflict. The fact that a chemical is or is not a carcinogen or that a lake is or is not acidified is an example of dissonance. Typically, some evidence supports one hypothesis, different evidence the other, and we are uncertain between the two. When the evidence is combined, probabilities may be assigned to each hypothesis. Thus, if a GIS analysis indicates that there is a 30% probability that lake ABC in a particular region is acidified, then there is a 70% probability that it is not acidified. With dissonance, a hypothesis cannot be both true and false at the same time, an outcome of Aristotle's law of the excluded middle.

Confusion is pure and potential conflict and often arises when the meaning of the evidence is unclear. For example, we may have evidence that dissolved organic carbon (DOC) levels are increasing in a particular lake. The level of DOC, however, plays a complex role in regulating tissue mercury levels in lakes. In drainage lakes, there generally is a positive relationship between DOC levels and tissue mercury levels because mercury is first complexed with humic material and then transported to the lake from the surrounding catchment area (Driscoll et al. 1994). In seepage lakes, however, most of the mercury arrives via atmospheric deposition (Grieb et al. 1990). Because elevated DOC levels generally inhibit biomethylation (Barkay et al. 1997), the relationship between DOC and tissue mercury levels in seepage lakes is the reverse of that observed in drainage lakes. Without information on lake type, we are confused about the meaning of the evidence of increasing DOC levels with regard to tissue mercury levels in a lake.

Methods

Many methods are available to quantify uncertainties in multiple-stressor assessments. The majority of methods are, however, strictly probabilistic and therefore deal only with uncertainty in the form of dissonance. Because the methods for quantifying uncertainty do not differ between multiple- and single-stressor assessments, we only briefly describe methods below. References to the literature are provided to assist readers who want to learn more about particular methods.

The general mechanics of any uncertainty analysis typically involve the following seven steps (see Finkel 1990; Hammonds et al. 1994; Moore and Elliott 1996):

1) Specify the risk-model equation. The model equation specifies how the inputs will be combined to estimate exposure, effects, and/or risk. It can range from the very simple (e.g., probabilistic quotient = exposure concentration/no-effects concentration) to the complex (e.g., food-web models). Unlike single stressors, the risk equation in a multiple stressor assessment must specify how the stressors will combine to exert their effects on receptors. This requirement can be difficult to achieve when the stressors interact in a nonadditive fashion or when the stressors cause different types of effects (e.g., mortality, decline in fecundity) to the population of interest. Reckhow et al. (1990) and a number of papers in Volume 15 of *Advances in Water Resources* (1992) discuss methods for calibrating, evaluating, and validating a model equation.

2) List all variables that will be specified as distributions. In general, it is preferable to keep this list as short as possible by specifying input distributions for only those variables that are likely to have an important influence on the output (Seiler and Alvarez 1996).

3) Generate a distribution for each input variable in the model equation. These often are referred to as probability-density functions. The choice of distribution depends on 1) the form of the observed data, which may be determined by graphical or goodness-of-fit statistical techniques, and 2) our basic understanding of the input variable, so that theory about distributions can be used to best describe the underlying reality. Mitchell Sharp's chapter in the classic text by Morgan and Henrion (1990), Haimes et al. (1994), Hattis and Burmaster (1994), Ott (1995), and Seiler and Alvarez (1996) discuss distributions commonly used in ecological risk assessment.

4) Determine and account for dependencies among input variables. This often is an overlooked aspect of an uncertainty analysis. Ignoring correlations among important input variables (e.g., spatial correlations of multiple stressors) can lead to under- or overestimates of risk (Ferson and Burgman 1995).

5) Generate the output distribution by combining the input distributions as specified in the model equation. This step often involves Monte Carlo analysis, but there is a variety of other possible methods.
6) Fine-tune the analysis. Sensitivity analysis can be used to determine important input variables by identifying which input variables have the highest correlations with the output variable. If reexamination of these variables reveals that they have little scientific support, then additional empirical data and expert knowledge should be obtained. Once the input variables and, if necessary, the model equation have been fine-tuned, the analysis is repeated. Fine-tuning of an uncertainty analysis typically involves numerous iterations.
7) Summarize the results, highlighting important implications for risk managers. A variety of graphical and statistical techniques can be used, the choice of which depends on the outputs and the statistical sophistication of the audience. Warren-Hicks and Moore (1998) discuss various means of communicating uncertainty to lay and scientific audiences. Managers and interested parties also should be informed of unresolved scientific controversies and sources of uncertainty that could not be included in the quantitative analysis (Finkel 1990; Covello and Merkhofer 1993).

Uncertainty estimates can be derived using analytical methods (often referred to as first-order error analysis or variance propagation). Analytical methods are easy to use for simple additive or multiplicative models in which the input variables are independent (see Morgan and Henrion 1990; Hammonds et al. 1994; Slob 1994). With a simple additive model, $Y = a + b + c$, for example, the mean of the output is equal to the sum of the mean values of the model parameters. The variance of the output, assuming statistical independence among the model parameters, is equal to the sum of the variances of the model parameters. In this example, the output distribution will tend to conform to a normal distribution. Multiplicative models ($Y = a \times b \times c$) can be reduced to an additive form by logarithmically transforming the model parameters: $\ln(Y) = \ln(a) + \ln(b) + \ln(c)$. In most multiple-stressor assessments, particularly those estimating population- and community-level risks, it is unlikely that simple additive or multiplicative models will be useful. The following describes several methods that can be used in multiple-stressor assessments.

Taxa-sensitivity distributions

A simple approach for incorporating variability in sensitivities of species to single or multiple stressors was developed by Parkhurst et al. (1996). The approach requires a distribution relating stressor intensity, concentration, or dose to the percentage of species or genera affected and a distribution of exposure in the environment. To estimate acute risks posed by a chemical, for example, the species- or genus sensitivity distribution usually is expressed as cumulative percentage of taxa LC_{50} or EC_{50}s versus concentration. For chronic risk estimation, the sensitivity distribution generally consists of estimates of low toxic effect following chronic exposures (e.g.,

EC_{20}, no-observed-effects level). Therefore, the effects portion of this analysis captures variability in species sensitivities but does not quantify uncertainties arising from lack of model fit or from estimation of the individual toxicity end-points. Once the effects and exposure distributions have been developed, they are integrated to produce a joint distribution that expresses risk as a curve showing the probabilities of effects of varying magnitude (i.e., percentage of taxa affected).

The taxa-sensitivity approach can be easily expanded to consider risks of multiple stressors. The approach assumes that the risks of individual stressors are additive, and thus the cumulative risks can be estimated by integrating the risks of all stressors (Parkhurst et al. 1997). The assumption of additivity is reasonable for related stressors with similar modes of action (e.g., chlorinated benzenes) but likely is inappropriate for disparate stressors (e.g., nutrient enrichment, heavy metals). In order to integrate risks, the risks of the individual stressors must share a common metric (e.g., mortality, growth). When additivity is not a reasonable assumption, but the stressors share a common metric, risk curves can be plotted together to facilitate comparisons and help managers prioritize issues. If the multiple-stressor assessment has a large spatial scale (e.g., watershed), then the analyses can be carried out for a variety of locations to illustrate how risk varies spatially.

The taxa-sensitivity distributions approach is a simple, although somewhat crude, way to estimate community-level risks in a multiple-stressors assessment. The main advantages are that implementation is easy, software that is easy to use is available from the Water Environment Research Foundation, and results are easily communicated to stakeholders and risk managers. The approach, however, overlooks some sources of uncertainty (e.g., uncertainty about statistical estimates of toxicity or model fit) and requires some rather simplistic assumptions (e.g., only direct effects to biota contribute to risk, the exposure distribution is spatially and temporally appropriate for all taxa included in the sensitivity distribution, etc.). Nevertheless, the approach is a useful one and can help determine which stressors, receptors, and locations require more in-depth quantitative uncertainty analyses.

Monte Carlo simulation

The most commonly used technique for estimating uncertainty in ecological risk assessment is Monte Carlo simulation. The reasons are obvious: it is conceptually easy to understand, easy-to-use software is available, and Monte Carlo simulation models can be incorporated into complex modeling systems. The basis for Monte Carlo analysis is straightforward. Point estimates in a model equation are replaced with probability distributions, samples are taken randomly from each distribution, and the results are tallied, usually in the form of a probability density function or cumulative distribution.

For multiple-stressor assessments involving complex ecological models, Monte Carlo simulation is likely the most feasible uncertainty-propagation technique currently available. Uncertainty analyses involving variance propagation likely would face nearly insurmountable analytical difficulties in models with tens or hundreds of variables (e.g., comprehensive aquatic systems model [CASM], see below). Monte Carlo simulation, however, requires large quantities of data to properly specify the model equation, input distributions, and the relationships between the input distributions. The fisheries assessments discussed in Chapter 1 indicate that for some multiple-stressor assessments, we may lack not only data on key input variables, but also the theoretical knowledge required to specify a risk model equation (Lackey [1996] expands on this theme for Pacific salmon assessments). As an alternative to empirical data, expert elicitation methods can be used to select and parameterize distributions or refine model equations (see Morgan and Henrion 1990; Meyer and Booker 1991). With this approach, probability should be regarded as representing a degree of reasonable belief based on existing information (i.e., the Bayesian view) rather than the frequency with which an event would occur in repeated trials. This view would seem to run counter to the underlying theory of the Monte Carlo method, which is grounded in the long-run frequency interpretation of statistics (Warren-Hicks and Butcher 1996). In practice, however, Bayesians employ Monte Carlo methods to generate prior distributions and to solve numerical problems within the Bayesian paradigm (Brand and Small 1995). The Bayesian interpretation of the output would be more akin to degree of belief (i.e., estimated probabilities are conditional upon the data observed) than to some close approximation of the "true" probability.

In this chapter we use Monte Carlo simulation in two case studies to illustrate how the method can be used in multiple-stressor assessments. The first is a relatively simple analysis showing how the combined risks of mercury and polychlorinated biphenyls (PCBs) to mink can be estimated. In this case study, much information was available to characterize the input distributions. We believe the outputs from simple, data-rich analyses such as this one are amenable to risk-based decision-making. The second application involves estimating risks of contaminants and nutrient enrichment to an entire aquatic food web. In this case study, there was little information available to characterize variability for the input distributions. Thus, the outputs from such an analysis are not intended as the basis for risk-based decision-making. Rather, uncertainty analysis in cases like this one can be more appropriately thought of as a tool for identifying important input variables, exploring assumptions (e.g., consequence of assuming additivity for metals effects), and conducting "what if" analyses for different scenarios (e.g., imposing nutrient enrichment on an already contaminated system).

Other methods

A variety of other probabilistic methods exist for quantifying uncertainty, including second-order Monte Carlo (see special issue of *Human and Ecological Risk Assessment* 2[4]), probability- bounds analysis (Ferson et al., 2000), and Bayes' theorem alluded to earlier (Berger 1985). Second-order Monte Carlo separates variability and incertitude into two dimensions in the inputs and then propagates these two aspects of uncertainty via nested Monte Carlo simulations. The result is a distribution of distributions that expresses uncertainty both from variability and incertitude about the parameters of the input variables. Probability-bounds analysis represents each uncertain input distribution within an entire class of probability distributions that conform with the available empirical information about the variable. When the class is very large, it reflects the poor state of knowledge about the input variable. Once the bounds on the input distributions have been determined, it is possible to compute the bounds for the output using RiskCalc™ (Applied Biomathematics, Setauket, NY). The main benefit of both second-order Monte Carlo and probability-bounds analysis is that they allow the analyst to be more forthright about what is known as empirical fact when characterizing input distributions. To our knowledge, these methods have not been applied to date in ecological risk assessments involving multiple stressors.

Fuzzy arithmetic can be used to incorporate uncertainty in the form of vagueness in an analysis. Fuzzy arithmetic is the arithmetic embodied in operations such as addition, subtraction, multiplication, and division of fuzzy numbers (Kaufmann and Gupta 1985). A fuzzy number is essentially a stack of intervals at each of infinitely many levels from 0 to 1, with 0 representing impossible values and 1 representing those values that are entirely possible. Fuzzy arithmetic can be thought of as a refinement of interval analysis in that it permits propagation of the uncertainty represented by fuzzy numbers through mathematical equations. A fuzzy number can represent vagueness because it does not have to obey the probability axiom of the excluded middle; an organism can be both long and short, a lake can be both acidified and not acidified. Although fuzzy arithmetic has yet to be applied in a multiple-stressors assessment, it ultimately may prove to be a valuable method for quantifying uncertainty, particularly in assessments in which vagueness may be an issue.

The choice of an appropriate method for quantifying uncertainty depends on the complexity of the risk analysis, the available information, the expertise of the assessor, and the sources of uncertainty (see brief guidance in Landis et al. 1998). Few methods exist in ecological risk assessment that can deal with uncertainties in the form of confusion and non-specificity. Perhaps our only recourse at this time is to formulate risk-assessment equations and data collection to minimize the impact of these uncertainties on the estimates of risk. Critical to accomplishing this task is to obtain a priori agreement from risk managers and interested parties on quantifiable definitions for terms included in statements of assessment goals. For example, the goal of preventing "eutrophication" could be restated as preventing a greater than 20% reduction in Secchi disk readings.

Ecological Modeling

Ecological systems are complex (Patten 1971–1976; Allen and Starr 1982; O'Neill et al. 1986), dynamic (Landis et al. 1998), and adaptive (Dobzhansky 1965; Holling 1986). These attributes, particularly adaptability, impose constraints on our ability to completely and accurately characterize ecological systems, including their responses to individual or multiple stressors. Mathematical models have been developed as heuristic tools for describing the structure and function of ecological systems since the beginnings of modern quantitative ecology (e.g., Lotka 1956).

Developing and applying ecological models combined with experiments and monitoring are an effective approach for characterizing ecological systems from a risk-assessment perspective. Earlier developments in theoretical ecology and modeling derived in no small part from such practical risk-management issues as insect pest control (e.g., Watt 1961) and fisheries management (e.g., Ricker and Foerster 1948; Ricker 1958; Saila 1972).

Issues

The following sections outline several important, largely unresolved issues that are central to effectively describing ecological system responses to stressors using ecological models. More general discussions concerning the use of ecological models in assessing risk have been published (Barnthouse et al. 1986; Emlen 1989; Bartell et al. 1992; Suter and Bartell 1993; Campbell and Bartell 1998) and our purpose is not to revisit these efforts. A comprehensive review of the ecological modeling process (see Patten 1971–1976; Caswell 1989) and existing ecological models (see Jørgensen et al. 1996) also lie beyond the scope of this chapter.

The issues addressed in this paper include 1) identification of model structure, 2) formulation of model processes, 3) estimation of model-parameter values, and 4) evaluation of model results. Where possible, these issues will be discussed in the context of multiple stressors.

Model structure

We define model structure broadly to include some representation of the ecological phenomena that are the foci of the modeling effort, along with a definition of pertinent boundaries and delineation of the spatial/temporal scale. Structure identifies the points of measurement and observation; ecological structure comprises the state variables in ecological models. The main issue concerns the identification of necessary and sufficient structure to include in development of an ecological model. Discussion of this issue can devolve to unproductive debates about "simple" versus "complex" models, particularly in the context of models used in environmental regulation.

From a risk-assessment perspective, a difficult modeling challenge lies in identifying the ecological structures needed to characterize accurately ecological responses to single and multiple stressors. The difficulty arises from the anticipation that ecological structures relevant to modeling one type of stressor (e.g., a toxic chemical) may differ from the structure needed to describe others (e.g., physical habitat alteration). Developing models of multiple stressors may require learning how to combine disparately scaled ecological structures effectively into a common modeling framework.

Process formulation

The mathematical functional relationships specified among the model state variables (i.e., process) can assume different forms depending on the purpose of the model, ecological understanding, and availability of data. While recognizing the inherent nonlinearity of ecological systems, early model developers commonly described the dynamics of ecological systems using linear equations and constant coefficients (see, for example, Smith 1969; Patten 1971, 1972). Reasons for linear process formulations emphasized in early ecological models included 1) computational constraints (both hardware and software), 2) the analytical tractability of linear models, and 3) the relative absence of nonlinear mathematical descriptions of ecological processes.

As ecological understanding increased and modeling progressed, theoretical ecologists and model developers derived nonlinear equations that more realistically described important ecological processes (e.g., predation) (Holling 1966; DeAngelis et al. 1975). Such formulations have become the common parlance of ecological models, and current modeling practices typically involve the use of different combinations of linear and nonlinear process formulations, depending largely on the purpose of the model.

Using models to assess the ecological impacts of single or multiple stressors can be accomplished only through the derivation of equations that integrate the exposure and effects relationships. Such formulations depend, of course, on the basic ecological structure of the model; structure and function are interdependent in nature and in models. Acute mortality as a population response to stress has been modeled by adjusting mortality-rate constants in the models in relation to the magnitude of stress. Sublethal toxic responses have been formulated as adjustments to multiple physiological process equations, including nonlinear terms, in describing changes in population growth as a function of exposure to individual stressors, including phenolic compounds (Bartell et al. 1992), pesticides (Hanratty and Stay 1994), and toxic metals (Bartell 1994). Clearly, much work remains to be done in formulating ecological responses to multiple stressors.

Parameter estimation

Having defined structure and formulated processes, the modeler must derive numerical values for the resulting collection of parameters in order to calculate results. An entire complement of parameter values is rarely available for site-specific application of ecological models. Model- parameter values commonly constitute a collage of system-specific values combined with values derived from similar and not-so-similar systems. Important modeling issues concern the accuracy and generality of parameter values and the reliability of the data used to estimate them.

Using models to assess risks posed by multiple stressors exacerbates any difficulties in estimating parameter values by simply increasing the number of familiar parameters that must be assigned values or by defining novel model parameters for which fewer data might be available. The sensitivity of model performance to model-parameter values has become a focal point in model evaluation, including models used to assess ecological risks (e.g., Bartell et al. 1992).

Model performance

Model calculations rarely are accepted at face value. Questions and challenges concerning the accuracy of model results, especially for models applied in a regulatory context, are essentially immediate and continue over the "life span" of model application. A comprehensive and detailed treatment of concepts and methods pertaining to model evaluation easily could occupy this entire volume.

One unresolved issue concerns the a priori establishment of performance criteria for model results to be accepted or rejected in assessing ecological risks. The answer to "How good is good enough?" has received scant attention from the regulatory community or from among the regulated. In the absence of well-specified performance criteria, the use of model results in regulation or planning may require supplemental interpretation and evaluation by individuals trained and experienced in the use of such models. Such expertise may be applied to determine the degree of confidence to be placed on model results. The issue of model performance is further complicated by the development and implementation of models that address multiple stressors and endpoints; it is reasonably anticipated that these models will perform better for some stressors and endpoints and less well for others. The issue of performance criteria, left unresolved, can lead to arbitrary and inconsistent model "validation by acclimation" or to the cynical dismissal of all model results because any model can be pushed to the point of failure.

A related concern includes the duality in ecological model purpose and application: models constructed for basic research are intended to be falsified. Such model failures are viewed positively as defining the next important research objectives. Models used with regulatory or planning intentions are expected to produce accurate, reliable results. Such results may serve as the basis for environmental decisions that entail measurable consequences in dollars or lost resources; model utility is paramount. Suspicions can arise when the same model is used for both basic research and enforcement of environmental regulations.

This dual nature of the model development and application may be addressed effectively by limiting regulatory applications to those circumstances in which the model has been accurately and reliably used in the past (i.e., the domain of application) (Mankin et al. 1975), while additional basic research and development serves to increase this model domain. Such an approach may prove even more powerful if incorporated into an adaptive-management strategy where decisions can be reviewed and revised in relation to environmental monitoring, as well as in relation to improvements in model performance. At the very least, managers and other users of model results in making decisions must be aware of the developmental and evolutionary nature of ecological models used in assessing ecological risks.

Methods

The value of ecological modeling is due both to the process and the results produced. The modeling process is the point at which understanding is gained and science advances. The assessment and regulatory communities benefit to the extent that models usefully extend such gains in practical applications.

Methods have been developed to address the modeling issues previously outlined. The following sections describe several of these methods and their potential application to redress the issues of concern in ecological modeling.

Model structure

Formalized procedures of system identification have been derived to help model developers define and identify ecological structures that are sufficient to describe measured dynamics in ecological systems (e.g., Mulholland and Sims 1976). An often simpler alternative to the rigors of formal system identification lies in the addition, deletion, or aggregation of state variables in different instantiations of the same model. Model performance can be evaluated in relation to model complexity by comparing the alternative constructs. Formal rules have been derived for aggregating structure in linear models (Ziegler 1976, 1979); less formal, heuristic guidelines have been developed for nonlinear models (Gardner et al. 1982; Bartell et al. 1988). Parsimony in the modeling process suggests that adding ecological structures that fail to improve model performance leads to unnecessarily complex models; too much structure can even diminish model performance. In contrast, models lacking sufficient structure to describe the phenomena of interest will perform poorly even if the other aspects of the model are perfectly known.

One challenge in structuring ecological models to assess multiple stressors lies in the expectation that different degrees of ecological detail may pertain to different stressors, e.g., aquatic system responses to excessive nutrients, toxic chemicals, low dissolved oxygen, and increased sediment loads. Correlations among ecological responses to two or more stressors may help reduce the required model complexity; disparate scales involved in modeling the responses to different stressors could increase the necessary model complexity. The final model complexity may be determined by the ecological structure required to describe the most complicated stress-response relationships.

As suggested above, the relevant spatial and temporal scales of both the ecological entities of concern and the different stressors can play an important role in determining the structure of ecological models developed for risk assessment. Accurately describing the impacts of disparately scaled stressors on ecological structure or processes with similar scale incompatibilities may require the use of several differently scaled and structured risk assessment models.

Process formulation

Alternative equations describing the same ecological phenomena have accumulated in the ecological modeling literature. Formal guidance for selecting among alternative process formulations has not been well developed in ecological modeling. For example, several functional relationships have been derived to equate the relationship between light intensity and photosynthesis; each has an underlying basis in theory, each has been compared to data, and each has been used in developing ecological models that include a mathematical description of primary production. Likewise, different equations have been formulated to describe the feeding relationship between a predator and its prey (Holling 1966; DeAngelis et al. 1975). The basis for selecting among alternative process equations is infrequently included in model documentation and appears to reflect the preferences of different model developers.

Methods for developing equations that describe ecological responses to stressors range from purely empirical analysis of exposure-response data, to postulation of alternative formulations based on similarity to previously modeled phenomena, to derivation of process-oriented relationships from considerations of fundamental physics, chemistry, biology and ecology.

Parameter estimation

Several methods for estimating model parameter values are routinely practiced by modelers. The most straightforward and advantageous circumstance is to have site-specific data that directly quantify the model parameters. The next preferred approach is to have site-specific data that describe the dynamics of interest. Such data can be used to "calibrate" the model parameter by systematically adjusting their values in relation to pre-specified performance criteria. The calibrated values should be carefully examined for ecological feasibility; several methods (e.g., subplex, Monte Carlo filtering) permit the use of a priori definition of realistic parameter values (i.e., ranges, distributions, fuzzy numbers) as part of the calibration process, and the final values will be constrained by these definitions.

In the absence of site-specific data, the procedures mentioned above can be applied to data obtained from other similar systems. In addition, model parameter estimates can be derived from physical, chemical, biological or ecological theory. Finally, values of model parameters can be obtained from analysis of studies published in the technical literature. In practice, many or all of the methods for estimating values of model parameters may be used to arrive at a complete set of parameters in the implementation of ecological models.

Model performance

The validation of ecological and numerical models has been the subject of basic (Grant 1962; Naylor and Finger 1967; Naylor et al. 1969; Mankin et al. 1975; Caswell 1976; Collins 1980; Rice and Cochran 1984; Turner et al. 1989; Oreskes et al. 1994; Rykiel 1996) and applied (e.g., Campbell and Bartell 1998; Bartell et al. 1992; Burns 1986; Gardner et al. 1980, 1990) research. While the models are simplifications of natural systems, and are by definition invalid, it is possible to delineate the circumstances in which model results are consistent with data. That is, model utility can be quantified, within the constraints of available data (Mankin et al. 1975).

A variety of methods has been developed for comparing model results with data. Perhaps the most straightforward approach is simply to plot model results against observations. Perfect agreement between model results and observations would define a straight-line relationship with a slope of 1.0. Deviations in model:data comparisons are readily evident from inspecting these kinds of plots.

More detailed numerical methods of model analysis are presented by the authors referenced above. The concepts and methods described by Mankin et al. (1975) are particularly relevant to models used for both environmental assessment and basic research. That is, model utility can be evaluated for assessments of circumstances that are well within the domain of current model applicability. At the same time, basic research and development can proceed to extend model domain.

Case Study: Combined Risks of Mercury and Polychlorinated Biphenyls to Mink

Over 50 years of operations, storage and disposal of wastes from the U.S. Department of Energy Y-12 nuclear weapons facility at Oak Ridge, Tennessee have resulted in the contamination of water, sediment, biota, and flood-plain soils of East Fork Poplar Creek (EFPC). A preliminary assessment revealed that methylmercury and PCBs were the contaminants of greatest concern. Because these contaminants are persistent and accumulate in tissues and biomagnify up the food chain, piscivorous wildlife were identified as the biota at greatest risk of exposure. Moore et al. (1999a, 1999b) estimated the risks posed by methylmercury and PCBs to two piscivorous species, mink and belted kingfishers. This case study provides a brief synopsis of the Moore et al. (1999a, 1999b) probabilistic risk assessment and shows how the analysis can be extended to estimate cumulative risks of methylmercury and PCBs to mink. We do not estimate cumulative risks of methylmercury and PCBs to kingfishers here because Moore et al. (1999a) showed that the risks of PCBs to this species were very low.

Total daily intake for female mink exposed to mercury in EFPC was calculated using the following equation:

$$TDI = C_{air} \cdot NIR_{air} + C_{water} \cdot NIR_{water} + MR_{fw} \cdot \sum_{i=1}^{3} \frac{C_i \cdot MeHg{:}Hg_i \cdot P_i}{AE_i \cdot GE_i}$$

Equation 4-1,

where TDI is exposure (μg/kg body weight/day);

C is concentration of mercury in air (μg/m^3), water (μg/L), and tissue (μg/g);

NIR is the intake rate normalized to 1 kg body weight;

P is the proportion of each prey item in the diet;

$MeHg{:}Hg$ is the proportion methylmercury to total mercury;

AE (unitless) is the assimilation efficiency of mink that consume fish ($i = 1$);

invertebrates ($i = 2$), or mammals ($i = 3$);

GE (kcal/g) is the gross energy of fish, invertebrates, or mammals; and

MR_{fw} (kcal/day) is the metabolic rate of wild female mink.

With this equation, uncertainties in each of the inputs used in the allometric equation for NIR for food can be propagated in the probabilistic exposure analysis. Concentrations of total mercury in each medium were multiplied by the proportion methylmercury to total mercury because methylmercury is the most toxic form of the metal. For PCBs, exposure was estimated for Aroclor 1260 because this is the most commonly detected congener profile in tissue samples from EFPC. The exposure equation was the same as for mercury, except that the methylmercury to total mercury conversion factors were removed.

The distributions and distribution parameters used in the exposure analyses are summarized in Table 4-1. Detailed descriptions of data sources and justification for the distributions selected are provided in Moore et al. (1999a). Input distributions were assigned as follows: lognormal distributions for variables that are right skewed with a lower bound of zero and no upper bound (e.g., tissue concentrations), beta distributions for variables bounded by 0 and 1 (e.g., proportion of a prey item in the diet), normal distributions for variables that are symmetric and not bounded by 1 (e.g., gross energy of prey items), and point estimates for minor variables (e.g., concentration in air).

Monte Carlo analyses were conducted to combine the input distributions as specified in Equation 4-1. Each analysis included 10,000 trials and Latin Hypercube Sampling to ensure adequate sampling from all portions of the input distributions. Negative correlations between dietary input distributions for mink were included in the analyses. Figure 4-1 shows the resulting exposure distributions for mink exposed to methylmercury and PCBs.

In order to express risk as probabilities of effects of differing magnitude, we need to derive dose-response curves that subsequently can be integrated with the exposure

Table 4-1 Input variables used in the Monte Carlo exposure simulations for total daily intake of methylmercury and PCBs by female mink near EFPC, Oak Ridge, Tennessee

Variable	Chemical	Distribution	Parameters
Air ($\mu g/m^3$)	Mercury	Point estimate	0.00663
	PCBs	Point estimate	0.01
Air intake rate (m^3/day)	Both	Point estimate	1.83
Water concentration ($\mu g/L$)	Methylmercury	Point estimate	0.0006
	PCBs	Point estimate	0.006
Water intake rate (L/day)	Both	Point estimate	0.093
Concentration in invertebrates ($\mu g/g$)	Mercury	Lognormal	$\bar{x} = 1.045, s = 0.119$
	PCBs	Lognormal	$\bar{x} = 0.451, s = 0.182$
Concentration in fish ($\mu g/g$)	Mercury	Lognormal	$\bar{x} = 0.389, s = 0.0441$
	PCBs	Lognormal	$\bar{x} = 0.748, s = 0.302$
Concentration in mammals ($\mu g/g$)	Mercury	Lognormal	$\bar{x} = 0.588, s = 0.067$
	PCBs	Lognormal	$\bar{x} = 0.218, s = 0.088$
Proportion methylmercury in fish tissue	Mercury	Beta	$\alpha = 38.2, \beta = 1.25,$ scale = 1
Proportion methylmercury in invertebrates	Mercury	Beta	$\alpha = 3, \beta = 3$, scale = 0.34
Proportion methylmercury in mammals	Mercury	Beta	$\alpha = 3, \beta = 3$, scale = 0.24
Assimilation efficiency—Fish	Both	Beta	$\alpha = 65, \beta = 8$, scale = 1
Assimilation efficiency—Invertebrates	Both	Beta	$\alpha = 65, \beta = 8,$ scale = 0.96
Assimilation efficiency—Mammals	Both	Beta	$\alpha = 65, \beta = 8,$ scale = 0.93

Table 4-1 continued

Variable	Chemical	Distribution	Parameters
Gross energy—Fish (kcal/g)	Both	Normal	$\bar{x} = 1.20, s = 0.24$
Gross energy—Invertebrates (kcal/g)	Both	Normal	$\bar{x} = 0.80, s = 0.12$
Gross energy—Mammals (kcal/g)	Both	Normal	$\bar{x} = 1.70, s = 0.28$
Metabolic rate of wild female mink (kcal/day)	Both	Lognormal	$\bar{x} = 256, s = 130$
Proportion fish in diet	Both	Beta	$\alpha = 5, \beta = 4.5, \text{scale} = 1,$ $r_{fish:invert} = -0.26,$ $r_{fish:mammal} = -0.94$
Proportion invertebrates in diet	Both	Beta	$\alpha = 3, \beta = 7, \text{scale} = 0.35,$ $r_{invert:mammal} = 0.03$
Proportion mammals in diet	Both	Beta	$\alpha = 4, \beta = 4, \text{scale} = 0.74$

distributions. For methylmercury, several long-term feeding studies (93 to 183 days) with female mink have been conducted using similar protocols (Aulerich et al. 1974; Wobeser et al. 1976; Wren et al. 1987a; Chamberland et al. 1996). These studies were combined to produce a toxicity dataset with 11 treatment levels. The endpoint was female mortality. The concentration-response relationship for female mortality versus methylmercury concentration in the diet was then estimated using the generalized linear model (GLM) framework with a probit-link function and a binomial-error distribution. In order to convert effect concentrations to doses, the probit concentration-response model was combined with the food-intake rate for captive female mink. Bleavins and Aulerich (1981) found that captive female mink have a mean food-intake rate of 160 g/day (normalized to a 1 kg female mink) with a standard deviation of 10.

For PCBs, the results of three long-term feeding studies (Aulerich and Ringer 1977; Jensen et al. 1977; Aulerich et al. 1985) on the effects of Aroclor 1254 to number of kits born alive per exposed female were combined to produce a toxicity dataset with nine treatments. The GLM approach with a log link function and Poisson error distribution was used to determine the concentration-response relationship. For this analysis, we assumed that Aroclor 1254 and Aroclor 1260 would exhibit similar toxicity to mink reproduction; this assumption is supported by the limited evidence available for other mammals (Eisler 1986). Effect concentrations were converted to doses using the same approach described above for methylmercury.

Moore et al. (1999a) conducted Monte Carlo simulations to estimate total daily intakes of each contaminant by mink and then integrated the resulting exposure distributions with their respective dose-response curves to estimate risks. The

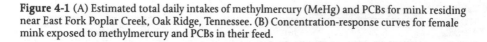

Figure 4-1 (A) Estimated total daily intakes of methylmercury (MeHg) and PCBs for mink residing near East Fork Poplar Creek, Oak Ridge, Tennessee. (B) Concentration-response curves for female mink exposed to methylmercury and PCBs in their feed.

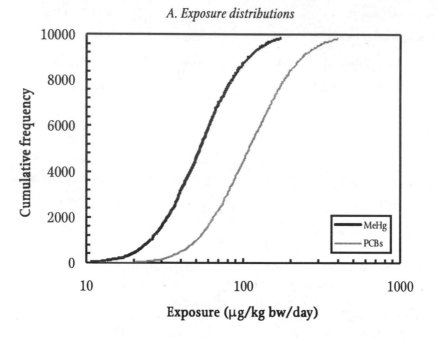

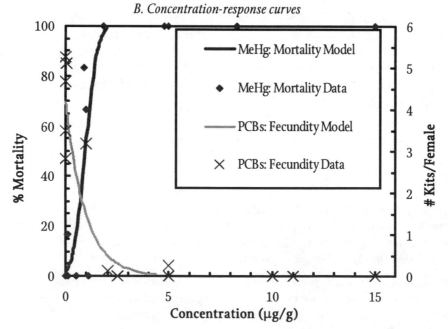

Figure 4-1 (C) Dose-response curves for female mink exposed to methylmercury (mortality) and PCBs (fecundity) in their diet. (D) Exceedence risk curves for female mink exposed to methylmercury, PCBs, and both contaminants.

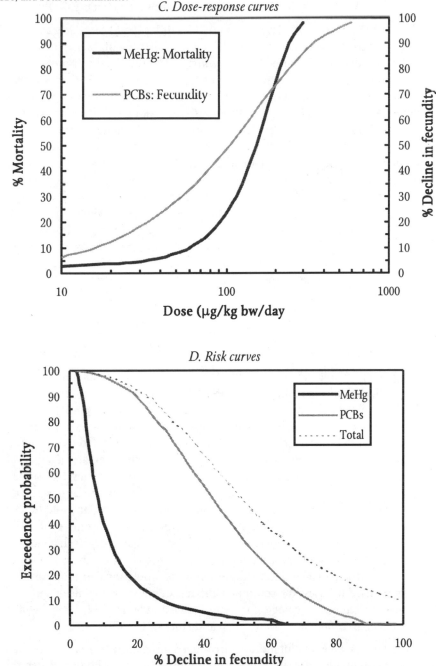

results indicated that methylmercury poses a moderate risk to female mink (24% probability of at least 15% mortality) and PCBs pose a very serious risk to mink (52% probability of at least a 50% decline in reproductive fecundity) (Figure 4-1).

The effects measures for methylmercury and PCBs differ (adult mortality and reproductive fecundity, respectively), which poses a potential problem when estimating cumulative risks posed by methylmercury and PCBs (i.e., cannot combine "apples and oranges"). In the case of methylmercury, limited data show that female mink able to survive to time of mating reproduce normally even at dietary concentrations exceeding the chronic LC_{50}. In a long-term feeding study, Wren et al. (1987a, 1987b) showed that exposure to 1 $\mu g/g$ methylmercury in the diet caused 67% mortality to adult female mink but had no significant effect on number of kits born per surviving female, percent kit survival to 5 weeks, or average weight of kits at 1, 3 and 5 weeks. Therefore, for female mink chronically exposed to methylmercury, it seems reasonable to equate percent mortality of adult females to percent reduction in fecundity. For this reason, adding the methylmercury and PCBs risk curves (Figure 4-1) seems a reasonable approach for estimating cumulative risks. Mortality caused by methylmercury is of more concern, however, because its effects on reproduction are permanent, whereas the effects of PCBs on reproduction could be reduced by reducing exposures during future breeding cycles.

Case Study: Assessing Effects of Contaminants and Nutrient Enrichment Using an Aquatic Food-web Model

Estimating the probable impacts of multiple stressors on the production dynamics of phytoplankton and zooplankton requires a number of assumptions concerning ecological complexity. In this discussion, the term "ecological complexity" refers to ecological structure and organization: individuals, populations, and communities (Ruggiero et al. 1994). Increased ecological complexity is interpreted to mean more ecological structure, more interactions among these structures, greater average strength of interaction, more pathways by which energy passes through, or some combination of these (Begon et al. 1996). Ecological complexity can be described and quantified only partially; the simplification of ecological structure and function inherent to quantitative study produces errors of aggregation (Gardner et al. 1982; Bartell et al. 1988). Assessing impacts of multiple and single stressors depends on adequate structural characterization of the system. This assertion applies whether physical and mathematical models, experimental manipulations, or monitoring programs are used to assess the combined impacts of physical, chemical, and biological disturbances to ecological systems (Allen and Starr 1982; O'Neill et al. 1986; Bartell et al. 1988; Pimm 1991; Allen and Hoekstra 1992).

In most situations where pollutants are introduced into natural waters, more than one toxic or potentially toxic substance is present; the larger the body of water, the more likely it is that mixtures of pollutants will be present (Eaton 1973). Exposure to combinations or mixtures of chemicals can result in significant toxicity even when the individual chemicals do not occur at toxic concentrations. Determination of an impact from exposure to a single contaminant is comparatively well established (e.g., O'Neill et al. 1982, 1983; Bartell 1990; Bartell et al. 1992); however, quantitative methods for characterizing impacts from exposures to chemical mixtures are less well-developed (Haas et al. 1997).

Four types of actions from joint effects of complex mixtures have been identified: similar, dissimilar, interactive, or non-interactive (Plackett and Hewlett 1952). Joint action can be classified further into simply additive, more than additive (synergy or potentiation), less than additive (antagonism), and no interaction (Plackett and Hewlett 1952). In the case of complex mixtures, the analysis can become complicated because the joint actions of different pairs may be of different types (Nirmalakhandan et al. 1994). Results of laboratory toxicity studies indicate that for combinations of heavy metals, joint effects may be additive (Thompson et al. 1980; Enserink et al. 1991), more than additive (synergism or potentiation) (Eaton 1973; Babich and Stotzky 1983; Spehar and Fiandt 1986; Winks 1990; Haas 1992; Cuvin-Aralar and Aralar 1993; Naddy et al. 1995; Pelgrom et al. 1997), or less than additive (antagonistic) (Roales and Perlmutter 1974; Van Puymbroeck et al. 1982; Haas 1992; Naddy et al. 1995). In some experiments, the toxic response of metal combinations was dominated by one metal (Eaton 1973; Broderius and Smith 1979; Naddy et al. 1995). In addition, studies of striped bass survival when exposed to mixtures of Al, Cd, Cu, Cr, and Zn in tributaries of the Chesapeake Bay were used to evaluate a method for assessing ecological impacts of contaminant mixtures developed by Logan and Wilson (1995).

In this case study, we examine the implications of different models of joint metal toxicity (i.e., As, Cu, and Cd) on ecological risks estimated by using a modification of the CASM (Bartell et al. 1992; DeAngelis et al. 1989). The purpose of this study was to develop a mathematical representation of experimental mesocosms (1 m^3) in order to examine the potential ecological impacts of three metals introduced simultaneously to the mesocosms.

The CASM and its modification used in this study also have the capabilities to examine other ecological stressors, either individually or in combination. The model can be used to examine the implications of nutrient enrichment by simulated additions (or reductions) of dissolved inorganic N, P, and Si, or particulate organic matter. Impacts of dissolved oxygen depletion on population dynamics, community structure, and ecosystem function can be addressed in a similar manner. Possible impacts of reduced light availability (e.g., due to atmospheric pollution, volcanoes, nuclear winter) can be addressed by modifying input data files to the CASM. Finally, implications of thermal pollution or climate change can be explored by manipulating water temperature. Of course, modifying any one of these potential stressors invariably brings others into play owing to the feedback mechanisms and interactions inherent to CASM and other similarly complex models.

Model description

For the current study, the CASM was modified to simulate the production dynamics of an experimental marine mesocosm. The model comprises 22 state variables that define mesocosm primary producers and 17 state variables for consumers (Figure 4-2). In this figure, arrows indicate the flow of carbon into the next trophic level. Dashed lines indicate a group of organisms that is involved in the interaction. If a line or arrow passes through the dashed line surrounding a group of organisms, only the indicated size class/life-cycle stage is involved in the interaction. To simplify this figure, anemones, chironomids, fish, clams, and oysters have been grouped into the category higher-order consumers. A combined taxonomic and size-based approach was used to define three size categories (2 to 10 μm, 10 to 20 μm, and > 20 μm) for flagellates (FL), dinoflagellates (DF), cryptophytes (CR), pennate diatoms (PD), centric diatoms (CD), and cyanophytes. The remaining three producer-state variables included picoplankton (< 2 μm), *Rhizoselenium*, and benthic algae.

Modeled consumers include four size classes of microzooplankton (< 20 μm, 20 to 50 μm, 50 to 100 μm, and 100 to 200 μm), four state variables representing aggregate life stages of *Acartia* (eggs + non-feeding nauplii, nauplii, copepodites, and adults), ctenophores, fish (*Fundulus heteroclitus*), bacterioplankton, heterotrophic nanoflagellates, clams (*Macoma*), oysters, anemones, chironomids, and sediment bacteria. This model structure was determined primarily by the food-web structure measured in experimental mesocosms.

The revised mesocosm model calculates daily changes in biomass (gC/m^3) of each state variable using physiological process description based on bioenergetics (carbon equivalent). DeAngelis et al. (1989) provide the detailed governing equations. Values of primary producer biomass in the model change in relation to daily values of surface irradiance, water temperature, dissolved inorganic P, dissolved inorganic N, and dissolved Si.

One model assumption derived from the experimental conditions is that the initial algal components essentially are adapted to the measured water temperatures; temperatures routinely are observed to change only by 1 or 2 °C during the duration of an experiment (30 to 40 days), and the phytoplankton in the model "acclimate" to changing input-temperature values by adjusting their optimal temperatures for growth. Population-specific relations between light intensity and photosynthesis rates are determined by light-saturation values defined for each phytoplankton population (Park et al. 1974). Differential nutrient utilization is determined by population-specific values of half-saturation constants and Michaelis-Menten-Monod functions for N, P, and Si. Primary producer populations lose biomass daily to modeled grazers (e.g., zooplankton, clams, oysters). The experimental mesocosm

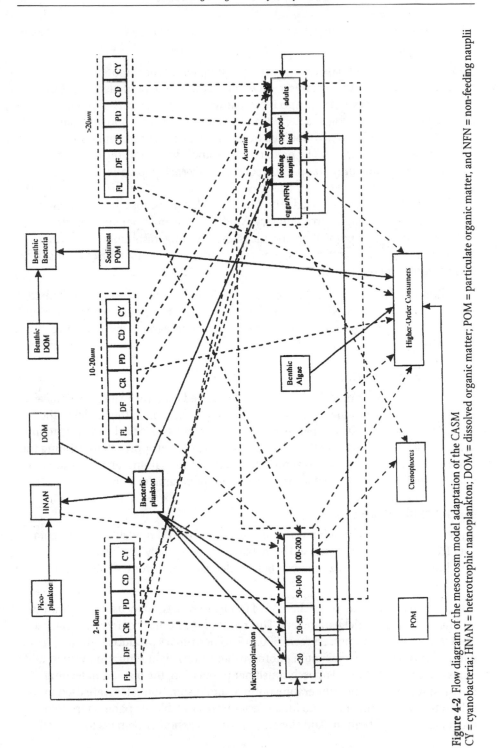

Figure 4-2 Flow diagram of the mesocosm model adaptation of the CASM
CY = cyanobacteria; HNAN = heterotrophic nanoplankton; POM = particulate organic matter; DOM = dissolved organic matter; and NFN = non-feeding nauplii

was stirred continuously; therefore, plankton sinking rates (day^{-1}) were defined as zero for this study.

Values of consumer biomass change daily as a function of consumption minus energetic-based losses to respiration, excretion, locomotion, predation, and (for fish only) the costs of digestion (i.e., specific dynamic action). The consumption equation calculates feeding as a normalized product of predator and prey biomass (DeAngelis et al. 1975, 1989), modified by the preference of predator i for prey j (w_{ij}), the assimilation of prey j by predator i (a_{ij}), and a handling efficiency for predator i consuming prey j (he_{ij}). Food consumed by each population is either assimilated, excreted, or egested. The egested portion is re-mineralized by modeled bacteria populations and recycled nutrients are added to the dissolved nutrient pools assuming a constant stoichiometry. Modeled consumer populations are distinguished by their population-specific rates of feeding, respiration, excretion, locomotion costs, prey preferences, prey assimilation, and temperatures for maximum feeding and respiration.

In addition to daily biomass values for each model population, the model calculates concentrations of dissolved N, P, Si, and dissolved oxygen. Total system production and respiration also can be calculated for each day, or integrated over an entire simulation.

Parameter estimation

Preliminary values for model parameters were derived from the primary technical literature. These values then were revised through calibration of the model to the results of initial mesocosm experiments (Tables 4-2 and 4-3). The detailed structure of the model, combined with the taxonomic and size-based approach to defining the populations, provided the opportunity and challenge to examine a large number of relevant studies and construct prior distributions of parameter estimates.

Model calibration

The objective of the calibration was to fit the revised CASM model to experimental data from mesocosms not exposed to metals. This potentially can involve the simultaneous variation of as many as 660 model parameters for the fully implemented model.

Previous sensitivity analyses of the CASM model were used to focus the calibration on known critical model parameters. This reduced the number of model parameters used in the calibration process from 660 to 70. For primary producers, these parameters include the maximum photosynthetic rates, light saturation values, and half saturation constants. For each consumer population, the maximum feeding rate, respiration-specific temperature optima, and respiration rates were used in calibration. If experimental data for a species were available, its parameters were included in the calibration. Additionally, maximum assimilation rates for several

Table 4-2 Listing of producer parameter values used during simulations

Compartment	hp gC/m^3	si $E/m^2/d$	ps $1/d$	xkp $\mu gP/L$	xkn $\mu gN/L$	xks $\mu gSi/L$
picoplankton	9.17E–03	9	2.52	0.038	0.70	0.00
flag 2–10 µm	0.00E+01	9	1.90	0.300	0.480	0.00
flag 10–20 µm	0.00E+01	9	1.36	0.300	0.480	0.00
flag >20 µm	0.00E+01	9	1.10	0.300	0.480	0.00
dino 2–10 µm	4.50E–03	40	1.00	0.150	7.570	0.00
dino 10–20 µm	2.19E–02	40	1.06	0.150	7.570	0.00
dino > 20 µm	6.35E–02	40	0.70	0.150	7.570	0.00
crypt 2–10 µm	4.50E–03	12	1.00	0.035	0.700	0.00
crypt 10–20 µm	2.19E–02	12	1.06	0.385	7.700	0.00
crypt > 20 µm	6.35E–02	12	0.80	0.068	1.400	0.00
pdiatom 2–10 µm	5.24E–05	20	2.12	0.056	1.278	1.59
pdiatom 10–20 µm	1.23E–04	20	2.08	0.037	1.024	1.59
pdiatom > 20 µm	3.23E–01	20	1.11	0.030	1.327	1.59
cdiatom 2–10 µm	5.10E–02	20	1.55	0.145	0.948	1.08
cdiatom 10–20 µm	2.48E–01	20	1.60	0.580	1.759	2.10
cdiatom > 20 µm	7.19E–01	20	1.71	2.381	2.519	3.37
cyano < 3 µm	0.00E+01	6	2.96	0.018	0.210	0.00
cyano 3–10 µm	1.26E–05	6	2.59	0.035	0.210	0.00
cyano 10–20 µm	3.18E–05	6	2.69	0.035	0.210	0.00
cyano > 20 µm	1.87E–02	6	1.09	0.030	0.210	0.00
benthic algae	0.00E+01	6	0.50	0.035	0.700	0.00
Rhizoselenium	0.00E+01	6	0.50	0.035	0.700	0.00

Abbreviations: hp = initial consumer biomass; si = light saturation constant; ps = photosynthetic rate; xkp = half-saturation constant for phosphorus; xkn = half-saturation constant for nitrogen; xks = half-saturation constant for silica

Table 4-3 Listing of consumer parameter values used during simulations

Compartment	bc	tc	cmax	rsda	tr	rs	u	sdy	cm
	gC/m³	₀C	m³/gC/d	1/d	₀C	1/d	1/d	1/d	1/d
MZ < 20 μm	1.77E–02	22	50.5500	0.00	27	0.940	0.005	0	0.01
MZ 20–50 μm	6.08E–03	22	3.4250	0.00	27	0.880	0.005	0	0.01
MZ 50–100 μm	0.00E+01	22	9.3500	0.00	27	0.760	0.003	0	0.00
MZ 100–200 μm	4.42E–02	22	2.1330	0.00	27	0.670	0.003	0	0.00
Eggs/NFN	0.00E+01	22	0.0000	0.00	27	0.840	0.035	0	0.07
Nauplii	1.13E–01	22	5.4480	0.00	27	0.840	0.035	0	0.07
Copepodites	3.54E–01	22	1.0860	0.00	27	0.230	0.040	0	0.06
Adult Acartia	7.20E–01	22	0.7200	0.00	27	0.170	0.020	0	0.05
Ctenophores	0.00E+01	22	0.7200	0.00	27	0.170	0.020	0	0.05
Fish	1.23E–00	22	0.7975	0.02	35	0.146	0.080	0	0.02
Bacterioplankton	2.00E–00	22	11.6700	0.00	27	1.000	0.060	0	0.06
HNAN	2.23E–01	32	11.4400	0.00	27	1.020	0.040	0	0.06
Oysters	4.48E–01	22	0.8562	0.00	26	0.193	0.060	0	0.05
Anemones	2.39E–00	22	0.2815	0.00	35	0.039	0.060	0	0.05
Chironomids	5.83E–01	22	0.8200	0.00	27	0.170	0.020	0	0.05
Clams	5.88E–01	22	1.1320	0.00	35	0.421	0.020	0	0.05
Sediment bacteria	0.00E+01	22	15.5000	0.00	27	1.000	0.060	0	0.06

Abbreviations: *MZ*: microzooplankton; *NFN*: non-feeding nauplii; *HNAN*: heterotrophic nanoplankton; *bc*: initial consumer biomass; *tc*: temperature for maximum feeding; *cmax*: maximum assimilation coefficient; *rsda*: metabolic cost of digestion; *tr*: temperature for maximum respiration; *rs*: maximum respiration rate; *u*: excretion rate; *sdy*: cost of locomotion; and *cm:* non-predator mortality for consumers.

consumers were included because the model showed high sensitivity to these parameters.

A modified version of the Nelder-Mead Simplex method for function minimization was used to calibrate the mesocosm model to the mesocosm data (Nelder and Mead 1965). In what is called a "subplex" method, Rowan (1990) applies the Nelder-Mead Simplex Method to sub-spaces of the whole parameter space instead of modifying all parameters at the same time. The subplex is effective for models with large numbers of parameters and provides fast convergence of an error function relating model output and experimental results to a minimum value (Rowan 1990). The accuracy of the model result was estimated according to

$$e = \frac{abs(m - x)}{\min(m,x)}$$

Equation 4-2,

where *e* is the error, *m* is the population-specific biomass calculated by the model, and *x* is the experimental value of the biomass of the corresponding mesocosm population. Total error was calculated as the sum of all population errors. This procedure attempted to optimize acceptable model performance while keeping parameter values within realistic ranges suggested by published information. To examine the potential for the subplex calibration results to be influenced by inadvertently optimizing to local minima in the error terms, calibrations were repeated several times using different initial estimates of the model parameters.

Calibrations that produced wildly divergent estimates of the model parameters were not used to define the final model parameter values used in the simulations of ecological response to multiple stressors.

Results of the model calibration demonstrated the ability of the subplex method to optimize model performance while maintaining realistic values of model parameters. The calibrated model parameters are listed in Tables 4-2 and 4-3. Model:data agreement generally was within an order of magnitude, with the exception of the clams, which showed very close calibration, and the fish, which showed an approximately 17-fold underestimate by the model. These calibrations were constrained by having essentially an initial and final measured value to use in the subplex method. Mixed calibration results also were obtained for the phytoplankton. The modeled dinoflagellate and cryptophyte populations proved difficult to match with the experimental values, while the pennate diatoms, centric diatoms, and cyanophytes were calibrated well within an order of magnitude.

Metals exposures

The multiple stressors addressed in this study included the potentially toxic metals As, Cd, and Cu. The model examined the ecological effects of exposing model populations to a mixture of these metals. Simulations were based on constant metal inputs used in the mesocosm experiments. The model did not incorporate the complex chemistry of metals in aquatic systems, but used daily inputs of freely dissolved metal ion (typically the most toxic form) to the mesocosm. Metals were introduced on Day 6 and increased on Day 7 to the desired concentration in the model and the experiments. Constant amounts were introduced for the remainder of the experiment. The resulting daily exposure concentrations were increased systematically and decreased in a series of simulations performed with different representations of the joint toxicity of the three metals.

Concentration-response functions

Independent of the assumed model for joint toxicity of the metals, the sublethal ecological effects of exposure were modeled by changing the values of the bioenergetics parameters (O'Neill et al. 1982, 1983; Bartell et al. 1992; Bartell 1990, 1994). Probit-scaled concentration-response functions were developed for each model population and each metal using published toxicity data for the corresponding or similar species. The toxicity data were compiled from the U.S. Environmental Protection Agency's (USEPA) Water Quality Criteria documents and the U.S. Fish and Wildlife Service's (USFWS) Contaminant Hazard Reviews (USEPA 1980, 1985a, 1985b, 1986, 1987; Eisler 1985, 1988). When toxicity data were not available for specific taxonomic groups, data from the most closely related taxonomic group were used.

The slope of the concentration-response functions varied for each modeled population; the shape of the function was defined by the LC_{50}/EC_{50} assigned to the model population and by assuming that zero exposure implies zero impact. Using these functions, an exposure concentration specified an expected bioenergetics-based toxic response. The bioenergetics equations were solved for each modeled population to calculate the toxic effects factor, e_i, that produced the expected toxic response. The e_i values were calculated on a daily time scale in relation to daily changes in the exposure concentration. The e_i values scale from 0 (no effect) to 1.0 (100% mortality). For example, if the exposure concentration for a metal equaled the concentration at which a 50% decrease would be expected over a 4-day period based on the toxicity data, the model calculated an effects factor, e_i, that would produce the expected decrease in biomass for the population over that duration of exposure. Using this approach, e_i values were calculated separately for each model population and each metal.

Joint metal toxicity

Three alternative hypotheses concerning the expression of multiple metal toxicity were explored using the CASM. These hypotheses were implemented by combining the e_i values calculated independently for population exposure with each individual metal.

Additive metal toxicity model

The e_i values determined separately for exposure to each metal were summed to produce an overall additive effects (ae) factor for each population i:

$$ae_i = minimum(1.0, (e_{i,As} + e_{i,Cd} + e_{i,Cu}))$$

Equation 4-3.

However, the value of ae_i was constrained to 1.0 according to the overall model construct.

Antagonistic metal toxicity model

The geometric mean of the e_i values was selected to represent an antagonistic response to multiple-metal exposure. Using this model, the most severe toxic response is reduced by the process of averaging the toxic responses; the geometric mean appears appropriate for averaging across chemical exposures (O'Neill et al. 1982, 1983). For each population i, the geometric mean effects factor (ge) was calculated as

$$ge_i = \frac{e_{i,As} \cdot e_{i,Cd} \cdot e_{i,Cu}}{n}$$

Equation 4-4,

where n (n ranged from 1 to 3) is the number of non-zero exposures. We did not include e_i values equal to 0 in estimating this antagonistic response to multiple exposures. Thus, if zero exposure occurred for all three metals on any modeled day, the resulting ge_i was equal to 0 (i.e., no toxic effect). If all three metals were present at acutely toxic concentrations (i.e., $e_i = 1.0$ for each metal), the ge_i value was defined as 1.0; the antagonistic effect was assumed not to occur for acutely toxic circumstances.

Maximum single metal toxicity model

The third expression of multiple-metal toxicity reduces the representation to a single exposure, the most toxic, as determined by the comparative value of the effects factors calculated separately for each metal exposure. Thus, for each modeled day of exposure, the maximum e_i (*me*) value for population i was used in estimating ecological risk:

$$me_i = maximum(e_{i,As}, e_{i,Cd}, e_{i,Cu})$$ Equation 4-5.

As with the other expressions of multiple-metal toxicity, the me_i values ranged between 0 and 1.0.

These selected expressions of multiple-metal toxicity had the desirable property that zero exposure produced no toxic effects and acutely toxic conditions produced maximum effects factors. The main difference among these alternative expressions was the contribution of each metal toxicity to the overall population response for $0 <$ exposures $< LC_{50}/EC_{50}s$. This was the point of the analyses, given that the CASM was designed to estimate ecological risks in relation to sublethal exposures.

Toxicity and population production

Figure 4-3 illustrates the effects of multiple-metal exposure on the population size of modeled cryptophytes. Under control conditions (i.e., zero exposure), the population grows throughout the course of the simulated mesocosm experiment. With increasing exposures, the toxic effects on the production dynamics of this species is evident. These results demonstrate that the approach for modeling toxic effects in the CASM does produce results that are consistent with expectations based on concentration-response relationships expressed through alterations of the basic bioenergetics parameters for model populations.

Uncertainty analysis and risk estimation

The e_i values were calculated under model conditions that simulated the laboratory tests used to generate the toxicity data (e.g., constant temperature, absence of food); the resultant effect factors were then used in the context of the entire food-web model with changing environmental conditions and exposure concentrations. The accuracy and precision of the e_i values will be influenced at least by the success of the bioenergetics-based model in usefully describing the dynamics of the model populations, the mapping of single toxicity values to many model populations and the extrapolation of toxic effects measured under test conditions to the mesocosm environment. To represent these uncertainties in the model, each e_i value was assigned to a normal distribution with a standard deviation equal to the mean value

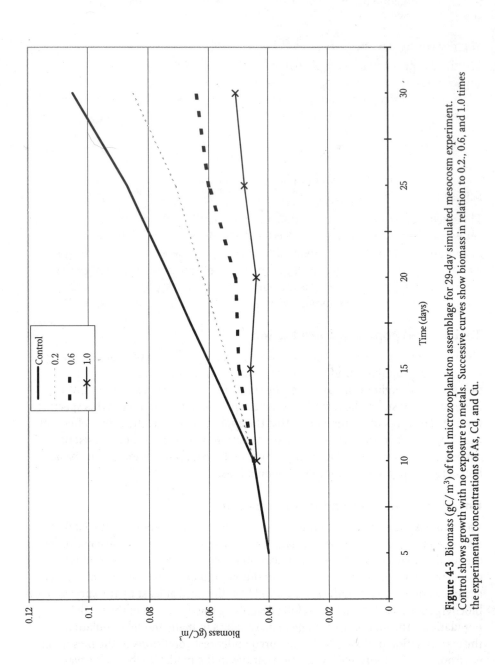

Figure 4-3 Biomass (gC/m³) of total microzooplankton assemblage for 29-day simulated mesocosm experiment. Control shows growth with no exposure to metals. Successive curves show biomass in relation to 0.2, 0.6, and 1.0 times the experimental concentrations of As, Cd, and Cu.

(i.e., CV = 100%). This assumption introduced a bias toward predicting an impact when one might not be observed (Bartell et al. 1992). At the same time, this assumption provides equal mathematical weight to toxicity and uncertainty, which reduces the likelihood of simulating severe ecological impacts solely as the result of high uncertainty.

To estimate the probable impact of exposure to metals on the production dynamics of the modeled plankton, 100 independent simulations were performed for each metal exposure scenario and for each joint toxicity expression. Each simulation used a separate, stratified-random sample from each distribution of e_i values for the modeled populations. Risk was calculated as the frequency of simulations that exceeded different magnitudes of population reduction integrated over the 29 days of these simulated mesocosm experiments. Thus, the smallest non-zero risk that could possibly be estimated using this methodology was $1/100 = 0.01$; the greatest risk was, of course, $100/100 = 1.0$.

Scenarios for risk characterization

Two general scenarios were examined in relation to CASM risk estimation for multiple stressors. The first examines the implications of alternative hypotheses concerning the expression of joint toxicity of metals on risk estimates. The second explores the implications of risks resulting from the combined effects of metals and nutrient enrichment.

Exposure to multiple metals and expression of toxicity

The simulated "control" mesocosm used in model calibration was exposed to different magnitudes of metal exposure concentrations in repeated simulations and ecological risks estimated. The daily concentrations of exposure for each of the three metals used in the experiments were multiplied by constants (0.5, 1.0, 1.5, and 2.0) to produce different exposure scenarios. Risks of different magnitudes of population reduction were estimated from the model results for each exposure scenario and expression of multiple toxic effects. Figures 4-2 and 4-3 illustrate the results summarized for modeled centric diatoms and the microzooplankton.

The results demonstrate a decreasing probability of increasing impacts consistent with the general quantitative concept of risk (Kaplan and Garrick 1981). The results also demonstrate that the risk functions for scenarios of increased exposure do not simply scale linearly (i.e., the risk functions are not all parallel) using the CASM methodology. This is apparent for all three assumptions concerning joint toxicity, although the geometric mean effect factors more closely approximate linear scaling of risk in relation to increased exposures. This nonlinear ecosystem- model response is potentially important because "quotients" calculated using the model input metal toxicity data and exposure regimes do scale linearly. Consequently, a plot of risk versus quotients for centric diatoms (or microzooplankton) would not be linear, which makes it difficult to extrapolate from quotients to ecological risk. Simply put, quotients do not characterize ecological risks, particularly when multiple stressors are involved (Bartell 1996).

The assumption concerning joint toxic effects did make a difference in the resulting estimates of ecological risk. The additive model consistently produced the highest risk estimates for any of the modeled exposure scenarios. The antagonistic toxicity model produced the lowest estimates of risk. The maximum toxic effect model produced intermediate results. This general pattern resulted for centric diatoms (Figure 4-4), microzooplankton (Figure 4-5), and all the other food- web components that had non-zero risks in these simulations. Interestingly, the general shapes of the risk functions for any selected exposure regime differed according to the underlying model of joint toxic effects. Apparently, different assumptions (i.e., models) of joint toxic effect do not introduce simple bias to risk estimates. That is, risks produced by one joint toxic effect model do not scale or extrapolate linearly to risk estimates resulting from alternative assumptions concerning joint effects.

The CASM estimates of risks posed by three metals to microzooplankton also demonstrated the possibility for indirect food-web effects to influence the assessment. The scenario of 2x the nominal exposure resulted in lower risks than the 1.5x scenario for both the additive and maximum effects models of joint toxicity. For the additive model, the risks associated with a 2x exposure differed little and were in some instances lower than risks posed by the 1x exposures. Analysis of the model calculations suggested that this counterintuitive response resulted from the acutely toxic impacts of 2x enrichment on several phytoplankton species, including centric diatoms. This released other less-sensitive model algal populations from competition (light, nutrients) and increased the food supply to the microzooplankton. The subsequent increased growth of the microzooplankton offset some of the direct toxic effects on microzooplankton and reduced risk compared to the 1.5x exposure scenario.

Combined exposure to metals and nutrients

The apparent importance of indirect effects that propagate through complex ecological systems on risk estimation (e.g., Figure 4-5) led to a series of CASM simulations for combinations of metal exposures and nutrient enrichment. The CASM was executed for nutrient regimes that were 0.2, 0.4, 0.6, 0.8, 1.0, and 2.0 times the nominal inputs for dissolved inorganic N and P. For each nutrient regime, the exposure concentrations of the three toxic metals were multiplied by the same series of values. One hundred simulations were performed for each combination of nutrient and metal regime. These simulations were based on the additive model for joint toxic effects of metals. The null hypothesis was that ecological risk for any metal exposure regime would be independent of simulated nutrient inputs to the model mesocosm.

The results demonstrated the potential interaction between nutrient enrichment and metal exposures in determining ecological risks using the CASM. For example,

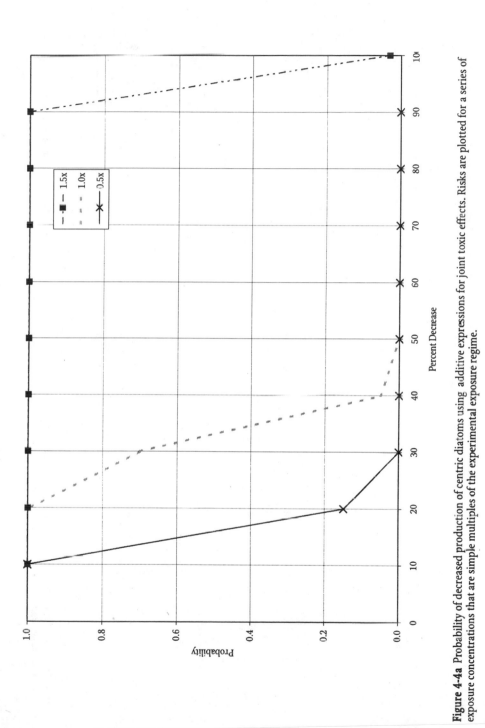

Figure 4-4a Probability of decreased production of centric diatoms using additive expressions for joint toxic effects. Risks are plotted for a series of exposure concentrations that are simple multiples of the experimental exposure regime.

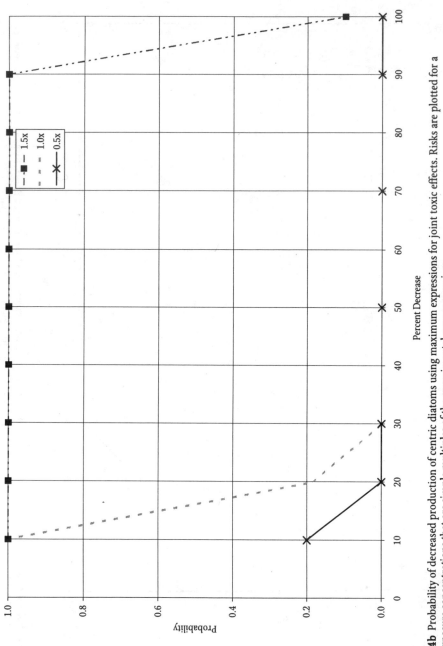

Figure 4-4b Probability of decreased production of centric diatoms using maximum expressions for joint toxic effects. Risks are plotted for a series of exposure concentrations that are simple multiples of the experimental exposure regime.

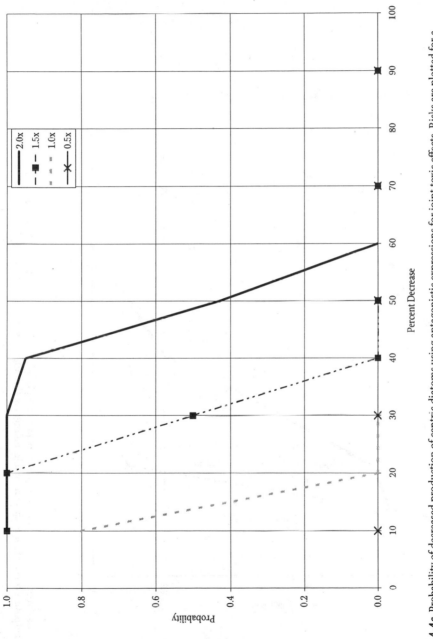

Figure 4-4c Probability of decreased production of centric diatoms using antagonistic expressions for joint toxic effects. Risks are plotted for a series of exposure concentrations that are simple multiples of the experimental exposure regime.

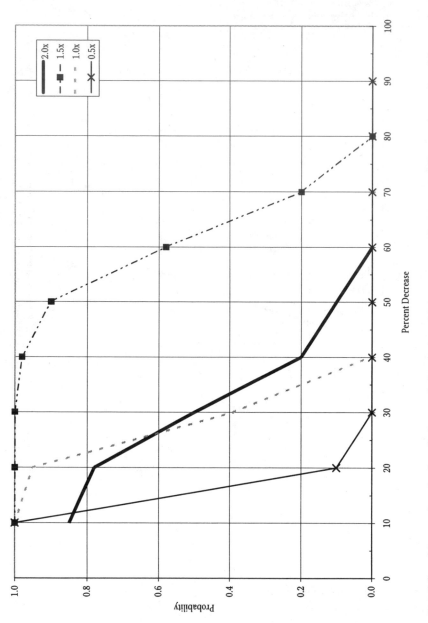

Figure 4-5a Probability of decreased production of microzooplankton using additive expressions for joint toxic effects. Risks are plotted for a series of exposure concentrations that are simple multiples of the experimental exposure regime.

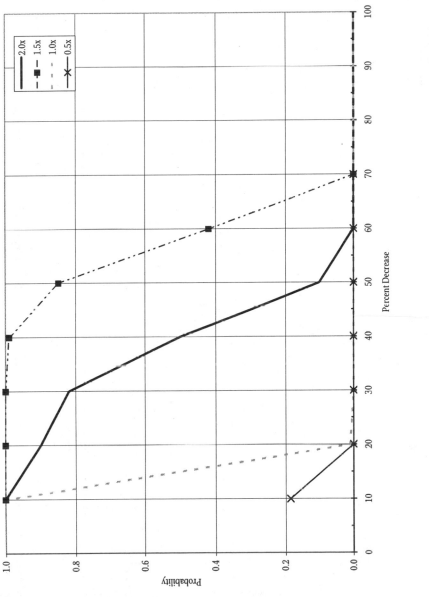

Figure 4-5b Probability of decreased production of microzooplankton using maximum expressions for joint toxic effects. Risks are plotted for a series of exposure concentrations that are simple multiples of the experimental exposure regime.

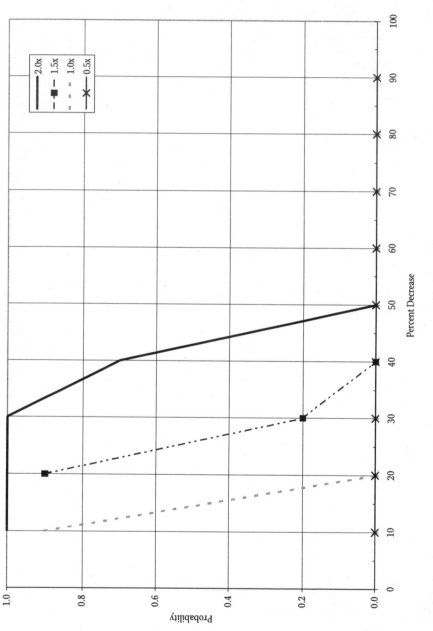

Figure 4-5c Probability of decreased production of microzooplankton using additive antagonistic expressions for joint toxic effects. Risks are plotted for a series of exposure concentrations that are simple multiples of the experimental exposure regime.

Figure 4-6 summarizes the probabilities of observing at least a 10% decrease in the overall production of cryptophytes during the 29-day simulations. The results suggest that the cryptophytes are generally at high risk of at least a 10% reduction; the probabilities are 1 or nearly 1 for many of the combinations of nutrients and metals. However, risks decline in relation to increasing nutrient availability in simulations involving toxic metal exposures at 0.8x the nominal concentrations, as well as for nutrient loadings ranging from 0.4 to twice the nominal values. The model suggests that growth stimulated by increased nutrient availability begins to counterbalance metal toxicity for cryptophytes. The inference is that more productive systems might be less susceptible to toxic metal stress.

Toxicity	Risk					
2.0	1	1	1	1	1	1
1.0	1	1	1	1	1	1
0.8	1	1	1	1	1	0.99
0.6	1	1	1	1	1	0.86
0.4	1	1	1	0.68	0.35	0.01
0.2	1	0.06	0	0	0	0
	0.2	0.4	0.6	0.8	1	2
	Nutrients					

Figure 4-6 Probability of a 10% decrease in cryptophyte production versus exposure concentrations for As, Cu, and Cd and varying nutrient inputs

Teasing apart risk sensitivity and uncertainty analyses

The risks posed to model populations by exposure to multiple metals were examined in detail using methods of numerical sensitivity and uncertainty analyses. The purpose of these analyses was to understand the relative contribution of direct and indirect effects of multiple-metal toxicity on the risk estimates produced by CASM.

Sensitivity analysis

Numerical sensitivity analysis was performed by varying 220 of the bioenergetics parameters required to perform the CASM simulations. These parameters were defined as normal distributions with a coefficient of variation of 1%. These relatively small parameter perturbations have been demonstrated to numerically approximate the partial derivative of the model state variables to the parameters for similarly structured models (Gardner et al. 1982). Parameter values were randomly selected from these distributions using a stratified-random sampling procedure. One hundred sensitivity simulations were performed; within each simulation, the CASM was run 100 times with random samples from the distributions of toxic effects factors. Each sensitivity analysis thus entailed 10,000 model simulations.

The analysis focused on the variability of the risk of a 50% reduction in the production of each modeled population. Each set of randomly selected parameter values was saved along with the estimates of risk for each model population. Basic statistics were calculated for each risk estimate. The sensitivity of the risk estimates to parameter variation was described by a Sensitivity Index (SI). The SI was calculated as the square of the simple correlation between each parameter and each risk estimate, multiplied by 100. For each model population, the top ten ranking model parameters were identified in relation to their contribution to variability associated with the corresponding estimates of risk.

Uncertainty analysis

Uncertainty analyses were performed to examine model behavior when parameter values were permitted to vary more than 1% of their mean value. These analyses begin to explore model performance when parameter variation that is more characteristic of the experimental mesocosms is used in the model simulations. The uncertainty analyses used the same procedures as the sensitivity analyses, except that model parameter coefficients of variation were increased 10-fold (i.e., to 10% of the mean values).

Results

Sensitivity Index values were calculated for all model populations and model parameters. Selected results for pennate diatoms and microzooplankton are presented in Tables 4-4 and 4-5. These tables list the 10 most sensitive model parameters, the corresponding SI values, and a description of each parameter. The sensitivity analysis for pennate diatoms estimated the probability (i.e., risk) of a 50% decrease in production as 0.76 (SD = 0.39). The production of pennate diatoms was more sensitive to parameters of other phytoplankton populations and grazers than to its own growth parameters (Table 4-4b). All of the listed parameters, except the *rsp29* and *u12*, occur in nonlinear terms in the model and might reasonably be expected to be controlling parameters. This pattern of parameter sensitivities suggests that metal toxicity exerts its influence on pennate diatoms largely through indirect impacts on competing phytoplankton species and the populations that graze on pennate diatoms.

Sensitivity analysis of risks posed by multiple metals to microzooplankton demonstrated that the risk of a 50% decrease in production was 0.39 (SD = 0.43) (Table 4-5b). The sensitivity analysis also emphasized the indirect effects contributing to risk. Parameters that determined the production of phytoplankton food for these consumers were most important. However, in contrast to the analysis of pennate diatoms, the microzooplankton parameter (*u11*) was the third most sensitive, indicating that direct toxic effects on microzooplankton were also important.

The results of the uncertainty analyses suggest that the risk of a 50% decrease in pennate diatom production is 0.95 (SD = 0.17); increased variability in the parameters produced a higher risk estimate with less variability compared to the sensitivity results (Table 4-4a). The important parameters further reinforce the suggestion

Table 4-4 Results of (a) uncertainty analysis [1] and (b) sensitivity[2] for pennate diatoms

Rank	Parameter	SI	Description
1	rs42	4.8	Max. respiration rate, HNAN
2	u51	4.8	Excretion rate, oysters
3	cmax23	4.5	Max. feeding rate, adult acartia
4	rs54	4.1	Max. respiration rate, clams
5	si110	3.8	Light saturation, cryptophytes > 20 μm
6	u52	3.3	Excretion rate, anemone
7	xkn28	2.9	N half-saturation, cyanophytes 3–10 μm
8	cmax11	2.7	Max. feeding rate, microzooplankton < 20 μm
9	xkn18	2.7	N half-saturation, cryptophytes 10–20 μm
10	xks21	2.5	Silica half-saturation, pennate diatoms 2–10 μm

[1] Risk of 50% decrease in pennate diatoms: mean = 0.95, SD = 0.17, n = 100

Rank	Parameter	SI	Description
1	ps26	21.5	Max. photosynthesis rate, centric diatoms > 20 μm
2	tc53	9.3	Temperature dep. of feeding, chironomids
3	rs14	8.3	Max. respiration rate, microzooplankton 100–200 μm
4	ps24	8.2	Max. photosynthesis rate, centric diatoms 2–10 μm
5	xkp210	6.1	P half-saturation, cyanophytes > 20 μm
6	rsp15	5.9	Photorespiration rate, dinoflagellates 2–10 μm
7	cmax52	5.8	Max. feeding rate, anemone
8	rsp29	5.4	Photorespiration rate, cyanophytes 10–20 μm
9	xkp15	5.4	P half-saturation, dinoflagellates 2–10 μm
10	u12	5.4	Excretion rate, microzooplankton 20–50 μm

[2] Risk of 50% decrease in pennate diatoms: mean = 0.76, SD = 0.39, n = 100

that risks to pennate diatoms are indirect and mediated through food-web interactions. In contrast to the sensitivity analysis, several of the higher order consumers (e.g., oysters, clams, acartia) become important to pennates with increased variability in the model parameter values. Note that the half-saturation constant for silica for pennates does show up in the analysis, thereby demonstrating that it is possible to show direct toxic impacts using the CASM methodology.

Table 4-5 Results of (a) uncertainty analysis[1] and (b) sensitivity[2] for the microzooplankton community

Rank	Parameter	SI	Description
1	rs42	4.8	Max. respiration rate, HNAN
2	u51	4.8	Excretion rate, oysters
3	cmax23	4.5	Max. feeding rate, adult acartia
4	rs54	4.1	Max. respiration rate, clams
5	si110	3.8	Light saturation, cryptophytes > 20 μm
6	u52	3.3	Excretion rate, anemone
7	xkn28	2.9	N half-saturation, cyanophytes 3–10 μm
8	cmax11	2.7	Max. feeding rate, microzooplankton < 20 μm
9	xkn18	2.7	N half-saturation, cryptophytes 10–20 μm
10	xks21	2.5	Silica half-saturation, pennate diatoms 2–10 μm

[1] Risk of 50% decrease in microzooplankton: mean = 0.75, SD = 0.24, n = 100

Rank	Parameter	SI	Description
1	ps26	21.5	Max. photosynthesis rate, centric diatoms > 20 μm
2	tc53	9.3	Temperature dep. of feeding, chironomids
3	rs14	8.3	Max. respiration rate, microzooplankton 100–200 μm
4	ps24	8.2	Max. photosynthesis rate, centric diatoms 2–10 μm
5	xkp210	6.1	P half-saturation, cyanophytes > 20 μm
6	rsp15	5.9	Photorespiration rate, dinoflagellates 2–10 μm
7	cmax52	5.8	Max. feeding rate, anemone
8	rsp29	5.4	Photorespiration rate, cyanophytes 10–20 μm
9	xkp15	5.4	P half-saturation, dinoflagellates 2–10 μm
10	u12	5.4	Excretion rate, microzooplankton 20–50 μm

[2] Risk of 50% decrease in microzooplankton: mean = 0.39, SD = 0.43, n = 100

The uncertainty analysis for microzooplankton similarly resulted in an increase in the estimated risk (0.75) and a decrease in variability about this estimate (SD = 0.24) (Table 4-5a). Indirect effects related to food availability dominated the top three sensitive parameters, while competitive interactions with chironomids and nauplii also were important. Metal impacts on the feeding rate of microzooplankton (direct effect) ranked number six in this analysis.

Discussion

Mathematical models will continue to play an important role in assessing ecological response to disturbance. While not offered as a replacement for experiments or whole-system manipulations, such models may provide process-level understanding of effects observed in experiments or field tests. Importantly, models may be the only recourse for estimating impacts for certain stressors in which the objective is to keep the experiment from happening (e.g., exotic species introductions, novel chemicals) or in which whole-system manipulations are ill advised or not permitted (e.g., chemical pollution). Therefore, it is necessary to understand the performance of these models in relation to the assumptions and rationales that provide the basis for their construction and use.

The mesocosm model represents a testable hypothesis concerning ecological effects of multiple stressors. If future mesocosm experiments produce results that are consistent with the additive toxicity assumption, then the mesocosm model cannot be rejected immediately. The important point is to establish an operational feedback between results of the mesocosm model and mesocosm experiments. The model can be used to help understand the results of the experiments, to design future experiments, and to simulate experiments that cannot be performed because of constraints in time or resources. Results of future mesocosm experiments will provide continued opportunities to evaluate the accuracy and usefulness of the CASM model. This complex modeling approach may prove applicable for only those few experimental systems that can be described and measured in commensurate detail.

An alternative approach for estimating risks could be developed by simplifying the structure of the CASM to reflect known major direct and indirect causal pathways involved in the expression of ecological responses to single or multiple stressors. These pathways might be identified in relation to the dominant flows of energy through the system or in relation to ecological structures and processes that prove highly sensitive to the stressors of concern. These simplified models may be applied more generally to other similar systems impacted by different stressors.

Conclusions

Methods for quantifying uncertainty and estimating ecological risk at higher levels of organization have been developed. Increasingly, their use is being advocated in ecological risk assessment guidance manuals (e.g., Environment Canada Priority Substances Assessment Program; Environment Canada 1997) and elsewhere (e.g., Landis et al. 1998). Their application in ecological risk assessments, however, is relatively rare. Multiple-stressor case studies that have used these methods are even more rare. Thus, we do not have a wealth of experience to draw upon. Nevertheless, if we wish to conduct multiple stressor assessments, particularly prospective assessments, uncertainty propagation and ecological modeling methods will be required to estimate risks in a credible fashion at levels of organization that matter to society. The value of the probabilistic CASM and other similar ecological modeling methods is that they provide the ability to explore what could occur in the future given different combinations and levels of stressors in the environment. Using these and other similar modeling approaches, we may develop the capability to intelligently manage watersheds and larger regional systems to prevent calamities from single or multiple stressors.

Acknowledgments—Drs. Dwayne Moore and Steven Bartell are employed by The Cadmus Group, Incorporated. The CASM study was supported by The Academy of Natural Sciences under the University of Maryland Biotechnology Institute Award SC3527553 for support of the project entitled: "The Importance of Understanding Ecological Complexity to Predicting Effects of Multiple Stressors on Coastal Systems"; this award is referred to by the National Oceanic and Atmospheric Administration (NOAA), the Prime Funding Agency, as NA66RGO129. The authors also wish to thank the International Life Sciences Institute for funding preparation of this paper, and Donald DeAngelis, Anne Fairbrother, Alan Maki, Kelly Munkittrick and Larry Barnthouse for their reviews of the first draft.

References

Allen JC. 1990. Factors contributing to chaos in population feedback systems. *Ecol Model* 51:281–298.

Allen TFH, Hoekstra TW. 1992. Toward a unified ecology. New York: Columbia University.

Allen TFH, Starr TB. 1982. Hierarchy: perspectives for ecological complexity. Chicago IL: University of Chicago.

Aulerich RJ, Ringer RK. 1977. Current status of PCB toxicity to mink, and effect on their reproduction. *Arch Environ Contam Toxicol* 6:279–292.

Aulerich RJ, Bursian SJ, Breslin WJ, Olson BA, Ringer RK. 1985. Toxicological manifestations of 2,4,5',–2',4',5'–, 2,3,6,2',3',6'–, and 3,4,5,3',4',5'– hexachlorobiphenyl and Aroclor 1254 in mink. *J Toxicol Environ Health* 15:63–79.

Aulerich RJ, Ringer RK, Iwamoto S. 1974. Effects of dietary mercury on mink. *Arch Environ Contam Toxicol* 2:43–51.

Babich H, Stotzky G. 1983. Synergism between nickel and copper in their toxicity to microbes: mediation by pH. *Ecotoxicol Environ Saf* 7:576–587.

Barkay T, Gillman M, Turner RR. 1997. Effects of dissolved organic carbon and salinity on bioavailability of mercury. *Appl Environ Microbiol* 63:4267-4271.

Barnthouse LW, O'Neill RV, Bartell SM, Suter GW. 1986. Population and ecosystem theory in ecological risk assessment. In: Poston TM, Purdy R, editors. Aquatic ecology and hazard assessment, 9th Symposium. Philadelphia PA: American Society for Testing and Materials). p 82–96.

Bartell SM. 1990. Ecosystem context for estimating stress-induced reductions in fish populations. *Am Fish Soc Symp* 8:167–182.

Bartell SM. 1994. Estimating sublethal toxic effects and ecological risks in coastal systems. In: Dyer KR, Orth RJ, editors. Changes in fluxes in estuaries. Olsen & Olsen. p 211–214.

Bartell SM. 1996. Some thoughts concerning quotients, risks, and decision-making. *Hum Ecol Risk Assess* 2:35–43.

Bartell SM, Cale WG, O'Neill RV, Gardner RH. 1988. Aggregation error: research objectives and relevant model structure. *Ecol Model* 41:157–168.

Bartell SM, Gardner RH, O'Neill RV. 1992. Ecological risk estimation. Boca Raton FL: Lewis.

Begon M, Harper JL, Townsend CR. 1996. Ecology: individuals, populations, and communities. Boston MA: Blackwell Science. 1068 p.

Berger JO. 1985. Statistical decision theory and Bayesian analysis. New York: Springer-Verlag.

Bleavins MR, Aulerich RJ. 1981. Feed consumption and food passage time in mink (*Mustela vison*) and European ferrets (*Mustela putorius furo*). *Lab Anim Sci* 3:268–269.

Brand KP, Small MJ. 1995. Updating uncertainty in an integrated risk assessment: conceptual framework and methods. *Risk Anal* 15:719–731.

Broderius SJ, Smith Jr LL. 1979. Lethal and sublethal effects of binary mixtures of cyanide and hexavalent chromium, zinc, or ammonia to the fathead minnow (*Pimephales promelas*) and rainbow trout (*Salmo gairdneri*). *J Fish Res Board Can* 36:164–172.

Burns L. 1986. Validation and verification of aquatic fate models. In: Proceedings of a workshop on environmental modelling for priority setting among existing chemicals; 11–13 November 1985; Munich, Germany. Munich, Germany: Ecomed. p 148-172.

Campbell KR, Bartell SM. 1998. Ecological models and ecological risk assessment. In: Newman MC, Trojan CL, editors. Risk assessment: logic and measurement. Chelsea MI: Ann Arbor Press. p. 69–100.

Caswell H. 1976. The validation problem. In: Patten BC, editor. Systems analysis and simulation in ecology. New York: Academic. p 313–325.

Caswell H. 1989. Matrix population models: construction, analysis and interpretation. Sunderland MA: Sinauer Associates. 328 p.

Chamberland G, Belanger D, Dallaire A. 1996. Urinary protein excretion of semi-domesticated mink in a chronic methylmercury study. *J Toxicol Environ Health* 47:285–297.

Collins CD. 1980. Formulation and validation of a mathematical model of phytoplankton growth. *Ecology* 61:639–649.

Covello VT, Merkhofer MW. 1993. Risk assessment methods: approaches for assessing human and environmental risks. New York: Plenum. 319 p.

Cuvin-Aralar MLA, Aralar EV. 1993. Effects of long-term exposure to a mixture of cadmium, zinc, and inorganic mercury on two strains of tilapia *Oreochromis niloticus* (L.). *Bull Environ Contam Toxicol* 50:891–897.

DeAngelis DL, Bartell SM, Brenkert AL. 1989. Effects of nutrient recycling and food-chain length on resilience. *Am Nat* 134:778–805.

DeAngelis DL, Goldstein RA, O'Neill RV. 1975. A model for trophic interaction. *Ecology* 56:881–892.

Dobzhansky T. 1965. Adaptness and fitness. In: Lewontin RC, editor. Population biology and evolution. New York: Syracuse University. p. 109–122.

Driscoll CT, Schofield CL, Munson R, Holsapple J. 1994. The mercury cycle and fish in the Adirondack Lakes. *Environ Sci Technol* 28:136-143.

Eaton JG. 1973. Chronic toxicity of a copper, cadmium and zinc mixture to the fathead minnow (*Pimephales promelas* Rafinesque). *Water Res* 7:1723–1736.

Eisler R. 1985. Cadmium hazards to fish, wildlife, and invertebrates: a synoptic review. U.S. Fish and Wildlife Service (USFWS) Biological Report 85(1.2).

Eisler R. 1986. Polychlorinated biphenyl hazards to fish, wildlife, and invertebrates: a synoptic review. U.S. Fish and Wildlife Service (USFWS) Biology Report 85(1.7).

Eisler R. 1988. Arsenic hazards to fish, wildlife, and invertebrates: a synoptic review. U.S. Fish and Wildlife Service (USFWS) Biological Report 85(1.12).

Emlen JM. 1989. Terrestrial population models for ecological risk assessment: a state-of-the-art review. *Environ Toxicol Chem* 8:831–842.

Enserink EL, Maas-Diepeveen JL, Van Leeuwen CJ. 1991. Combined effects of metals: an ecotoxicological evaluation. *Water Res* 25:679–687.

Environment Canada. 1994. A framework for ecological risk assessment at contaminated sites in Canada: review and recommendations. Ottawa ON: Prepared by C. Gaudet, EVS Environmental Consultants, and ESSA. Scientific Series No. 199.

Environment Canada. 1997. Environmental risk assessments of priority substances under the Canadian Environmental Protection Act: guidance manual. Ottawa ON: Chemicals Evaluation Division, Commercial Chemicals Evaluation Branch, Environment Canada.

Ferson S, Burgman M. 1995. Correlations, dependency bounds and extinction risks. *Biol Conserv* 73:101–105.

Ferson S, Ginzburg LR, Akçakaya HR. 2000. Whereof one cannot speak: when input distributions are unknown. *Risk Anal* (in press).

Finkel AM. 1990. Confronting uncertainty in risk management: a guide for decision-makers. Washington DC: Center for Risk Management, Resources for the Future.

Foran JA, Ferenc SA, editors. 1999. Multiple stressors in ecological risk and impact assessment. Pensacola FL: SETAC. 115 p.

Gardner RH, Cale WG, O'Neill RV. 1982. Robust analysis of aggregation error. *Ecology* 63:1771–1779.

Gardner RH, Hetterlingh J-P, Kamari J, Bartell SM. 1990. Estimating the reliability of regional predictions of aquatic effects of acid deposition. In: Kamari J, editor. Impact models to assess regional acidification. London: Kluwer. p. 185-207.

Gardner RH, Mankin JB, Emanuel WR. 1980. A comparison of three carbon models. *Ecol Model* 8:313–332.

Grant DA. 1962. Testing the null hypothesis and the strategy and tactics of investigating theoretical models. *Psych Rev* 69:54–61.

Grieb TM, Driscoll CT, Gloss SP, Schofield CL, Bowie GL, Porcella DB. 1990. Factors affecting mercury accumulation in fish in Upper Michigan peninsula. *Environ Toxicol Chem* 9:919–930.

Haas CN. 1992. A new approach for the analysis of mixture toxicity data. *Water Sci Technol* 26:2345–2348.

Haas CN, Kersten SP, Wright K, Frank MJ, Cidambi K. 1997. Generalization of independent response model for independent action. *Chemosphere* 34:699–710.

Haimes YY, Barry T, Lambert JH. 1994. When and how can you specify a probability distribution when you don't know much. *Risk Anal* 14:661–706.

Hammonds JS, Hoffmann FO, Bartell SM. 1994. An introductory guide to uncertainty analysis in environmental and human health risk assessment. Oak Ridge TN: Oak Ridge National Laboratory, U.S. Department of Energy.

Hanratty MP, Stay FS. 1994. Field evaluation of the littoral ecosystem risk assessment model's predictions of the effects of chlorpyrifos. *J Appl Ecol* 31:439–453.

Harwell M, Gentile J, Norton B, Cooper W. 1994. Ecological significance. Ecological risk assessment issue papers. Washington DC: U.S. Environmental Protection Agency (USEPA). EPA/630/R-94/009.

Hattis D, Burmaster DE. 1994. Assessment of variability and uncertainty distributions for practical risk analyses. *Risk Anal* 14:713–730.

Hoffman FO, Hammonds JS. 1994. Propagation of uncertainty in risk assessments: the need to distinguish between uncertainty due to lack of knowledge and uncertainty due to variability. *Risk Anal* 14:707–712.

Holling CS. 1966. The functional response of invertebrate predators to prey density. *Mem Entomol Soc Can* 48:1–85.

Holling CS. 1986. The resilience of terrestrial ecosystems: local surprise and global change. In: Clark WC, Munn RE, editors. Sustainable development of the biosphere. Laxenburg, Austria: International Institute of Applied Systems Analysis. p. 292–317.

Jensen S, Kihlstrom JE, Olsson M, Lundberg C, Orberg J. 1977. Effects of PCB and DDT on mink (*Mustela vison*) during the reproductive season. *Ambio* 6:239.

Jørgensen SE, Halling-Sørensen B, Nielsen SN, editors. 1996. The handbook of environmental and ecological modelling. Boca Raton FL: CRC Lewis. 672 p.

Kaplan S, Garrick BJ. 1981. On the quantitative definition of risk. *Risk Anal* 1:11–27.

Kaufmann A, Gupta MM. 1985. Introduction to fuzzy arithmetic: theory and applications. New York: Van Nostrand Reinhold.

Klir GJ. 1989. Is there more to uncertainty than some probability theorists might have us believe? *Int J Gen Syst* 15:347–378.

Klir GJ, Folger TA. 1988. Fuzzy sets, uncertainty, and information. Englewood Cliffs NJ: Prentice-Hall.

Lackey RT. 1996. Is ecological risk assessment useful for resolving complex ecological problems? In: Stouder DJ, Bisson PA, Naiman RJ, editors. Pacific salmon and their ecosystems: status and future options. New York: Chapman and Hall. p 525–540.

Landis WG, Moore DRJ, Norton SB. 1998. Ecological risk assessment: looking in, looking out. In: Douben, PET, editor. Pollution risk assessment and management. Chichester, UK: Wiley. p 273–309.

Logan DT, Wilson HT. 1995. An ecological risk assessment method for species exposed to contaminant mixtures. *Environ Toxicol Chem* 14:351–359.

Lotka AJ. 1956. Elements of mathematical biology. New York: Dover. 465 p.

Mankin JB, O'Neill RV, Shugart HH, Rust BW. 1975. The importance of validation in ecosystem analysis. In: Innis GS, editor. New directions in the analysis of ecological systems. La Jolla CA: Simulation Councils Proc. Ser. p 63–71.

May RM. 1974. Biological populations with non-overlapping generations: stable points, stable cycles and chaos. *Science* 186:645–647.

May RM, Oster GF. 1976. Bifurcations and dynamical complexity in simple ecological models. *Am Nat* 110:573–599.

McNeill D, Freiberger P. 1993. Fuzzy logic. New York: Simon and Schuster. 319 p.

Meyer MA, Booker JM. 1991. Eliciting and analyzing expert judgement: a practical guide. New York: Academic.

Moore DRJ. 1998. The ecological component of ecological risk assessment: lessons from a field experiment. *Hum Ecol Risk Assess* 4:1103–1123.

Moore DRJ, Biddinger GR. 1995. The interaction between risk assessors and risk managers during the problem formulation phase. *Environ Toxicol Chem* 14:2013–2014.

Moore DRJ, Elliott BJ. 1996. Should uncertainty be quantified in human and ecological risk assessments used for decision-making? *Hum Ecol Risk Assess* 2:11–24.

Moore DRJ, Sample B, Suter GW, Parkhurst BR, Teed RS. 1999a. A probabilistic risk assessment of the effects of methylmercury and PCBs on mink and kingfishers along East Fork Poplar Creek, Oak Ridge, Tennessee. *Environ Toxicol Chem* 18:2941–2953.

Moore DRJ, Sample B, Suter GW, Parkhurst BR, Teed RS. 1999b. Risk-based decision making: the East Fork Poplar Creek case study. *Environ Toxicol Chem* 18:2954–2958.

Morgan MG, Henrion M. 1990. Uncertainty: a guide to dealing with uncertainty in quantitative risk and policy analysis. Cambridge, UK: Cambridge University.

Mulholland RJ, Sims CS. 1976. Control theory and the regulation of ecosystems. In: Patten BC, editor. Systems analysis and simulation in ecology, Vol 4. New York: Academic. p 373–388.

Naddy RB, LaPoint TW, Klaine SJ. 1995. Toxicity of arsenic, molybdenum and selenium combinations to *Ceriodaphnia dubia. Environ Toxicol Chem* 14:329–336.

Naylor TH, Finger JM. 1967. Verification of computer simulation models. *Manage Sci* 14:B92–B101.

Naylor TH, Wertz K, Wonnacott T. 1969. Spectral analysis of data generated by simulation experiments with econometric models. *Econometrica* 37:333–352.

Nelder JA, Mead RA. 1965. A simplex method for function minimization. *Computer J* 7:308-313.

Nirmalakhandan N, Arulgnanendran V, Mohsin M, Sun B, Cadena F. 1994. Toxicity of mixtures of organic chemicals to microorganisms. *Water Res* 28:543–551.

O'Neill RV, Bartell SM, Gardner RH. 1983. Patterns of toxicological effects in ecosystems: a modeling study. *Environ Toxicol Chem* 2:451–461.

O'Neill RV, DeAngelis DL, Waide JB, Allen TFH. 1986. A hierarchical concept of ecosystems. Princeton NJ: Princeton University.

O'Neill RV, Gardner RH, Barnthouse LW, Suter GW, Hildebrand SG, Gehrs CW. 1982. Ecosystem risk analysis: a new methodology. *Environ Toxicol Chem* 1:167–177.

Oreskes N, Shrader-Frechette K, Belitz K. 1994. Verification, validation, and confirmation of numerical models in the earth sciences. *Science* 263:641–646.

Ott WR. 1995. Environmental statistics and data analysis. Boca Raton FL: Lewis. 313 p.

Park RA, et al. 1974. A generalized model for simulating lake ecosystems. *Simulation* 23:33–50.

Parkhurst BR, Warren-Hicks WJ, Cardwell RD, Volosin J, Etchison T, Butcher JB, Covington SM. 1996. Methodology for aquatic ecological risk assessment. Alexandria VA: Water Environment Research Foundation. Contract No. RP91-AER-1.

Parkhurst BR, Warren-Hicks WJ, Creager CS. 1997. Methods for assessing watershed-scale aquatic risks for multiple stressors. In: Dwyer FJ, Doane TR, Hinman ML, editors. Environmental toxicology and risk assessment: modeling and risk assessment, 6th Vol. Philadelphia PA: American Society for Testing and Materials. STP 1317.

Patten BC, editor. 1971. Systems analysis and simulation in ecology, Volume I. New York: Academic.

Patten BC, editor. 1972. Systems analysis and simulation in ecology, Volume II. New York: Academic.

Patten BC, editor. 1971–1976. Systems analysis and simulation in ecology. 4 vols. New York: Academic.

[PCC] The Presidential/Congressional Commission. 1997a. Framework for environmental health risk management. Final Report, Volume 1. Washington DC: The Presidential/Congressional Commission on Risk Assessment and Management. 64 p.

[PCC] The Presidential/Congressional Commission. 1997b. Risk assessment and risk management in regulatory decision-making. Final Report, Volume 2. Washington DC: The Presidential/Congressional Commission on Risk Assessment and Management. 213 p.

Pelgrom SMGJ, Lock RAC, Balm PHM, Bonga SEW. 1997. Calcium fluxes in juvenile tilapia, *Oreochromis mossambicus,* exposed to sublethal waterborne Cd, Cu, or mixtures of these metals. *Environ Toxicol Chem* 16:770–774.

Pimm SL. 1991. The balance of nature? Ecological issues in the conservation of species and communities. Chicago IL: University of Chicago. 434 p.

Plackett RL, Hewlett PS. 1952. Quantal responses to mixtures of poisons. *J R Stat Soc, B* 14:141–154.

Reckhow KH, Clements JT, Dodd RC. 1990. Statistical evaluation of mechanistic water-quality models. *J Environ Eng* 116:250–268.

Rice JA, Cochran PA. 1984. Independent evaluation of a bioenergetics model for largemouth bass. *Ecology* 65:732–739.

Ricker WE. 1958. Handbook of computations for biological statistics of fish populations. *Bull Fish Res Board Can* 119: 300 p.

Ricker WE, Foerster RE. 1948. Computation of fish production. *Bull Bingh Oceanogr Coll* 11:173–211.

Roales RR, Perlmutter A. 1974. Toxicity of methylmercury and copper, applied singly and jointly, to the blue gourami, *Trichogaster trichopterus*. *Bull Env Contam Toxicol* 12:633–639.

Rose KA, Cowan Jr JH, Houde ED, Coutant CC. 1993. Individual-based modelling of environmental quality effects on early life stages of fishes: A case study using striped bass. *Am Fish Soc Symp* 14:125–145.

Rowan TH. 1990. Functional stability analysis of numerical algorithms. [Ph.D. Dissertation]. Austin TX: The University Texas at Austin.

Rowe WD. 1994. Understanding uncertainty. *Risk Anal* 14:743–750.

Ruggiero LF, Hayward GD, Squires JR. 1994. Viability analysis in biological evaluations: concepts of population viability analysis, biological population, and ecological scale. *Conserv Biol* 8:364–372.

Rykiel Jr EJ. 1996. Testing ecological models: the meaning of validation. *Ecol Model* 90:229–244.

Saila SB. 1972. Systems analysis applied to some fisheries problems. In: Patten BC, editor. Systems analysis and simulation in ecology, Volume 2. New York: Academic. p. 331–372.

Schaffer WM, Kot M. 1986. Chaos in ecological systems: the coals that Newcastle forgot. *Trends Ecol Evol* 1:58–63.

Seiler FA, Alvarez JL. 1996. On the selection of distributions for stochastic variables. *Risk Anal* 16:5–18.

Slob W. 1994. Uncertainty analysis in multiplicative models. *Risk Anal* 14:571–576.

Smith EP, Shugart HH. 1994. Issue paper on uncertainty in ecological risk assessment. In: Ecological Risk Assessment Issue Papers. Washington DC: Risk Assessment Forum, U.S. Environmental Protection Agency (USEPA). EPA/630/R-94/009. p. 8-1–8-53.

Smith FE. 1969. Effects of enrichment in mathematical models. In: NAS Symposium, Eutrophication: causes, consequences, correctives. Washington DC: National Academy of Sciences. p 631–645.

Spehar RL, Fiandt JT. 1986. Acute and chronic effects of water quality criteria-based metal mixtures on three aquatic species. *Environ Toxicol Chem* 5:917–931.

Spromberg JA, John BM, Landis WG. 1998. Metapopulation dynamics: indirect effects and multiple discrete outcomes in ecological risk assessment. *Environ Toxicol Chem* 17:1640–1649.

Suter GW, Bartell SM. 1993. Ecosystem-level effects. In: Suter GW, editor. Ecological risk assessment. Chelsea MI: Lewis. p 275–308.

Thompson KW, Hendricks AC, Cairns Jr. J. 1980. Acute toxicity of zinc and copper singly and in combination to the bluegill (*Lepomis macrochirus*). *Bull Environ Contam Toxicol* 25:122–129.

Turner MG, Costanza R, Sklar FH. 1989. Methods to evaluate the performance of spatial simulation models. *Ecol Model* 47:18–28.

[USEPA] U.S. Environmental Protection Agency. 1980. Ambient water quality criteria for copper. Washington DC: U.S. Office of Water, USEPA. EPA-440/5-80-036.

[USEPA] U.S. Environmental Protection Agency. 1985a. Ambient water quality criteria for arsenic. Washington DC: U.S. Office of Water, USEPA. EPA-440/5-84-033.

[USEPA] U.S. Environmental Protection Agency. 1985b. Ambient water quality criteria for cadmium. Washington DC: U.S. Office of Water, USEPA. EPA-440/5-84-032.

[USEPA] U.S. Environmental Protection Agency. 1986. Ambient water quality criteria for nickel. Washington DC: U.S. Office of Water, USEPA. EPA- 440/5-86-004.

[USEPA] U.S. Environmental Protection Agency. 1987. Ambient water quality criteria for zinc. Washington DC: U.S. Office of Water, USEPA. EPA-440/5-87-008.

[USEPA] U.S. Environmental Protection Agency. 1998. Guideline for ecological risk assessment. Washington DC: Office of Research and Development, USEPA.

Van Puymbroeck SLC, Stips WJJ, Vanderborght OLJ. 1982. The antagonism between selenium and cadmium in a freshwater mollusc. *Arch Environ Contam Toxicol* 11:103–106.

Warren-Hicks WJ, Butcher JB. 1996. Monte Carlo analysis: Classical and Bayesian applications. *Hum Ecol Risk Assess* 2:643–649.

Warren-Hicks WJ, Moore DRJ, editors. 1998. Uncertainty analysis in ecological risk assessment. Pensacola FL: SETAC. 277 p.

Watt KEF. 1961. Use of a computer to evaluate alternative insecticidal programs. *Science* 133:706–707.

Winks KL. 1990. Effects of metal mixtures on *Pimephales promelas* larval growth in water and sediment exposures [M.S. Thesis]. Dayton OH: Wright State University.

Wobeser G, Nielsen NO, Schiefer B. 1976. Mercury and mink II. Experimental methyl mercury intoxication. *Can J Comp Med* 40:34–45.

Wren CD, Hunter DB, Leatherland JF, Stokes PM. 1987a. The effects of polychlorinated biphenyls and methylmercury, singly and in combination, on mink. I: uptake and responses. *Arch Environ Contam Toxicol* 16:441–447.

Wren CD, Hunter DB, Leatherland JF, Stokes PM. 1987b. The effects of polychlorinated biphenyls and methylmercury, singly and in combination, on mink. II: Reproduction and kit development. *Arch Environ Contam Toxicol* 16:449-454.

Zeigler BP. 1976. The aggregation problem. In: Patten BC, editor. Systems analysis and simulation in ecology, Volume 2. New York: Academic. p 299-311.

Zeigler BP. 1979. Multilevel multiformalism modeling: an ecosystem example. In: Halfon E, editor. Theoretical systems ecology. New York: Academic. p 17–54.

CHAPTER 5

Environmental Decision-making for Multiple Stressors: Framework, Tools, Case Studies, and Prospects

Mark A. Harwell and John H. Gentile

The Need to Manage Multiple Environmental Stressors

The issue of understanding the ecological risks from multiple stressors has come to the forefront at this time for several reasons. First, while it is clear that the U.S. has made substantial progress in improving many of the more egregious environmental problems of the 1960s through implementation of chemical-by-chemical, end-of-pipe legislation like the Clean Air Act, Clean Water Act, and the Federal Insecticide, Fungicide, and Rodenticide Act, the case can be made that we are approaching an asymptote in further environmental improvements on these issues. This is a result of both the increased expense in removing smaller and smaller residual quantities of toxic chemicals from environmental media and the fact that the more fixable parts of the system have been fixed. In other words, further environmental improvements by using this approach are becoming more difficult precisely because it has been so successful.

In addition, as shown though the relative risk rankings of the Unfinished Business (USEPA 1987a, 1987b), Reducing Risk (USEPA SAB 1990a, 1990b; Harwell et al. 1992), and Integrated Risk (USEPA SAB 1999) projects, the greatest ecological risks at the national level in the U.S. are associated with stressors other than chemicals.

CHAPTER PREVIEW

Multiple Stressors in Ecological Risk and Impact Assessment: Approaches to Risk Estimation. Susan A. Ferenc and Jeffery A. Foran, editors.
©2000 Society of Environmental Toxicology and Chemistry (SETAC). ISBN 1-880611-40-6

For example, the most recent of these exercises, the Integrated Risk Project (IRP), proposed that the highest ecological risks in the U.S. derive from habitat alteration, hydrological modification, over-harvesting of living marine resources, invasive exotic species, and global climate change (Table 5-1) (USEPA SAB 1999). These results are consistent with the Unfinished Business and Reducing Risk reports. These are physical or biological stressors that, for the most part, are not regulated under the traditional legislative mandates of USEPA. Moreover, these stressors are not highly localized but typically involve anthropogenic activities and ecological consequences on regional to even global scales.

Table 5-1 Relative ranking of ecological risks at the national scale[1]

Highest ecological risks	High ecological risks	Medium ecological risks	Low ecological risks	Unknown but potentially important risks
Hydrologic alterations	Turbidity/ sedimentation	Disease/pest outbreaks	Oil spills	Endocrine disruptors
Harvesting marine living resources	Habitat fragmentation	Nutrient additions	Acid deposition (forests)	Genetically engineered organisms
Habitat conversion	Pesticides	Physical habitat disruption	Hg/MeHg	
Climate change		Acid deposition (lakes)	No_x/SO_2	
Introduction of exotic species		Altered fire regime	Radionuclides	
		Altered salinity regime	Noise pollution	
		Persistent toxic organics	Light pollution	
		Heavy metals other than Hg	Groundwater contamination	
		DO/BOD	Thermal pollution	
		Harvesting freshwater resources		
		Tropospheric ozone/UV-B		
		Toxic inorganics		
		Acid mine drainage		

Source: USEPA SAB 1999
[1] This ranking assumes enforcement of current environmental laws and regulations.

Finally, there is a trend toward increased attention to regional-scale environmental issues. This is partially because new frameworks are emerging to deal with these issues, especially concepts such as ecosystem management and ecological sustainability (Lubchenko et al. 1991; IEMTF 1995a, 1995b; Christensen et al. 1996; Harwell et al. 1996). But it is also because there is increased awareness that the environmental quality of life that people experience is visibly tied to their living conditions, whether it is overcrowding and pollution driving to work or while on vacation, constraints on water usage, excessive prices for seafood, or loss of recreational opportunities. Regional-scale environmental issues have become increasingly important, including the preservation of remnant old-growth forests, recovery of salmon in the Pacific Northwest (Tuchman et al. 1996; Chapter 1, this volume) and saving the Everglades in South Florida (Davis and Ogden 1994; Florida Governor's Commission 1995; Harwell et al. 1996).

These factors, among others, mean that there is now a convergence between the requirement to understand ecological risks from multiple stressors and the requirements for effects-based environmental decision-making. This includes the need for a systematic framework for addressing multiple-stressor, regional-scale ecological issues, as well as analytical and statistical tools for characterizing multiple stressor/multiple ecological effects relationships. We will discuss issues that have to be addressed in meeting these needs, draw lessons from the other articles in this volume on analytical and statistical tools, propose a framework for bringing science more effectively to bear on the effects-based environmental decision-making, and consider a regional-scale case study.

Terminology

The terminology used to describe the risk effects to human health and ecology from both natural and anthropogenic environmental stress can be classified into two general categories. First, the terms *cumulative risk*, *effects*, and *impacts* have been used to denote the accumulation of risk/effects resulting from the incremental addition of stressors to the environment. This terminology has its origins in the Council on Environmental Quality (CEQ) regulations for implementing the National Environmental Policy Act of 1969 (NEPA) that requires environmental impact statements to "anticipate a cumulatively significant impact on the environment" (38 CFR 1500.6). Cumulative impacts are defined in this legislation as "the impact on the environment which results from the incremental impact of the action when added to other past, present, and reasonably foreseeable future actions."

The term multiple stressor has its origins in the field of ecotoxicology and historically has been used to denote the interactions among multiple chemicals. A valuable contribution of the multiple-stressor concept was that it stressed the need to account for multiple chemical interactions when formulating regulatory policy that was based, principally, on laboratory studies of individual chemicals. However, the risks and impacts from multiple stressors, as used in this chapter, are placed in a broader context, including both prospective (predictive) and retrospective (diagnostic) assessments and reflecting the current position being adopted in both the Canadian and U.S. environmental regulatory communities.

This broader and more integrated view is reflected in the US Environmental Protection Agency Science Policy Council's recent guidance on the planning and scoping phase of cumulative risk assessments (USEPA 1997). The guidance notes that risk assessments within the Agency are moving from the single chemical, human cancer analyses to integrated assessments involving suites of natural and anthropogenic stressors in multiple media with a variety of adverse effects on humans, individual species, communities, and ecosystems. The guidance notes that the term *cumulative risk assessment* relates to a wide variety of risks and situations, from multiple chemicals affecting a single endpoint to combinations of chemical, physical, and biological stressors affecting many ecological and human systems. The guidance is clearly focused on an integrated approach that can accommodate that range of interpretations of cumulative risks. It specifically defines cumulative risk assessment to be "the consideration of the aggregate ecologic and human health risk to the target entity caused by the accumulation of risk from multiple stressors operating through multiple pathways and originating from multiple sources" (USEPA 1997).

While we recognize that there remains a healthy dialogue regarding the terminology used in this field, we suggest that these perspectives do not necessarily reflect distinct scientific problems, nor do they require unique analytical frameworks to arrive at solutions. Granted, there are always site-specific differences that will require the selection of unique analytical methods, models, and measurements. For example, the models and methods chosen to analyze the risks from the multiple-source release of multiple chemicals within a riverine system would likely be quite different from those used to assess the causes of regional ecological degradation from physical, chemical, and biological stressors to the Florida Keys coral reef tract or for evaluating what would be necessary to achieve a specified level of protection for a valued ecological resource. However, we contend that these apparent differences are simply variations on the same basic theme that can be addressed using a single ecological assessment framework (USEPA 1992, 1998; Gentile et al. 1993). Further, we suggest that the framework that has been developed for ecological risk assessments is appropriate, with some modifications, for assessing human-health risks, especially when endpoints other than cancer and stressors other than single chemicals are considered. In later sections of this chapter, we will elaborate more on the proposed process for doing effects-based assessments. For now, we believe this is all the same fundamental problem, and solving this class of problems is the challenge to advancing the next generation of environmental decision-making.

Classification of Cumulative Effects: A Hierarchical Framework

The context within which ecological assessments are conducted is a multidimensional space defined by a variety of ecosystem types within which is a hierarchy of potential environmental receptors and endpoints that interact with several categories of potential stressors over a range of spatial and temporal scales (Figure 5-1). It is exactly this complexity that confounds our attempts to analyze quantitatively or qualitatively the cumulative ecological effects of multiple stressors. Therefore, it is not surprising that there is continuing debate regarding terminology and strategies for analyzing and communicating the ecological and environmental effects from multiple stressors. Certainly, it is not our intention to resolve this debate but to propose a classification that reduces the dimensionality of this n-dimensional problem and provides a template for evaluating current knowledge and tools.

We certainly recognize that there are other possible classification schemes and that in reality complex environmental problems cannot realistically be reduced to a single categorical dimension without the risk of oversimplification and potentially inappropriate generalization. For example, a single-chemical stressor that is highly lipophillic and persistent may exert its action over a wide geographic range and a long period of time. Similarly, a non-chemical stressor, such as overfishing, may act over a very small spatial scale (e.g., a coral reef). Thus, this classification is intended to provide a framework for organizing and evaluating the problem.

The following is a proposed hierarchical classification that attempts to encompass the range of environmental problems resulting from multiple stressors (Table 5-2). The four tiers include
- Class 1: a single-chemical stressor and single ecological receptor;
- Class 2: multiple-chemical stressors and their interactions acting on a single ecological receptor;
- Class 3: multiple-chemical stressors and their interactions acting on multiple ecological receptors; and
- Class 4: multiple classes of stressors (chemical, physical, and biological) from multiple sources and their interactions acting upon multiple ecological receptors.

In this classification schema, Classes 1 through 3 are ecotoxicological in nature and apply primarily to predictive assessments for one or more chemicals with similar and different modes of action, but they do not have explicit spatial (site-specific) or temporal components. These types of assessments would be used to support such issues as toxic chemical registration, product development, and ambient water-quality criteria. Class 1 needs no further elaboration here, as it is limited to single-chemical assessments with one receptor and thus basically represents classical ecotoxicology.

Class 2 represents multiple chemicals with similar modes of action acting upon a single receptor. Here the individual chemicals can be considered to be additive in the form of toxic units or toxic equivalents (Ahlborg et al. 1994; Swartz et al. 1995; Foran and Ferenc 1999). For the Class 2 multiple-chemical model with a single receptor, analytical, numerical, and statistical methods are available (compare

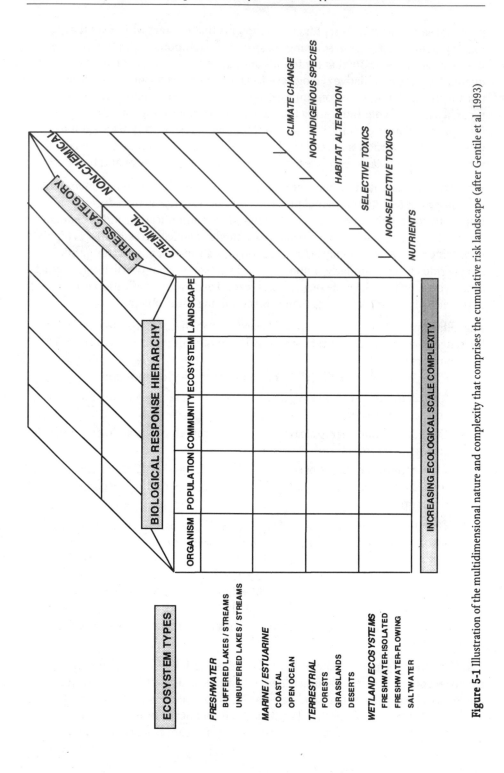

Figure 5-1 Illustration of the multidimensional nature and complexity that comprises the cumulative risk landscape (after Gentile et al. 1993)

Table 5-2 Classification scheme for organizing cumulative risks from multiple stressors into categories reflecting increasing complexity based on types of stressors, modes of action, degree of stressor interactions, and scale

Stressor types	Receptor	Mode of action	Interactions	Temporal	Spatial	Terminology
				Scale		
Single chemical	Single species	Single	No	Hours-months	None or local	Single stressor
Multiple chemical	Single species/populations	Similar	No	Hours-months	None or local	Multiple stressors
Multiple chemical	Single species/Populations	Dissimilar	Yes	Hours-months	None or local	Multiple stressors
Multiple chemicals	Multiple species/Populations	Similar	No	Months-years	Local-watershed	Multiple stressors
Multiple chemical	Multiple species/Populations	Similar	Yes	Months-years	Local-watershed	Multiple stressors
Multiple chemical	Multiple species/populations	Dissimilar	Yes	Months-years	Local-watershed	Multiple stressors/ Cumulative effects
Mutiple caterories and sources of stressors (e.g., physical, chemical, and biological)	Populations, comunities, ecosystems and landscapes	Dissimilar	Yes	Years to decades centuries - often unlimited time scales	Generally large (e.g., water-shed, regional)	Cumulative risks/ Effects/ Impacts

Chapter 3, this volume), but even for this tier, the requirements for empirical data are substantial and often are not satisfied. The Class 2 class of problems generally does not involve a spatially explicit or site-explicit component, and time is generally constrained experimentally.

Class 3 includes chemicals with different modes of toxic action and adds a diverse suite of ecological receptors, but it generally continues to focus on the individual-, or at most, population-level responses. Because the different ecological receptors likely will have differential response thresholds, the data needs will increase along with the degree of analytical difficulty. Now the analyses not only must include the contributions and interactions of the chemical stressors but also must address the problem of cumulating effects across multiple receptors at the species and/or population level. Further, when chemical substances have mixed modes of action and act independently, the *hazard rate* approach (Kooijman and Bedaux 1996) may be more appropriate. However, if there is evidence for interactions (e.g., synergism, antagonism, potentiation), then multivariate approaches, such as those discussed in Chapter 3, are more appropriate. Class 3 experimental and data requirements are substantial and will require sophisticated methods to cumulate effects (e.g., numerical models, cumulative distribution functions, etc.). Generally, Class 3 retains the "multiple stressor" terminology, but with the addition of multiple receptors and ecological effects comes a shift, in some arenas, to the terms *cumulative effects* and *cumulative risks*. Class 3 assessments do not have spatial or temporal components.

Class 4 deals with single, site-specific assessments such as a hazardous waste sites in which multiple classes of stressors operate through a variety of pathways and affect multiple ecosystems or ecosystem components. Class 4 represents a major shift in analytical complexity because it includes multiple-stressor categories (i.e., physical, chemical, and biological) operating on multiple receptors representing different levels of biological complexity (e.g., populations, communities, landscapes). This level of complexity includes both natural and anthropogenic stressors and their variability as well as defined site-specific spatial and temporal components. Moreover, the Class 4 cumulative effects or risks from multiple stressors may be assessed for current conditions resulting from past actions or for future conditions anticipated from planned actions. Whether retrospective or prospective, temporal and spatial scales are defined in terms of the site of interest (e.g., hazardous waste sites, power plants, etc.). The analytic and data requirements for these types of analyses increase by an order of magnitude over previous tiers. Modeling must now be spatially explicit and dynamic (compare Chapter 4), perhaps requiring the integration of hydrodynamic, toxicological, and population or ecosystem models, all of which require substantial data to parameterize and calibrate. Here we encounter another subtle shift in terminology, to cumulative environmental effects or impacts, reflecting the more comprehensive and inclusive nature of the stress regime and hierarchy of environmental responses.

Class 4 focuses on watershed and regional assessments and specifically addresses multiple sources and natural variability both in the present and future. At this level, the risks or impacts may cumulate over indeterminate spatial and temporal scales, beyond the boundaries of the original problem setting, or the problem may be more complicated by the future addition of multiple sources of stress to the system. The restoration of South Florida and the Everglades, discussed below, is an example of the Class 4 type of assessment problem, wherein on a regional spatial scale many different societal drivers or sources contribute a host of physical, chemical, and biological stressors expressing considerable natural variability and affecting a diversity of ecological systems from population to landscape levels. Class 4 assessments force us to address the regional distribution and accumulation of risks and effects to determine the cumulative impact of all of our actions, thus obviating what Odum (1982) called the "tyranny of small decisions." Class 4 assessments necessarily involve the statistical and modeling tools of less complex problems (following Chapters 3 and 4) but further require weight-of-evidence approaches and, ultimately, expert judgment and adaptive management (compare Chapter 1).

The proposed classification provides a context for examining a variety of analytical and decision paradigms and the available methods, models, and measures to assess the environmental consequences of multiple stressors over a range of stressor categories, ecological, temporal, and spatial scales. A simple typology representing the status of our current knowledge and capabilities is presented in Figure 5-2. This typology is intended to be a qualitative impression based upon the authors' understanding of the present state of the science. The intensity of the shading reflects our degree of knowledge and capabilities, with the darkest area representing our greatest understanding and capabilities and the lightest shading our area of least knowledge. It is clear that as scale and complexity increase, our ability to assess cumulative effects quantitatively decreases. In fact, it is only at Classes 1 and 2 that we can quantitatively assess cumulative effects with any degree of confidence. Assessing cumulative effects at higher tiers still remains qualitative, often relying on expert judgment. Clearly, the research needs lie in the latter area, and this is where resources should be focused both on qualitative and quantitative techniques. This may require a reexamination of the utility of conventional reductionist concepts, paradigms, and techniques in favor of more holistic approaches. We believe that expert judgment and weight-of-evidence approaches are appropriate tools for addressing problems at all the tiers. Further, expert judgment is perfectly acceptable and necessary as input from science to the decision-making process, and falsely expecting or demanding quantification and precision may be inappropriate and may inhibit rather than facilitate timely decision-making.

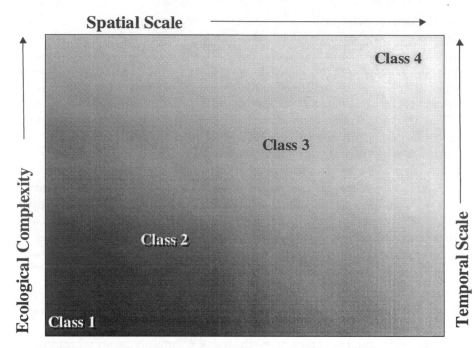

Figure 5-2 Illustration of the decrease in knowledge and understanding of classes of cumulative risks with increasing complexity and scale

Cumulative Effects Assessment Frameworks

The phenomena of cumulative environmental change and its implications for society have numerous examples in history. Environmental change typically results from ubiquitous human activities, which feature a multiplicity of small, independent decisions by numerous individuals. These incremental environmental changes from apparently insignificant decisions have been referred to as "destruction by insignificant increments" (McTaggart-Cowan 1976). Recognition that "cumulative impacts can result from individually minor but collectively significant actions taking place over a period of time" (40 CFR 1508.7) led to CEQ regulations requiring that cumulative impacts be addressed in all environmental impact statements being conducted under NEPA. While this Act correctly focuses attention on the importance of incremental impacts to the environment, it does not 1) address the mechanisms by which effects accumulate, 2) provide a framework or guidance on how to conduct cumulative risks and impact assessments, or 3) provide guidance for determining the significance of incremental change.

Cumulative effects assessment paradigms have at their foundation a multistage causal model comprised of the following components: 1) causes or sources of ecological change; 2) a process or pathway of change, including direct, indirect, and nonlinear, and interactions and synergisms; and 3) the resulting environmental effects (Cocklin et al. 1992; Spaling and Smit 1993; Harwell et al., in press). This model can be used as the basis for developing a variety of typologies for classifying and analyzing cumulative environmental effects. For example, Baskerville (1986) classified cumulative environmental effects by the system's response to perturbations; Cline et al. (1983) employed a matrix approach to facilitate analyzing direct or indirect impacts as well as additive incremental or cumulative impacts. Stakhiv (1991) added a temporal dimension (past, present, and future), while Lane et al. (1988) characterized cumulative effects based on their primary driving force and their spatial patterns. Other typologies of cumulative effects differentiate effects primarily on the basis of temporal and spatial attributes (CEARC/NRC 1986; Sonntag et al. 1987; Bedford and Preston 1988; Preston and Bedford 1988). Nevertheless, all of these approaches are organized around one or more elements of the multistage causal model. Collectively, they recognize multiple sources of causation, the reality of complex interactions and interrelationships among causes and the resulting stress to the environment, and the need to address cumulative environmental change within a variable spatial and temporal context. However, the operational utility of these typologies has yet to be tested rigorously in an applied environmental setting (Cocklin et al. 1992).

Attributes of Cumulative Effects Assessment Approaches

A variety of approaches has been proposed for systematically analyzing and evaluating the significance of the incremental change in environmental effects as the result on one or more anthropogenic activities. The more prevalent approach uses variations on the multistage causal model to assess cumulative effects associated with past, present, and future human activities. A second, and until recently, less-common approach utilizes regional planning principles to determine societal preferences among a set of resource allocation choices. This approach uses methods of multi-attribute preference elicitation to determine social norms. These norms function as decision rules for comparing and ranking alternative choices and to trade off environmental, economic, or political objectives as the basis for designing and choosing among alternative scenarios. This approach views cumulative effects assessment as a correlate to regional or comprehensive planning (Jacobs and Sadler 1990; Davies 1991; Stakhiv 1991) and includes multiple goal orientation, the role of social norms in determining goals, and a participatory role of stakeholders and society in decision-making (NRC 1996). Of course, the implicit assumption of both these approaches is that the results will be used by decision-makers and the public to lead to better-informed decisions.

While at first glance the planning/goal setting and causal model approaches may seem disparate, in reality they are quite complementary and necessary for effective decision-making. This interdependence characterizes the current dialogue within the risk assessment community that is focusing on ensuring that societal values, preferences, and norms, as well as stakeholder interests, are reflected in the goals of the assessment. This integration is particularly important in watershed and regional environmental assessments, in which decisions are driven more by societal and political processes than by compliance with specific regulations. Consequently, "planning" becomes essential for determining the most efficacious and productive way to engage and define society's role and contribution to the CEA process (compare NRC 1996).

A logical extension of this thinking is the recognition that most, if not all, scientific assessments are only one element in a broader risk-management rubric that includes economics, social preferences, politics, and special interest groups (Figure 5-3; after van Leeuwen et al. 1998). Recognition of the role of these elements in the decision-making process is essential if one is to develop a scientific assessment framework that is responsive to and reflective of society's needs and interests. USEPA's risk assessment guidelines, for example, have explicitly included a planning phase at the beginning of the process that is a major departure from health-risk assessments (NRC 1983; USEPA 1998). The intent is to elicit and include input from a range of sectors in the initial scoping and planning to ensure that the assessment is attuned to what society values ecologically and addresses the correct questions. This becomes particularly important in regional-scale assessments in which

Figure 5-3 Factors influencing risk management decisions

transboundary regulatory and societal preferences become more important and in which there is no overarching decision-making framework for addressing these issues and resolving conflicts. In Chapter 2, Munkittrick and McMaster clearly emphasize the need for a planning process that engages the public and stakeholders in the decision-making process. They correctly point out that the decision-making process often may ignore the issue of ecological significance (i.e., ignore ecologically relevant impacts) in favor of societal acceptance of issues of little ecological importance. Consequently, Canada is incorporating the issue of "societal acceptability" into its decision-making process. An important attribute for any CEA framework, therefore, is that it should provide the forum and mechanism for including the public, stakeholders, regulators, and decision-makers in the process.

In addition to recognizing that cumulative risk or effects assessment approaches must exist within a risk-management framework, they must also be flexible, dynamic, iterative, and adaptable to a variety of situations. For example, USEPA's Ecological Risk Assessment Guidelines (USEPA 1992, 1998) were deliberately designed to be general and applicable to the full range of assessment problems by recognizing three classes of assessments: stressor-directed, effects-directed, and value-directed. Another important attribute of an assessment framework is that it must be iterative, thus allowing both the scientist and the decision-maker to explore a variety of scientific and management options.

It is important that a cumulative risk assessment framework is able to address current conditions, future conditions assuming no management action, and future conditions in which management actions will add or reduce stress to the environment. In South Florida, we have successfully applied USEPA's ecological risk assessment framework, both retrospectively to determine the causal stress-response relationships that have resulted in the current unsustainable state of the Everglades and prospectively to forecast anticipated ecological changes over space and time for a variety of plausible management actions. Classifying current conditions is a necessary step in any cumulative effects assessment if one is to hope to be able to assess the incremental ecological changes that will result from management actions. As was clearly stated in Chapter 2, one must know where they are if there is to be any hope of determining the impacts of additional sources of stress to a given environment. Likewise, in human-health risk assessments, the issue is incremental risk from an action above current baseline conditions.

Finally, the most important attribute in a cumulative effects assessment framework is the ability to forecast future change from existing conditions. Without this predictive capability, one can address only current conditions that obviously represent only one point in space and time. This would have limited value and utility to the decision-maker who is asked to make decisions whose consequences will occur in the future. Given this background, let us examine how well several cumulative effect frameworks satisfy these necessary attributes.

Cumulative effects assessment framework comparisons

Five cumulative risk assessment or impact frameworks are compared using the proposed attributes (Table 5-3). Lee and Gosselink (1988) proposed a method for assessing cumulative impacts for bottomland hardwood forests (Figure 5-4). What is unique about this framework is that it addresses the linkage between cumulative effects and the regulation of cumulative impacts through a scientific goal-setting process, something that was absent from earlier works (Sonntag et al. 1987; Preston and Bedford 1988). This framework also suggests a mechanism for developing institutional memory that is critical to tracking the efficacy of decisions. However, this framework does not explicitly address the role of planning and the role of the public in setting goals for the environment. Rather, it views goals as solely ecological and within an existing regulatory context. We have found in the South Florida case study that both science and the public must be involved in goal setting: science provides the boundaries and constraints as to what is possible, and society decides at what point along the continuum of potentially sustainable states it prefers the system to be (Harwell et al. 1996). The most important omission in Lee and Gosselink's (1988) framework is the absence of a risk-based predictive component that provides the manager the ability to analyze scenarios and forecast plausible outcomes before action is taken.

The biologically directed assessment framework, discussed in Foran and Ferenc (1999), while not explicitly dealing with risk management and regulatory issues, can readily be interfaced with them (Figure 5-5). This framework in many ways closely parallels the Lee and Gosselink framework, in that it deals well with the deductive elements of the analysis but lacks the inductive component, i.e., the ability to forecast the future likelihood of impacts from one or more management options or scenarios. The text accompanying this framework is a comprehensive and excellent resource that describes, in detail, each of the steps in this process (Foran and Ferenc 1999).

The effects-driven assessment framework proposed by Munkittrick and McMaster in Chapter 2 can be viewed as a combination of the Lee and Gosselink (1988), Suter et al. (1999), and risk-based frameworks (USEPA 1998) in that it recognizes the need for both a diagnostic component and a predictive component. However, it is important to note that the recent USEPA ecological risk assessment guidelines now more explicitly address both retrospective diagnostic/deductive types of assessments by identifying three assessment approaches: stressor-directed, effects-directed, and value-directed. Much of the criticisms that have been directed at the failure of USEPA's initial ecological risk assessment framework (e.g., Fairbrother et al. 1997) can be attributed to trying to force-fit all assessments into a stressor-directed option rather than adapting the framework to the specifics of the problem setting. Within the context of our classification typology, USEPA's stressor-directed approach is applicable to Class 1, 2, and perhaps 3 assessments, while USEPA's effects- and value-directed approaches are applicable to Class 3 and 4 assessments.

Table 5-3 Comparison of cumulative assessment frameworks

Attributes	Cumulative assessment framework				
	Lee and Gosselink 1998	Foran and Ferenc 1999	USEPA 1998	Munkittrick and McMaster	USEPA SAB 1999
Risk management/Regulatory context	Yes	No	Yes	Yes	Yes
Includes public, stakeholders, etc. in planning and goal setting	No	Yes	Yes	Yes	Yes
Can address stressor-, effects-, and Value-directed assessments	Unlikely	Yes	Yes	Yes	Yes
Single framework for retrospective, current, and prospective analyses	No	No	Yes	Yes	Yes
Has epidemiological and diagnostic capability	Yes	Yes	Yes	Yes	No
Can assess current condition resulting from historical causes	Yes	Yes	Yes	Yes	Yes
Has ability to forecast outcomes of multiple scenarios	No	No	Yes	Yes	Yes
Can predict incremental changes	Unlikely	No	Yes	Yes	Yes
Can evaluate significance of changes	Maybe	No	Yes	Yes	Yes

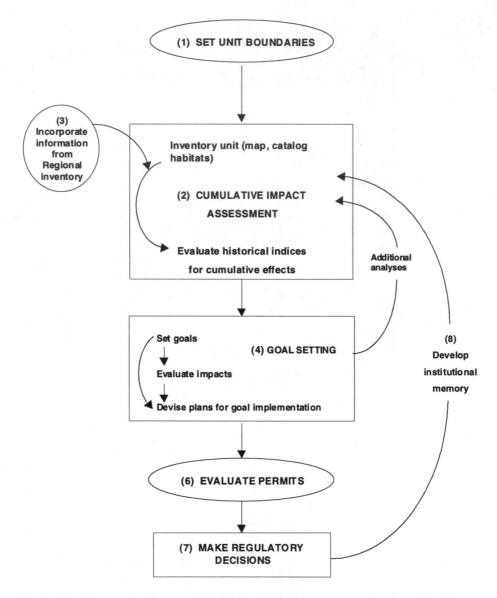

Figure 5-4 Major steps in the proposed cumulative impact assessment procedures (modified from Gosselink and Lee 1987)

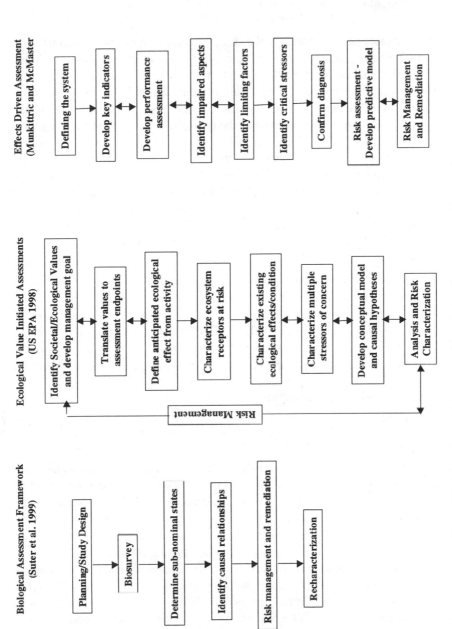

Figure 5-5 Comparison of three proposed cumulative effects assessment frameworks

Our experience in South Florida suggests that USEPA's effects- and value-directed pathways work quite well at Classes 3 and 4. Thus, there appears to be more congruence than disparity in these approaches.

Given the plurality of CEA strategies, the choice of approach depends upon the question. There are generally two broad categories of questions asked by stakeholders and decision-makers. First, what are the current state and condition of the ecosystem (or some component thereof) and what are the underlying causes for its degradation? If the focus of the assessment is retrospective, i.e., understanding the causes that have led to the current state of the ecological system, then the Lee and Gosselink (1988), Suter et al. (1999), and first half of the Munkittrick and McMaster (Chapter 2) frameworks are sufficient, as is the framework proposed by Fairbrother et al. (1997). Similarly, the planning and problem-formulation phase of USEPA's ecological risk assessment framework (USEPA 1998), if the effects- and value-directed options are used, will fully address these questions. However, the USEPA Science Advisory Board's Integrated Environmental Decision-Making Framework (USEPA SAB 1999) (Figure 5-6) does not explicitly address this question, but it could be modified to do so.

If, however, the question involves forecasting the probability, magnitude, extent, or duration of impacts that will result from remedial management options or the addition of new activities, then only those frameworks with an explicit risk-based assessment component will be sufficient. The USEPA (1992), USEPA SAB (1999), and Munkittrick and McMaster frameworks provide this capability, as does the "inductive logic" component of Fairbrother et al. (1997) (Figure 5-7).

The case for a single cumulative effects assessment framework

The commonality among the CEA approaches suggests that it is time to explore the utility and value of a single, comprehensive cumulative risk/effects assessment framework and accompanying guidance. Why a single paradigm? In 1983, the National Research Council (NRC) published its seminal study "Risk Assessment in the Federal Government: Managing the Process." This study was commissioned to develop a single unified strategy for conducting human-health risk assessment from the plethora of risk approaches being used at that time for chemical-induced cancer risks. Similarly when USEPA published the "Framework for Ecological Risk Assessment" (USEPA 1992), the explicit intent was to develop a general, flexible strategy for conducting assessments that could be tailored to fit specific needs in environmental decision-making (e.g., from support for pesticide registration to prospective assessments of the ecological consequences of multiple stressors). The guidelines that resulted from both these activities represent the consensus of a broad base of scientists, policymakers, the public, and stakeholders.

Moving to a unified approach for both human-health risks (NRC 1983) and ecological risks (USEPA 1992) has accomplished several objectives. First, it removed from

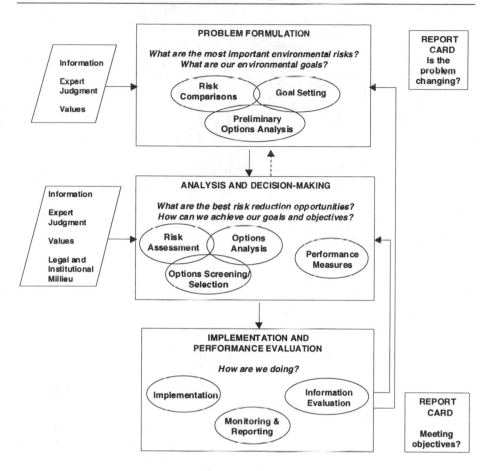

Figure 5-6 Integrated environmental decision-making framework (SAB/ IRP Draft Report)

the discussions the issue of which approach/paradigm to follow, and it allowed the decision-making process to be focused on the results and interpretation of the risk assessment without being confused by methodological arguments. This was very important within USEPA as well as within the regulated community because it provided a "level playing field" for all parties, and it made the process more transparent and less subject to manipulation. Achieving consensus on the assessment process and framework also served to identify the priority research topics (e.g., endpoints, uncertainties, etc.) and thus served as a mechanism for directing resources. By applying the same process to a variety of case studies, site-specific information needs were identified and used to direct research development for a wide variety of methods, models, and measures. Finally, these paradigms served as a research tool to identify clearly both the types of data and the analytical and decision-making methods necessary to perform a creditable assessment.

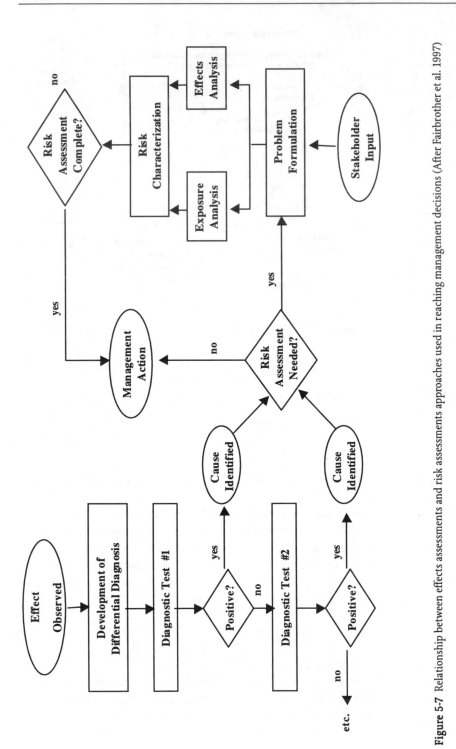

Figure 5-7 Relationship between effects assessments and risk assessments approaches used in reaching management decisions (After Fairbrother et al. 1997)

The USEPA has recognized the need for guidance in this area and recently has begun the process of developing a cumulative risk assessment framework initially for human-health risk assessments. It may be useful to begin a parallel process for ecological assessments, either within or outside USEPA, that would draw upon a broad base of international expertise. The USEPA risk assessment guidelines may be useful as a point of departure for this consensus exercise for several reasons: it already has extensive national and international acceptance and use as an assessment strategy and it provides a robust framework that can be adapted to include elements of other approaches. Further, the USEPA ecological risk framework has flexibility in design and explicit links to the public, stakeholders, and managers and includes a retrospective problem-formulation phase followed by a forecasting and analysis phase that provides a complete assessment strategy and one that is ideally suited to assessing the cumulative ecological effects for a wide range of scenarios. Cumulative effects assessments at Classes 3 and 4, which have stressor-directed as well as effects- and valued-directed components, will require an integrated assessment framework that seamlessly integrates both retrospective and prospective components.

In a later section, we explore the use of the USEPA framework in support of the ongoing ecosystem-restoration process in South Florida, and its extensive reliance on sound science to support complex environmental decision-making, as an excellent example of the Class 4 category of environmental decision-making.

Present Tools: Their Uses and Limitations

In this section, we discuss some issues raised, tools tested, and lessons learned from the other articles in the present volume. Collectively, these articles explore the state of the science in multivariate statistical analyses; ecological model development, parameterization, and applications; uncertainty analyses; adaptive management; and case examples of environmental problem-solving.

Insights in statistics, or, The necessary, but insufficient, tools for all Classes

In Chapter 3, Fairbrother and Bennett discuss inferential, descriptive, and geographical multivariate statistical tools and their applicability in ecological assessments. An array of sophisticated tools are presented for exploring data on complex stressor/ecological effects situations and "mining information" in support of decision-making. The primary purpose of multivariate analyses for environmental assessments is to provide the means for weighting the ability of various stressors to cause change in an ecological endpoint. In addition, there is available a series of geographical information systems (GIS) tools for exploring spatially explicit information. The GIS tools allow these analyses to be placed within a spatial context. As Fairbrother and Bennett note, these techniques have not been used widely in ecological risk assessments or environmental impact analyses, in part because of the lack of training in multivariate analyses by ecologists. However, these statistical and GIS tools are now much more accessible with the widespread development and availability of computer software. Case examples are discussed regarding the applicability of these multivariate tools, including the linking of a spatially explicit dynamic simulation model of landscape dynamics with developmental scenarios of tropical countries (Dale et al. 1994) and the mapping of predicted air pollution distributions onto GIS layers of habitats for identifying vulnerable habitats and regions (Carruthers 1998).

Fairbrother and Bennett suggest that the first step in the application of multivariate techniques is to analyze statistical relationships within complex datasets. A key is to define the risk question appropriately so that the correct statistical tool can be utilized. They suggest that the second step is to put observed relationships into an ecological context, i.e., to ask if they make ecological sense, such that predictions are reasonable and consistent with ecological understanding. This fundamentally relates to the issue of ecological significance, i.e., distinguishing statistical differences from what actually makes a difference ecologically. There is a need to couple expertise in understanding ecological systems and their important attributes or endpoints with facility of the multivariate statistical tools. Clearly, appropriate multivariate statistical tools can provide tremendous guidance to decision-making, but this is likely to be through a weight-of-evidence approach rather than through demonstration of definitive causal relationships among multiple stressors and ecological effects. Moreover, it can be expected in most real-world situations that there will be a paucity of data and understanding about the ecosystem and stress-response relationships. Nevertheless, through careful selection and application of the appropriate multivariate tool to the problem at hand, even in the face of significant uncertainties, there can be tremendous guidance in the decision-making process. As discussed below, using these tools in support of the development of the conceptual model of the environmental problem can be powerful. It is worth mentioning that a Bayesian approach may be particularly appropriate here because it provides a more formal integration of "expert knowledge" and numerical data.

Lessons in ecological modeling, or, Training computers to think about things too complicated for humans

In Chapter 4, Moore and Bartell discuss two critical aspects of multiple-stressor ecological risk assessments: ecological modeling and uncertainty analysis. These authors note important characteristics of multiple-stressor (and effects-based) ecological risk assessments:

- These problems are typically very data-intensive in need but often lack sufficient data in reality.

- Consequently, analyses often are needed to reduce the dimensionality of the problem, such as through eliminating implausible scenarios or aggregating ecological components.
- Some types of resource management issues have large existing datasets (e.g., fisheries management) and thus may be more amenable to modeling and uncertainty analyses.
- For other problems that do not have large amounts of data, modeling analyses may be done to guide research to the most important factors needing parameter estimation, or to provide analyses to managers for risks in hypothetical scenarios addressing "what-if?" questions.

Moore and Bartell correctly state that ecological modeling may be the only means to characterize risks to valued ecological attributes or endpoints from multiple stressors, identify the more important sources of risks, and evaluate likely risk reduction options. In part, this is because of the complexity of the issues in multiple stressors, such as interactions among stressors and the likelihood of having multiple at-risk components of the ecosystem. Thus, while each individual stressor and each individual ecological endpoint may in a data-rich situation have reliable and sufficient dose-response data (not a typical situation, unfortunately), the prospect of having such information for all combinations of multiple stressors is nonexistent; the number of combinations quickly become astronomical as more stressors are added. Exacerbating this problem is the issue of multiple ecological endpoints for each stressor; for example, one stressor may differentially affect different life stages of a single important species and may have totally different effects on other species or processes in the same system. These points would be true even in the absence of the ever-present natural variability in dynamical ecological systems and processes across space and time. Thus, it is impossible to design and implement any field or laboratory experimental program that can completely characterize the causal stressor/effects relationships for all combinations of multiple stressors that may affect the full set of important components of a real ecosystem. The conclusion is that ecological modeling is the only solution.

Moore and Bartell also note correctly that problems involving multiple ecological stressors tend to focus attention at higher levels of organization (i.e., community-, ecosystem-, and landscape-level effects) in order to be relevant to society, in part because these usually involve environmental issues of larger scales, such as regional environmental management problems. Regional-scale environmental problems typically involve mixes of quite different types of stressors (e.g., chemical contamination, exotic species, and habitat alteration) occurring simultaneously. These also often include stressors that are distributed and affect ecological systems across widely different temporal and spatial scales, such as global climate change. Higher-level considerations are complex because 1) multiple species are affected differently, some with direct and others with only indirect effects; 2) processes and structural components may be simultaneously affected; 3) and the opportunity for nonlinear responses and thresholds increases. Consequently, assessing risks to higher levels of organization requires the use of ecological models because of the complexity of ecosystems, the difficulty and expense of field studies, the usual lack of appropriate controls for field and often even mesocosm studies, and, again, natural variability.

Even an ecological model-based assessment cannot address all components of the ecosystem; therefore, a process is needed that focuses on those specific ecological components that are valued by society. Further, all possible scenarios of combinations of multiple stressors and various management options cannot be examined, even using models; consequently, we need a systematic method, developed jointly by risk assessors and risk managers, to reduce those options down to manageable sets of scenarios. However, ecological models can substantially assist in that endpoint and scenario-reduction process.

Moore and Bartell provide guidance on ecological model development and utility. Four major aspects to model development and use are suggested. First is the development of the appropriate model structure, i.e., identifying the ecological components that need to be modeled with the interactions among modeled components and the stressor-effects relationships incorporated. This aspect of model development is difficult in part because the important stressor-effects relationships for one stressor may differ from another stressor and may differ from one ecological endpoint to another. The authors discuss the methods of ecological model system identification, including rules of parsimony and rules for aggregation.

The second step is the formulation of modeled processes, i.e., putting the relationships between components and between stressors and ecological endpoint effects into specific equations. In the past, ecological modelers often linearized nonlinear processes (i.e., simplified the processes to make them tractable mathematically). For example, this was done for stability analyses to characterize system response in the neighborhood of a steady-state situation. But linearization just does not reflect the real world, which generally is nonlinear or has thresholds or distinct transition points. Fortunately, however, we can now handle very complex nonlinear equations through numerical solution algorithms implemented on modern computers, so the mathematical analytical constraints of previous modeling efforts are no longer limiting the field of ecological modeling. The difficulty, however, now centers on having adequate information to chose the appropriate process formulation. Model formulation methods include looking for similar equations from other modeling studies reported in the literature, empirical analyses of data collected specific to the process at hand, and development of mechanistic relationships through hypothesis-testing experimentation.

The third step is parameter estimation, i.e., assigning the specific value to each parameter in the model equations. The difficulty here, as noted above, is that multiple stressors and multiple ecological endpoints mean that the modeler must parameterize a very large number of terms and simply may not have the data. In that case, the modeler needs to conduct sensitivity analyses to identify those parameters that make a difference in the model response. Then either the more important parameters can be better parameterized through experiments or further data collection, or variance terms may be applied to those parameters to reflect their uncertainty (further discussed below). Parameter estimation methods include using site-specific data on the parameter or on the modeled process, calibrating the model to specific system conditions by comparison with field information, making analogy to similar other systems that have been studied and modeled, and deriving numbers from the literature.

Finally, modeling results must be evaluated. Here the important questions are what degree of accuracy in model response is sufficient and over what range of conditions is the model reliable and for what conditions is it not? Ecological models developed for one set of conditions may not apply to another, especially if the model is based on empirical data and correlations rather than on mechanistic processes. Evaluation of model performance may be as simple as visually comparing graphical representations of model results versus data; in fact, this may be the best way to demonstrate confidence in the model, especially to non-modelers or to decision-makers. There are statistical analytical tools for more rigorously comparing the outputs of model simulations with actual data. These tools are covered in Chapter 3, as discussed above.

Characterizing uncertainties, or, Knowing what you don't know

Another important issue for assessing multiple ecological stressors affecting ecological systems, as discussed by Moore and Bartell in Chapter 4, is uncertainty analysis. Uncertainties are higher in multiple-stressor, multiple-endpoint situations because of the tremendous number of potential interactions, as discussed previously. Uncertainties are higher because of the much greater data needs that are typically unmet. The authors also note that most ecological risk assessments do not include uncertainty analyses, even though the tools for them are widely available. As a result, risk assessors and risk managers often are unaware of just how large the uncertainties really are. By contrast, appropriately done and transparent uncertainty analyses can actually reduce conflict among stakeholders, risk assessors, and risk managers while putting the importance of specific parameters or processes in better perspective and identifying the specific research needed to improve confidence in predictions.

Moore and Bartell discuss methods for uncertainty analyses, including providing a conceptual framework and clarifying the often confusing terminology about uncertainty. Seven steps in uncertainty process are described:

1) specify the risk equation to be analyzed;
2) list the specific variables to be assessed, with their distributions;

3) generate the distributions (i.e., probability distribution functions) for each variable of concern;

4) determine dependencies across input variables;

5) generate output distributions from the model equations;

6) conduct sensitivity analyses to identify the more important parameters and variances and fine tune the input variables, equations, and parameters; and

7) integrate the uncertainty analyses results and communicate them to risk managers.

Tools for multiple-stressor uncertainty analyses include multiple-species toxicity curves to show community-level sensitivities and Monte Carlo simulations with random assignment of specific variables within specified frequency distributions.

Moore and Bartell elaborate on the issues of ecological model applications and uncertainty analyses through two case studies. The first, on Hg and polychlorinated biphenyl effects on mink populations, was a case with many input data, allowing extensive uncertainty analysis on distributions of input parameters using Monte Carlo techniques for the simulation models. However, even this data-rich case study had little explicit information on interactions between the two stressors, and only one at-risk ecological component was assessed. The other case study deals with nutrient enrichment and chemical contaminants simultaneously affecting aquatic mesocosms. Here fewer data were available, and uncertainty and sensitivity analyses were primarily useful in identifying information needs, selecting plausible scenarios, and providing guidance to decision-makers through assessment of hypothetical scenarios.

Role of adaptive management, or, How to cover your assessments

Along with relying on multiple analytical tools and assessments, decision-making in the presence of uncertainties can be facilitated by using adaptive management. As presented by Holling (1978), adaptive management reduces the need for certainty, allows the adjustment of policies as societal values change, and accommodates natural variability in important ecological endpoints. Refining interim decisions after careful monitoring of endpoints can permit early reduction or mitigation of stress and can limit the consequences of a misjudgment. This approach calls for

- establishing appropriate monitoring for ecological endpoints judged to be responsive to management decisions;

- following the status and trends of the endpoints; and

- modifying management decisions based on evidence of the success, failure, or other more subtle measures of the efficacy of the management policy.

There often is the misconception that adaptive management is a trial-and-error strategy. Quite the contrary, a properly designed adaptive management strategy must have the power to discriminate changes caused by natural variability from those caused by management actions. Making this distinction requires examining the historic and future trends in the behavior of the endpoints of interest to estimate their natural variability.

There are limitations to this approach relating particularly to time lags regarding responses (e.g., controls on the emissions of chlorofluorocarbons may take several decades to be manifested in improved stratospheric ozone concentrations) or relating to societal and institutional factors (e.g., public and political perceptions that an environmental problem is "solved" and thus no longer of concern). Nevertheless, given the uncertainties and complexities, ecological risk management and environmental decision-making for Class 3 and 4 situations must be adaptive it they are to be successful. This concept has been incorporated into the risk assessment framework in the form of feedback loops that lead from decisions back to the problem formulation and analysis steps.

Examples of successful use of adaptive management are presented in Chapter 1. In both case studies, the Pacific Northwest salmon decline and the Chesapeake Bay striped bass and submerged aquatic vegetation (SAV) declines, the best use of qualitative and quantitative methods and available data failed to identify the definitive causal factors for the ecological effect. However, expert judgment was used in each case to select potential management options to employ, followed by monitoring to evaluate progress towards restoration goals. In the case of the Chesapeake Bay striped bass population, a moratorium on fishing was implemented in 1985, and within a decade the bass population had essentially recovered. Thus, while the stressor, overfishing, was not previously shown to be the primary causal agent for striped bass decline, the removal of that stressor effectively achieved the goal, even though the other stressors (toxic chemicals, eutrophication, sedimentation, acid deposition, anoxia) were not eliminated as causing effects. In fact, most of the potential stressors had been shown to cause biological effects in laboratory and field experiments.

In the case of the Pacific salmon, restoration goals have not yet been achieved and management options are still being analyzed. The retrospective analyses of potential stressors suggest a correlation between fish survival and dam locations along the streams of the Columbia River Basin, but no specific causal factor is clear. There is a co-occurrence of habitat alteration of these sub-basins with dam location, resulting in related stressors such as sedimentation, altered water temperatures, spawning habitat loss, altered pH, and metals contamination. But there were no clear spatial patterns of these habitat characteristics and fish survival rates, so causality is difficult to establish. Other analyses indicated that genetic dilution from extensive hatchery production was not a factor since the salmon population declines occurred prior to the massive influx of hatchery-reared fish. Consequently, the selection of preferred management options has not yet occurred.

For the Chesapeake SAV restoration case, management options have been chosen and implemented, including source controls for nutrients and toxic chemicals and active restoration through replanting, although no formal risk analyses were done to develop those management options. However, the SAV communities have not yet recovered significantly, based on the monitoring that has been done.

The time scale for recovery is a critical element in effective adaptive management. If the system response has long time lags, then the adaptive part of adaptive management must wait for sufficient time to elapse after the management option has begun; otherwise, management might bounce from one option to another without giving it a chance to work. If, however, the time frame is exceeded and there is still not adequate progress towards the goal of restoration, then the stressors that are being managed may not be the driving causal factors, or other stressors may be limiting recovery, and management policies need to be revised. In such a case of unmet management goals, it is very important to have a framework to develop hypotheses of causal factors for ecological effects and to provide a basis for initial and subsequent selection of management options. That framework should explicitly consider intrinsic time lags of restoration, through delays in stressor reduction and/ or delays in ecological responses to reduced stressor levels. This highlights, again, the important role that a well-developed conceptual model may play in multiple-stressor and effects-based environmental issues.

Effects-based assessments, or, Managing to achieve results

In Chapter 2, Munkittrick and McMaster emphasize 1) strategies and approaches to addressing cumulative environmental effects, 2) letting the system tell you about its current state and deducing how it got there, 3) using fish metrics as a tool to be used within those strategies, and 4) using an adaptive management strategy to monitor changes. The authors' main premise is that an effects-directed approach to assessing the cumulative effects of multiple stressors is the most appropriate approach and uses site-specific information to define the magnitude and extent of the problem, identify the causal factors, and develop performance benchmarks to guide the assessment.

In their review of existing strategies, Munkittrick and McMaster suggest that traditional approaches involving single chemicals with a single discharge or single episodes of discharges of multiple chemicals provide little useful information for cumulative assessments because they fail to account for already-existing upstream effects and the addition of new downstream sources. Their premise is that while traditional single-stressor ecological risk assessments have reduced environmental impacts, these approaches have not addressed the issue of "gross insults," which can be interpreted to mean multiple stressors. The authors contend that early risk assessments were generic in that they focused on single chemicals, used ecotoxicity data for often a handful of species at best, and had no spatial component.

While this remains true for Class 1 and 2 risk assessments for the registration of toxic chemicals and pesticides and product development, the majority of risk assessments are site-specific and address multiple chemicals and other stressors (Classes 3 and 4) (e.g., Superfund, regional and state risk assessments, hazardous waste sites, etc.). Consequently, the majority of site-specific studies are particularly well-suited to the approach espoused by the authors of letting the system define its current state, developing appropriate benchmarks for the desired future state of the system, taking the appropriate management actions, and instituting an effective adaptive management program to monitor change.

Ecosystem management is another important topic discussed in this chapter. Munkittrick and McMaster suggest that rather than managing ecosystems by prediction and extrapolation, it is better to manage them in an effects-focused and adaptive manner. Their effects-directed paradigm (Figure 5-5), which focuses on using site-specific information to understand the current condition of ecological resources, has three distinct stages. The first stage is designed to identify key endpoints, develop performance measures, identify impaired and limiting factors and critical stressors, and characterize the current state of the system. This stage is similar to that proposed by Fairbrother et al. (1997) and focuses on diagnostic and epidemiological approaches for understanding the causes of the current ecological condition, which allows for the development of management scenarios to forecast future risks or remediation. The second, or risk assessment, stage uses the information gathered in the first stage to develop a predictive risk model that is used prospectively to forecast changes in the system. This predictive component interfaces with the third, risk management and remediation stage of the Munkittrick and McMaster paradigm. Stage 1 of the Munkittrick and McMaster paradigm is consistent in principle with other effects-directed paradigms (Fairbrother et al. 1997; USEPA 1998) but adds a level of detail absent from the others.

Munkittrick and McMaster also address a variety of important risk management issues. The decision-making process, as they correctly state, is not exclusively a scientific process but relies on science to provide the necessary information on the types and distributions of change and their ecological and societal relevance. They note that some countries base their decisions on ethical concerns and public perceptions. In effects-driven assessments, the role of the public and stakeholders is to help evaluate the question of "acceptability." Further, effects-driven assessments focus the discussion on sustainability, acceptability, and the consequences of additional future changes rather than just on adverse effects. The authors propose a decision-making framework, based upon their fish-effects directed strategy, that can be used to determine sustainability, acceptability, and impacts that then are linked to a diagnostic module that investigates the causes of the problem and leads to mitigation.

In their description of the effects-directed process, the authors touch on important methodological issues. For example, they provide a detailed account of how to conduct an effects-directed assessment of cumulative effects using fish populations. The focus of this approach is to provide an understanding of the "performance" of the system and a description of system responses to interface meaningfully with the decision-making process, so that a determination of acceptability can be made. Other interesting points include discussion of the inverse relationship between specificity of ecological responses over different response times and ecological relevance and the need to use a suite of hierarchical responses rather than just a single endpoint. The authors also discuss the use of power analysis to establish how much change will constitute a significant impact. They suggest that the discussion of power levels and their implications for detecting change be discussed early in the design of the study. Further, if the power levels are found to be insufficient for the study, then either the study should be redesigned or the decision-making criteria should be adjusted. Finally, the authors reiterate the principles of ecoepidemiology that can be used to define causality (e.g., consistency, prediction, strength of association, specificity, and coherence).

We believe the chapters in this volume capture the current state and prospects for many of the analytical tools needed for conducting multiple-stressor and effects-based environmental assessments. In the following section, we focus on the upper tiers of our hierarchy (Classes 3 and 4), i.e., the most complex and difficult environmental problems, but also the ones most in need of scientific support for decision-making. We propose that the ecological risk assessment paradigm, properly implemented, is the most appropriate construct for addressing this class of environmental decision-making problems. After exploring some issues for this class of environmental problems, we further propose that the careful development of the ecological conceptual model is the single most important aspect of implementing the ecological risk framework for complex environmental problems.

Proposed Framework for Class 3 and 4 Environmental Problems: The Tried-and-True Ecological Risk Assessment Framework

We suggest that of the possible frameworks for assessing Class 3 and 4 environmental problems, the most robust and widely used is the ecological risk assessment framework. Recall that this framework (Figure 5-8) consists of three major components: Problem Formulation, Risk Analysis, and Risk Characterization.

Assessing Class 3 and 4 ecological risks from multiple stressors must begin with an exercise in problem formulation (USEPA 1992, 1998; Foran and Ferenc 1999). The purpose of the problem-formulation stage is to define the spatial, temporal, and biological scope of the risk assessment. This means that the problem-formulation stage is centered on the identification of the at-risk components of the ecological systems, the identification of the environmental stressors that may affect those

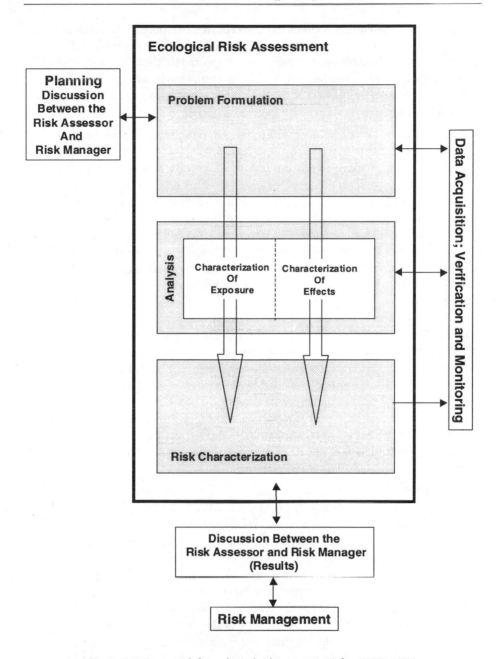

Figure 5-8 Framework for ecological risk assessment (after USEPA 1992)

components, the preliminary characterization of stress-response relationships, and the selection of the critical ecological endpoints for assessing environmental condition. These elements are most effectively captured through the process of developing a conceptual model; in fact, the conceptual model for the class of environmental problems of Class 4 should be the primary product of the problem-formulation stage.

The initial point of entry into the problem-formulation process is problem-determined, dealing either with a stressor-specific problem (e.g., projecting the effects from global climate change on ecosystems) or with an observed ecological effect problem (e.g., a large-scale die-off of seagrass). In either case, an important step in problem formulation is identifying the range of ecosystems and ecosystem components that are at risk from or affected by the stressors. If the problem is stressor-driven, sufficient information about the stressors is needed to help define the ecosystems and ecosystem components at risk. This information includes knowledge of the nature and properties of the stressors, their spatial and temporal scales, and their intensities. If the problem is ecological effects-driven, then observed change will be used to determine the at-risk ecosystems directly and, by extrapolation, the ecosystems at which no observed damage occurs at present but that also may be at risk. In addition to determining the different types of ecosystems that are at risk, problem definition defines the spatial extent of the ecosystems co-occurring with the stressors, focuses attention on the components of each at-risk ecosystem that may be directly or indirectly affected by the stressors, and determines the organizational scales that must be addressed (e.g., if consideration of population-level effects will suffice or if ecosystem- or landscape-level processes must also be evaluated). An explicit part of this determination is to consider both structural and functional aspects of each at-risk ecosystem in the context of potential direct or indirect effects from the stressors.

Another aspect of problem formulation is selecting ecological endpoints that are most appropriate for evaluating effects to the at-risk ecosystems. This process is necessary because the potential number and variety of ecosystem properties that could be affected by a human activity are virtually unlimited. Thus, for each ecosystem type at risk, the risk assessor must consider the specific properties of the ecosystem that, if sufficiently altered, would constitute a change in the ecosystem that is of ecological or societal importance. Next is the selection of ecological indicators or measures, defined as the specific properties of ecosystems that are measured or monitored to reflect on the state or the change of state of the ecological endpoints. Each selected endpoint should have one or more associated measures. These measures may be the endpoint itself (e.g., numbers of individuals in an endangered species population) or may relate to the endpoint directly (e.g., number of eggs produced per nesting pair of birds) or indirectly (e.g., area of wetlands in a region available for nesting habitat). Criteria proposed for selecting ecological measures include

- signal-to-noise ratio,
- frequency of false-positive and false-negative indications of an ecological effect,
- rapidity of response (e.g., for early-warning measures) versus degree of stress-specificity (e.g., diagnostic indication of a particular stress),
- statistical power (i.e., how much data would be required to demonstrate an effect),
- ease or economy of measurement,
- availability of historical databases, and
- comparability across ecological systems or environmental problems (Kelly and Harwell 1990).

Finally, problem formulation needs to address the critical issue of reference or benchmark conditions. These are essential if scientists, decision-makers, and stakeholders are to understand the relationships among historical, present, and potential future environmental conditions, i.e., the reference conditions provide the essential context for evaluating environmental goals and the success or failure of management to achieve those goals. Both the conceptual model development and the reference conditions characterization are elaborated more fully in a later section. These two aspects are central to the second stage of the ecological risk assessment framework: Risk Analysis.

In the risk-analysis stage for Classes 3 and 4, the tools discussed previously are used as appropriate; in particular, Moore and Bartell discuss the ecological modeling tools needed to handle the enormous complexity of Class 3 and 4 problems, while Fairbrother and Bennett detail the various classes of statistical tools needed to establish correlations, characterize spatial patterns, and distinguish experimentally causal effects of specific stressors and specific ecological responses. In addition, for the particular class of environmental problems of concern here, we have found that very often the scenario-consequence analysis approach is extremely useful.

The scenario-consequence analytical approach allows the prospective examination of complex environmental effects from a variety of human actions involving multiple drivers, multiple stressors, and multiple ecological consequences. The scenario-consequence analysis approach allows the bounding of potential environmental risks and is amenable to extensive sensitivity analyses to explore characteristics of the stress regime that contribute most to the risk. This approach involves developing a hypothetical set of conditions of an event or a management option (called scenarios) that have the following characteristics:

1) The scenarios are internally consistent, i.e., the parameters associated with an event are consistent with each other.

2) The scenario must specify all important factors needed to evaluate ecological effects. The central purpose of a scenario is to provide the specificity neces-

sary for assessments without having to rely only on historical analogs. So, for example, if a set of simulation models is to be used to assess consequences, the scenario must adequately specify all the parameters of the models.

3) The scenarios must be reasonable and scientifically defensible, i.e., the scenario needs to describe a set of conditions that are plausible, based on actual experience or on a set of reasoned, defensible assumptions.

4) The scenarios need not describe a "worst-case" set of conditions. In fact, for most complex ecological risk assessments, the concept of "worst-case" is inappropriate, since what might be worst-case for one stressor might not be for another.

5) Scenarios are developed to describe the range of conditions that plausibly might occur, forming the initial point of departure for conducting sensitivity analyses. The purpose is to allow the evaluation of the consequences of that range of conditions, so that particular scenario-specific parameters that would make a significant difference to the consequences to the ecological systems could be separated from that range of conditions that have little impact. This is very important in identifying the types of factors appropriate for risk management and in identifying those priority uncertainties upon which additional research could be optimally focused.

6) There is no need to assign any estimate of probability for any scenario. Each scenario may be considered to be conservatively plausible, but it is not necessary to assign a probability estimate to the occurrence of the particular scenario.

The risk-characterization stage for Classes 3 and 4 also needs to extend beyond the tools discussed previously on statistical determination of causal relationships (Chapter 3) to encompass a broader set of decision-making approaches. The approach we used in South Florida is equivalent to USEPA's Risk Characterization, which both estimates the risks and describes the significance of the changes within the context of uncertainty (USEPA 1992, 1998). The purpose of this phase of the assessment is to assemble all the information gathered from the planning, problem formulation, and analysis of the observed or predicted ecological effects. These effects are expressed in terms of the ecological endpoints or ecological valued components that have been determined to be of societal and/or ecological importance and reflective of the health or sustainability of the system.

Characterizing the risks or recovery for Class 3 and 4 assessments presents several challenges because of the complexities and interactions that typify large-scale assessments. Our knowledge, methods, models, measures, and information bases generally are very limited (Figure 5-2), thus requiring the development of innovative ways to estimate, interpret, and communicate assessments of risk and recovery. The following is a brief discussion of approaches that we have found particularly useful.

The initial estimation of risks at Classes 3 and 4 involves examining multiple lines of evidence. This is true for retrospective and prospective assessments. In the former, the focus is on understanding the causes that have resulted in the current state of the ecosystem as well as characterizing the status of ecological resources. In the latter, the focus is on projecting and interpreting the magnitude and extent of future change to the system as the result of some management actions. In either case, multiple lines of evidence are crucial to obtaining a sound understanding of the system state.

The lines of evidence employed at Classes 3 and 4 involve field observations, categorical rankings based upon expert judgment, the use of stressor-response relationships either singly or as distributions, and numerical models.

1) Field observations: Field observations, particularly historical, synoptic, or long-term monitoring and time series data, constitute a particularly important line of evidence that can be used to deduce not only the causes of environmental degradation but also the rate and geographic extent. This often requires using a variety of diagnostic or epidemiological techniques to understand the likely causal relationships and to apply criteria such as strength, consistency, specificity of response, and spatial and temporal coherence to affirm the interpretation (Hill 1965; Susser 1986). Of course the major advantage of using field data is that they can be used to evaluate multiple stressors and complex ecosystem relationships that would be otherwise impossible to duplicate in the laboratory (USEPA 1998). The statistical tools, especially spatially explicit ones, described in Chapter 3 are critical here.

2) Expert judgment: Professional judgment used in conjunction with qualitative evaluation techniques (e.g., fuzzy set theory, analytic hierarchy, Delphi approaches, etc.) likely will become more and more important in estimating the risks across multiple stressors and landscape types. These methods (Chapter 4) can be used to translate qualitative ranking or judgment information into a mathematical comparison that may have a high degree of confidence. Categorical ranking techniques are being used more widely to rank potential environmental risks from multiple stressors (Harris et al. 1994) or to identify the most important risks at a national level (USEPA SAB 1999). While categorical approaches are useful for assessing current risks and understanding the important causes, they, like field observations, have limited predictive power for forecasting future conditions as the result of modifying current conditions.

3) Stressor-effects data: A third line of evidence for characterizing risks is the classic single-chemical/single-receptor/stressor response curve or variations using cumulative distribution functions. These approaches are characteristic of Classes 1 and 2 and are particularly amenable to the multivariate statistical tools developed for ecotoxicology and discussed in Chapter 3. However, these

approaches become problematic as the number and variety of stressor types, modes of action, and interactions increase. The most important feature of these approaches is that they have the ability to predict, at least in theory if not always in practice, incremental change in the dependent variable (e.g., ecological effects) from a change in the dependent variable (e.g., intensity of one or more stressors). However, one persistent limitation of this approach is that it typically is determinate in space and time, which limits its applicability for regional-scale problems.

4) Numerical modeling: The fourth line of evidence, numerical modeling, integrates exposure and stress-response data as well as modifying factors to produce a forecast of both the magnitude and extent of ecological change over spatial and temporal scales. As Moore and Bartell discuss in Chapter 4, these types of models can be extremely complex, e.g., regional studies may require coupling landscape modules as inputs to hydrodynamic/water quality or air models that calculate the spatial and temporal patterns of exposures, which then are linked to population-, community-, or ecosystem-level models with built-in stress-response functions. Unfortunately, the development and calibration of integrated models are costly and data-intensive. On the other hand, as Moore and Bartell point out, simulation models are the only practical way to explore the multitude of potential combinations of stressors. While these models may be able to predict the intensity of one stressor, they are not capable of predicting the co-occurrence and interactions of more than one stressor, particularly if there are different classes of stressors (e.g., chemical and physical). Consequently, simulations using ecological models should be coupled with qualitative expert judgment techniques to forecast specific risks in complex systems.

A major problem for Class 3 and 4 risk assessments is interpreting the diversity of available data that are contained within several lines of evidence. One approach to increasing confidence in the interpretation and conclusions of the assessment is to conduct a weight-of-evidence analysis (Fox 1991; Menzie et al. 1996). This approach utilizes a suite of attributes for judging the measures and endpoints used in the assessment. These attributes include but are not limited to

- strength of association,
- site-specificity,
- stressor-specificity,
- data quality,
- stressor-sensitivity,
- spatial representativeness, and
- temporal representativeness.

These and other attributes can be weighted equally or unequally and used to evaluate each line of evidence. This approach also is based upon expert judgment and provides a basis for integrating qualitative and quantitative multiple lines of evidence.

Characterizing the risks from multiple stressors and sources over large, heterogeneous spatial and temporal scales presents many challenges. It is clear that our present state of science does not allow the routine quantification of risks for this level of complexity and that the tools that have developed for simpler problems are inadequate for the task at hand. The multivariate tools discussed in Chapter 3 in essence become overwhelmed by the complexity of Class 3 and 4 problems, and, realistically, there rarely are sufficient data to distinguish statistical differences among the enormous possible causal relationships. Similarly, the ecological models discussed in Chapter 4 are necessary but not sufficient by themselves to quantify risks; again, data availability is an issue, as is the broader issue of validation of the models for the set of complex stressors and interactions of a Class 3 or 4 problem at hand. In other words, the multivariate statistical tools and ecological simulation models, discussed in previous chapters, must be used to their fullest capacity, but even then they will almost always be found to be inadequate. Therefore, we suggest that a diverse, multiple-lines-of-evidence approach be used that incorporates field observations, diagnostic and epidemiological-type approaches, conceptual models, expert judgment, and quantitative statistical and numerical modeling approaches. We need to recognize and communicate to decision-makers that at these scales and complexities, data are often a limiting factor—thus expert judgment and our ability to generalize principles from one site to another become increasingly important. It is also important to emphasize that expert judgment comes not only from the scientific community but also from the local public who often have both historical knowledge and a "sense of place."

Issues to be Addressed for Assessing Class 3 and 4 Risks from Multiple Stressors and for Support of Effects-based Decision-making

For Class 3 and 4 environmental problems, following the ecological risk assessment paradigm as proposed above, there is a suite of issues that especially have to be addressed. Many of these issues emerge in the problem-formulation stage.

Issue of ecological endpoints

We define an ecological endpoint as an explicit expression of valued environmental attributes that can be defined in operational terms and are amenable to measurement or prediction. This definition highlights both ecological importance and/or relevance and societal value in defining ecological endpoints. Selection of ecological endpoints results from dialogue between the risk assessor and risk manager during the initial phase of the risk-assessment process and should reflect stakeholder perspectives. The process of selecting ecological endpoints is complex, involving the juxtaposition of societal and ecological values and perceptions that is confounded by the lack of a consensus definition of ecological health. Ecological endpoints may be structural (e.g., community diversity) or functional (e.g., rates of primary production). The endpoint should be relevant, having either ecological importance (e.g., keystone species, ecologically important processes) or societal importance (e.g., economically important, endangered, or aesthetic species). Selection of the ecological endpoint in part is a function of the nature of the stressor, i.e., some properties of the ecosystem may be known to be vulnerable to one stressor but not to another. Other criteria for selecting endpoints include natural variability of the endpoint; requirements of particular legislation or regulations; and availability of data, models, and knowledge about the specific endpoint that can be used for assessment. In any event, there should be a concerted effort to identify all attributes of the at-risk ecosystems that would be appropriate properties upon which to evaluate the condition of the ecosystem in the context of the stressors at hand. Ideally, a suite of ecological endpoints will be selected to ensure that the full range of ecosystem attributes are evaluated. Additionally, if there is a change in the ecosystem of importance, it should be reflected in the change of at least one or more of the selected ecological endpoints. Thus, the ecological endpoints, which are the ecological foundation of the risk assessment, must incorporate both ecological importance and social values, should be defined operationally, and can be measured directly or predicted from one or more environmental measures.

Issue of societal values and endpoints

One of the important characteristics of ecological endpoints is that they exist at the nexus of ecological and societal considerations. That is, an ecological endpoint may be selected because of its importance ecologically (e.g., a keystone species, a habitat-forming dominant species, the decomposition community). But an ecological endpoint also may be selected because of its importance to society, even if there is not a critical ecological role; examples include economically important species, noxious species, and endangered species (for which the population levels may be too low for a significant ecological role). Thus, we have argued that selection of ecological endpoints must be done jointly as a scientific process and as a societal goals process, i.e., choosing which attributes of ecosystems are societally important must reflect societal values and goals, not scientific issues. Similarly, because effects-based decision-making is at its core goals-driven, those must be the goals of society, not just of scientists. The USEPA SAB Integrated Risk Project (USEPA SAB 1999) included an important dialogue on environmental values and societal goals. While it is beyond the scope of this chapter to discuss how those values and goals are articulated, it must be noted that this is a critical step in the risk-assessment process for multiple stressors and for effects-based decision-making.

Issue of ecological significance

A critical element in the risk-assessment process calls for distinguishing environmental responses that matter from those that do not; that is, making a determination of the ecological significance of the risk (Gentile and Harwell 1998). The issue of ecological significance is fundamental to the entire ecological risk assessment process. There is no intrinsic ecological threshold for establishment of ecological significance, although many ecological issues are germane. What is significant and what is acceptable can be determined only through decision-making that takes place in the context of human values. Further, the issue of ecological significance is a meta-issue, i.e., it is relevant to several aspects of the ecological risk assessment process, such as selecting assessment endpoints, as well as interpreting the magnitude and nature of an ecological response and deciding what would be considered "acceptable" by both society and regulators. The basis for the emphasis on ecological significance is apparent, even if the specific elements are quite complicated:

- Virtually all components and processes in the environment exhibit natural variability continuously and simultaneously on many time scales.
- Virtually any human activity will result in a change to some component or process in the environment, although only anthropogenic changes that can be distinguished from natural variability warrant further consideration.
- Only a subset of detectable anthropogenic changes actually matters to the structure, functioning, or overall health of a particular ecosystem, and the criteria for defining such a subset (i.e., determining what matters) are in part ecological questions involving basic issues of stress ecology and in part societal questions involving human values and perceptions.

As noted in Chapter 3, statistical significance is not necessarily the same as ecological significance, which we define as changes in an ecosystem that are important in terms of its structure, functioning, and/or integrity. A statistically significant change may or may not be ecologically important. Conversely, a determination that something is ecologically significant may not necessarily require that statistical significance be demonstrated. The ecological risk assessment process is multilayered, with many different types of considerations incorporated into the decision-making process, including non-ecological factors. Relying strictly on stringent statistical tests is not compatible with this flexible paradigm. Moreover, decisions often have to be made when the data are too few or too noisy for a specified statistical criterion of confidence to be met. Again, the multivariate tools discussed in Chapter 3 are necessary but not sufficient for a determination of ecological significance.

Ecological significance relates to determining 1) whether a change that is detected or projected in the ecological system of concern constitutes a change of importance to the structure, function, and/or health of the system and exceeds a variance estimate (i.e., placed into the context of natural variability) and 2) whether such a change in the ecological system is of sufficient type, intensity, extent, and/or duration to be important to society. Both conditions are necessary and jointly sufficient for determining whether potential ecological change can be regarded as ecologically significant. There are several implicit assumptions in this definition:

- an ecological assessment endpoint, which is a benchmark of the risk assessment, is assumed to be the characteristic of the ecological system or its individual components of concern for which the significance of change is being evaluated;
- the ecological assessment endpoints represent structures or functions that are important to the health and sustainability of the ecosystem;
- the ecological assessment endpoints at least in part incorporate and reflect social values (society is defined in its broadest terms to include the perspectives and values of scientists, resource managers, policy analysts, regulators, politicians, special interest groups, and the lay public); and
- the explicit consideration of variance into the definition reflects the need to introduce an envelope of thresholds above which a detected or projected change in the assessment endpoint can be evaluated.

In reaching determinations of ecological significance and weighing them with economic, societal, or other factors in risk management, the decision-maker must accommodate the presence of uncertainties. For any environmental problem facing society today, there are uncertainties concerning, for example, 1) the way that ecological systems function and respond to stress and the way that recovery processes operate; 2) the availability of data at the various scales of interest; 3) requirements for extrapolating from laboratory or analog data to real-world ecosystems; and 4) the continual presence of natural variability in both the physicochemical environment and in biological organisms and processes. Uncertainty always will be a factor in risk assessment, regardless of how much research is conducted or how extensive a database is established. Thus environmental decisions must be made despite the uncertainties; otherwise, they literally never would be made. Using the weight-of-evidence approach, a 95% confidence level is not necessary and in many cases is not feasible. Rather, the risk manager and the decision-maker must make determinations based on information from analytical techniques and available databases. Chapter 4 offers guidance on how to characterize environmental uncertainties.

Comparative ecological condition

Another issue that must be addressed in assessing ecological risks from multiple stressors, and in effects-based decision-making in general, is how to compare the extant state of the ecosystem with other states of that ecosystem, such as disturbed, recovered, or desired states (Figure 5-9). A scheme is needed to address multiple ecological attributes, complex exposure regimes of multiple stressors, and reference

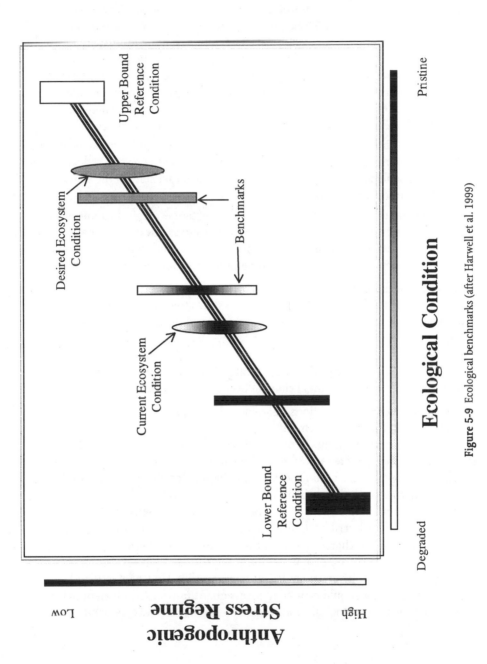

Figure 5-9 Ecological benchmarks (after Harwell et al. 1999)

ecological conditions, extant ecological conditions, and desired ecological conditions. We have proposed the following comparative conditions (Harwell et al. 1999):

1) Reference conditions: These are the bounding conditions for the essential physical, chemical, and ecological characteristics of the ecosystem, i.e., a descriptor of the critical attributes of the ecosystems at each end of the spectrum from a very high degree of disturbance to a very high degree of pristine ecological condition. In essence, the reference conditions identify the extremes of the spectrum of conditions for a particular ecosystem, and actual and desired conditions usually would fall between the extremes.

2) Desired conditions: These are descriptions of the essential characteristics of the system that reflect and capture the desired goal to be achieved, i.e., what society and science have determined to be the target state of the ecosystem that is to result from a restoration process.

3) Benchmark conditions: In many cases, the extant ecological condition is far removed from the desired condition, and progress towards restoration would be indicated more clearly if a set of intermediate conditions were established as milestones along the way to the complete restoration goals.

These milestones along the continuum of ecological states are the benchmarks, a more generic descriptor for distinct ecosystem states that can be used to evaluate just how well we are doing in achieving, or not achieving, an environmental goal. It is important to note that nothing in this framework is meant to signify static conditions; rather, each benchmark or reference condition, and the characterization of the actual ecosystem, explicitly incorporate natural variability and processes such as succession or other directional changes over time and space.

This set of comparative conditions (reference, desired, and benchmark) should be characterized in the specific terms of the selected ecological endpoints for the ecosystems of concern, discussed previously as those particular ecological or stressor attributes that are important to the ecosystem and/or to society. Consequently, they become the basis for evaluating the state or change of state of the ecosystem in the terms already identified as key descriptors of the ecosystem vis-á-vis the decision-making context. Thus, the benchmark, reference, and desired conditions are to be described in terms of both the ecological endpoints and the physical and chemical characteristics of the system. Finally, because the ecological endpoints are designed to be a parsimonious set, they are quite amenable to applications of the multivariate statistical tools described in Chapter 3, and, therefore, those tools should be used to assess quantitatively (if sufficient data are available) the extant ecological conditions vis-á-vis the reference, benchmark, and desired conditions.

Conceptual Models: Structure, Rationale, and Utility

The term conceptual model, while relatively new to ecological risk assessment and restoration, has been widely used as part of environmental impact assessment since the 1970s (Barnthouse and Brown 1994). Sanders et al. (1978) employed schematics to illustrate causal relationships and to generate "impact hypotheses" that would guide the collection and interpretation of monitoring data. Similarly, Beanlands and Duniker (1983) described the causal linkages between project activities, valued ecosystem components, and explicit impact hypotheses. Westman (1985) described a multi-phase impact assessment that corresponds closely to the conceptual model phase of an ecological risk assessment. Thus, the formalization of conceptual models within the risk and restoration process represents a natural evolution from earlier impact assessments. The common focus of these approaches was to illustrate the potential ecological impacts from multiple sources and types of environmental stress.

Conceptual models can be viewed as qualitative or descriptive statements of hypotheses concerning the nature of the potential causal relationships between human activities, the resulting natural and anthropogenic stressors, and their impacts on human and ecological systems (USEPA 1992, 1998). Thus conceptual models are an important initial step in the analysis of multiple stressors and cumulative effects (Foran and Ferenc 1999). While it is likely that all risk assessments will require a conceptual model, it is also likely that the conceptual models will vary with circumstances. For example, regulatory programs such as USEPA's pesticide and toxic chemical programs perform relatively standardized, non-site-specific assessments, using similar conceptual models, on large numbers of chemicals prior to issuance of a permit (Classes 1 and 2). Conversely, site-specific assessments (e.g., Superfund, NEPA, watersheds, etc.) require that conceptual models be developed separately for each assessment (Classes 3 and 4). Regardless of the application, conceptual models should be incorporated in all types of environmental assessment and recovery activities as a tool for describing the causal relationship between land uses, stressors, at-risk valued ecological resources, and their associated ecological endpoints and measures. For an excellent discussion and examples of types of conceptual models that can be constructed for complex ecological risk assessments and for assessing the risks from multiple activities, see Suter (1999a, 1999b).

Conceptual model development process

While it is desirable to maintain flexibility when developing conceptual models in order to accommodate the unique features of a site-specific situation, general guidance on the process, types of information, and rules can be developed. The following is a general description of a process for developing ecological conceptual site models for both anthropogenic and natural sources of stress across a range of scales and using existing information and understanding about ecosystem functioning:

- define the goals and objectives,
- delineate the spatial, temporal, and ecological scales and boundaries,
- inventory all resource use activities,
- describe sources of natural and anthropogenic stressors,
- identify the primary and secondary stressors of concern,
- describe contaminant release mechanisms and exposure routes,
- identify stressor-receptors co-occurrences,
- identify ecological values and endpoints,
- determine ecological measurements,
- develop full spectrum of risk hypotheses and causal pathways, and
- rank risk (recovery) hypotheses.

In addition to the steps described above, there are other principles to consider when structuring conceptual models. First is compatibility among spatial, temporal, and ecological scales. Often a series of spatially, temporally, and ecologically nested models are needed to represent the full range of ecological and societal concerns being examined, particularly at a regional scale such as South Florida. The development of a suite of nested models is important because often the response time for the expression or manifestation of changes in ecosystem structures and processes chosen as endpoints differs at regional, watershed, and local scales. In addition, spatial and temporal scales influence the selection of endpoints, measures, and sampling design used for monitoring, as well as the performance criteria chosen to measure the direction and progress of management actions. Another important issue is the level of detail, resolution, and aggregation necessary to capture and communicate fully the essential causal linkages for the setting. The level of aggregation is particularly important to the scientist and engineer who will be responsible for implementing management options and to the manager who will have to communicate with the public. Clearly, the former will require a finer level of detail than will the latter where the conceptual model is used as a communication tool. Consequently, regional-scale assessments likely will require a suite of conceptual models of differing levels of detail and aggregation commensurate with the audience to which they are intended to communicate.

Utility of conceptual models

A properly developed conceptual model effectively captures the scientific understanding of an ecosystem and its response to natural and anthropogenic stressors. We have found that the process of constructing a conceptual model can engage the scientific community in an important dialogue to articulate more clearly the individual perspectives of scientists regarding how an ecosystem functions and responds to stress. Assumptions and proposed relationships must be made explicit and defended, and, in the process, a consensus of the scientific community may emerge. The conceptual model can do much more, however. It can be an extremely effective tool for communicating to non-scientists or to scientists who have not previously focused on the environmental problem at hand. The communications function is very important for this class of complex problems for the very reason that they are complex, and a well-presented graphical representation of the conceptual model can make it clear to all what is meant by particular terms or categories, what linkages are considered relevant, etc. If the conceptual model development process continues through a relative ranking exercise, then the graphic can readily show what linkages, inputs, system components, etc., are most important and which are relatively minor. Further, if done properly, the conceptual model development process will identify the most important uncertainties about the ecosystem. Again, well-designed graphics can immediately show scientists and decision-makers alike those facets of the system that are both important and highly uncertain and the manner in which research resources should be prioritized. Finally, the conceptual model can be an extremely useful management tool when coupled to conceptual models for other connected systems. For example, we have facilitated the development of a societal conceptual model for the South Florida regional environment that directly couples to a series of ecological conceptual models for seagrass, hard-bottom, coral reef, and other ecosystems.

South Florida Case Study

In this final section, we draw upon the lessons learned from the other articles in this volume, illustrate the proposed use of the ecological risk assessment framework and associated development of conceptual ecological models and reference conditions, and explore the issues discussed in the previous section as a case example at the highest level of the Class 4 environmental problem. South Florida illustrates multiple-stressor issues, multiple-effect issues, multiple-endpoint issues, multiple spatial/temporal scale issues, and multiple societal goals issues, all cutting across a highly diverse and human-dominated landscape and seascape. The regional environmental stressors include

- massive habitat and hydrological alteration that has transformed the regional environment through the water management system, development of coastal shorelines, altered estuarine salinity regimes, altered fire regimes, and other habitat changes for the support of 5 million people;
- climate variability and change, with concomitant sea-level rise, changes in frequency of freezing events, changes in frequency of hurricanes, changes in frequency of drought and associated fires, and changes in sea surface temperatures;

- extreme over-exploitation of reef and estuarine fish and invertebrate populations and tremendous numbers of recreational-days of diving, boating, and other forms of physical contact with the environment;
- nutrients and other effluents from a highly urbanized environment located immediately adjacent to natural ecological areas;
- major agricultural activities, with runoff of pesticides, sediment, and other effluents;
- pervasive exotic species, some of which have become very well-established; and
- mercury from unknown origin at levels that preclude human consumption of many freshwater fish in parts of the region.

The region is also a case example for effects-based decision-making, with manifested effects including
- loss of whole classes of ecosystems, such as most pinelands;
- conversion of estuaries to lagoons and lagoons to estuaries;
- extensive die-off of seagrass communities in Florida Bay;
- periodic coral bleaching and overgrowth of corals by macroalgae; and
- reductions of important species such as wading birds (reduced by an order of magnitude), sea urchins (e.g., almost total loss of *Diadema*), and endangered species such as sea turtles, American crocodile, Cape Sable sparrow, manatee, Florida panther, and Everglades Kite.

Ecological risk assessment for South Florida

It is beyond the scope of this chapter to discuss all the stressors and effects in South Florida, so we focus on two major types of stressors and their effects to discuss anticipated risks and management options: 1) ecological effects from past hydrological modifications plus societal goals and ecological responses to prospective redesign of the water-management system and 2) prospective ecological risks from global climate change. These clearly fall within the upper portion of Class 4 and constitute a mixture of both stressor- and effects-based decision-making processes. The problem-formulation stage calls for developing a conceptual model of how the regional ecosystems function and are driven by the stressors of concern, so we begin with a brief description of the historical and present ecosystem.

The historical (pre-drainage) South Florida landscape was a hydrologically interconnected mosaic of habitats, including freshwater marshes, hardwood hammocks, cypress swamps, pinelands, mangrove swamps, freshwater lakes and streams, estuarine lagoons, and coral reefs (Harshberger 1914; Davis 1943; Douglas 1947; Craighead 1971; Duever et al. 1986; Gunderson 1994; Davis et al. 1994; DeAngelis 1994; Gleason and Stone 1994). A large and rapidly growing human population is perched on a narrow strip of land along the coast, highly dependent on the health of the environment for its economic base, i.e., tourism, recreational fishing, and agriculture. South Florida's climate varies seasonally and across years, with a distinct wet and dry season and with large differences in rainfall from year to year (see NOAA 1985, Duever et al. 1994, and Chen and Gerber 1990 for overviews of the climate regime). Regional precipitation is driven largely by local convection-generated thunderstorms, supplemented in some years by tropical storms and hurricanes. Seasonal variability is linked to the migration of the Bermuda high pressure system, and differences in its strength and location can lead to years of excessive flooding or consecutive drought (Chen and Gerber 1990; Duever et al. 1994; Obeysekera et al. in press). However, inter-annual variability in precipitation and the natural sequence of drought and wet years are major contributors to the high productivity and diversity of the region (Browder and Ogden in press; Kushlan 1989); for example, in very dry years only alligator holes remain wet, concentrating fish and invertebrate communities and providing a bonanza of food for wading birds, resulting in tremendous increases in bird populations (Robertson 1955; Craighead 1968; Bancroft et al. 1994). Episodic events have major impact on the region, including hurricanes and tropical storms, infrequent but highly damaging freezing events, and fires (Robertson 1962; Gunderson and Snyder 1994). The regional ecosystems have adapted to this natural variability, but anthropogenic changes have severely impaired the ability of the ecosystems to respond to natural variability, let alone climate change.

Sea-level rise is fundamental to the South Florida environment. The rate of sea-level rise was relatively slow, about 4 cm century^{-1} from 3200 BC to 1930 AD (ISS 1993; Wanless et al. 1994), resulting in the natural distribution of coastal wetlands and freshwater marshes, and allowing the shallow marine sediments and organic coastlines to build up, so that the coastal mangrove swamps prograded seaward even as sea levels rose. Similarly, the upward growth rates of the coral reefs was 0.65 to 4.85 m per 1000 years (Jaap and Hallock 1990), sufficient to accommodate sea-level rise during that period. However, tidal gauge records show a significant increase in the rate of sea-level rise: since 1930 the rate has averaged 30 to 35 cm century^{-1}, causing accelerated erosion of shorelines, saltwater intrusion, and landward movement of wetlands (Wanless et al. 1994). As a result, South Florida is very vulnerable to further sea-level rise if it exceeds the ecosystems' capacity to adapt. Human development certainly impairs the ability of such adaptation.

Effects of past hydrological modifications and prospective water management

In response to the climatic variability and the low relief of the region, the Central and South Florida Flood Control Project (C&SF), one of the world's largest water-management systems, was constructed by the U.S. Army Corps of Engineers to dampen hydrological variability, provide flood protection, and supply water to urban, agricultural, and natural systems (Light and Dineen 1994; USCOE 1994;

Solecki et al. in press). However, as a result of the water management system, only half of the natural Everglades remains, and the Greater Everglades is an endangered ecosystem whose sustainability is critically at risk (Davis et al. 1994; Harwell et al. 1996; Harwell 1997, 1998). Consequently, a major effort is underway to redesign the South Florida water-management system (Harwell 1998).

In order to project the implications of the South Florida ecosystem restoration, a set of causal hypotheses about ecosystem responses to the anthropogenic stressors of the region was developed and incorporated into a series of conceptual models. In this section, we briefly recount these hypotheses (Ogden et al. in press) about what caused the decline in the Everglades this century and discuss methods to assess whether proposed changes in the water-management system can lead to ecological restoration.

The first regional hypothesis concerns the spatial extent of the Everglades ecosystem. The pre-drainage wetlands of southern Florida covered an area of 28,000 km². This large spatial extent was essential 1) for the support of genetically and ecologically viable populations of species with narrow habitat requirements or large feeding ranges; 2) for the aquatic production necessary to support large numbers of higher vertebrates in a naturally, nutrient-poor environment; and 3) for sustaining habitat diversity created by natural disturbances and the regional patterns of topographical gradients and micro-topography. A major cause of the loss of ecological sustainability has been the 50% reduction in the spatial extent of the true Everglades (Ogden et al. in press). The second regional hypothesis relates to the dynamic water storage in the ecosystem: the pre-drainage wetlands of South Florida were expansive, interconnected, hydrological systems, characterized by an enormous capacity to collect and store water across multi-year time frames. Key components of the hydrological system were

- the large water storage capacity in the peat soils;
- the extremely slow flow rates associated with low topographical gradients and the density of the marsh vegetation;
- the interconnectiveness of flows within and across basin boundaries;
- the strong connections between surface and groundwater flows; and
- the large spatial extent of the basins.

Ogden et al. (in press) hypothesized that the substantially reduced water-storage capacity of the South Florida wetlands occurred because of the loss of peat soils, the storage limitations set by policy and structural limitations, the reduced total area of the systems, and the more rapid water conveyance through pumps and canals. This has caused regionally drier conditions and loss of natural patterns of hydroperiod. Further, these changes are responsible for system-wide collapses in production and survival of populations and in the availability of prey to larger aquatic vertebrates in the correct locations and at the proper times of the year relative to traditional reproductive and feeding patterns. The third hypothesis concerns sheet flow:

compartmentalization of the remaining Everglades into a series of Water Conservation Areas (WCAs) has substantially disrupted long-distance sheet flow through the marshes by impounding water and by rerouting water into fast-flow canal systems. The reduction in sheet flow and management-induced reductions in inter-annual hydropattern variability have been major contributors to regional changes in natural patterns of nutrient cycling and flow.

Based on these hypotheses and the nature of the South Florida environmental changes, Ogden et al (in press) concluded the following anthropogenic effects on the Everglades from human development this century:

- reduced areal extent of wetlands and flooding,
- shortened annual hydroperiods,
- lowered surface and groundwater levels,
- loss of sheet flow,
- alterations in timing and location of flows and in pre-drainage surface water-distribution patterns,
- moderations in the amplitude and inter-annual variability of seasonal and annual water depth patterns,
- reduced flows into the estuaries (Florida Bay and Biscayne Bay), and
- altered patterns of nutrient transport and concentration.

How does one assess the efficacy of specific management options in restoring the ecosystems, a sort of prospective ecological risk assessment? We focus on the potential effects on the Biscayne Bay of altered inputs of freshwater, resulting from climate change or from altered water management, that affect the Bay's salinity regime.

First, with respect to the ecological consequences of altered freshwater inputs to Biscayne Bay, a downstream recipient from the C&SF system, the analytical approach that we are developing involves a series of hydrological and ecological simulation models, each of which use various lines of evidence for model formulation and parameterization, following the steps detailed in Chapter 4. For example, the South Florida Water Management Model (SFWMM) (MacVicar et al. 1984; also, see the South Florida Water Management District Web site http://141.232.1.11/org/pld/hsm/sfwmm/index.html) has been developed over the past decade as a modeling tool to predict spatially explicit levels of surface water at thousands of nodes across the landscape, as well as canal discharge points. This model reflects the present water-management control structures, but it can be modified to represent the specific new configurations of the modified C&SF system. The SFWMM is driven by inputs of daily precipitation at many locations across the region, and a 30-year historical record is the default input, a period sufficient to cover most intra- and inter-annual changes in weather (excepting global climate change). Thus, as a part of the USCOE restudy process (USCOE 1998; www.restudy.org), a modified version of SFWMM was used to predict daily surface and canal water levels for 30-year periods under many scenarios of specific changes in the engineered structures and/ or water management schedules.

The SFWMM produces predictions of future freshwater inputs to Biscayne Bay through surface flow and through canal releases. The next step for assessing impacts on Biscayne Bay is to simulate the salinity regime that will occur under various climate conditions with and without the modifications in the C&SF system. For this, we are using the Biscayne Bay hydrodynamic model (Wang et al. 1988) to simulate the spatial and temporal distributions of salinity fields in the Bay, based on histori-cal weather and climate-induced changes in weather, again developed and param-eterized as suggested in Chapter 4. The Biscayne Bay hydrodynamic model has been validated through extensive measurements of currents and salinity, so there is a high confidence in its ability to predict recent conditions. This hydrodynamic model will produce a suite of salinity regimes reflecting a range of conditions, from pre-drainage, to present, to potential future alterations in the C&SF system and the regional precipitation regime. The next step is to evaluate the potential impacts of such an altered salinity regime on the distribution and productivity of the seagrass and hard-bottom communities of Biscayne Bay. For this we are using the CMEA seascape model, developed by Cropper et al. (in prep.) based on a previous seagrass model (Fong and Harwell 1994) and a new population-level model of sponges (Cropper and DiResta 1999). These models have been developed using a suite of lines of evidence about seagrass and hard-bottom communities, including extensive field studies, microcosm and mesocosm experimental studies, remote sensing and habitat classification, literature values on similar ecosystems in other areas, histori-cal information on Biscayne Bay, and expert judgment, all in concert with Moore and Bartell (Chapter 4). Again, they have been calibrated to Biscayne Bay and reasonably verified by extant conditions. The next step in the analytical process is to use the Biscayne Bay hydrodynamic model-derived salinity regimes as inputs to the ecological models to estimate the changes in productivity and extent of the benthic communities.

Subsequently, yet another ecological simulation model describing the spatially explicit fish and invertebrate communities and trophic structures of Biscayne Bay has been developed (Ault et al. 1999). That model, too, is based on extensive field studies and literature-derived relationships and parameters and has been verified against Biscayne Bay shrimp and fish populations. These populations are in part a function of the spatial extent and condition of the habitat, so changes in the benthic communities simulated by the seascape model will be used to drive the fish and invertebrate model. But they also are responsive to changes in water quality directly, so the salinity and turbidity regimes predicted by the hydrodynamic model also become drivers for the animal models.

How is this analysis extended to address multiple stressors? Again, the use of the simulation models is essential. As one example, a critical stressor on the Biscayne

Bay system is over-exploitation of the fish and invertebrate populations, either within the Bay itself or on the coral reef ecosystem to which it is linked that provides the dominant source of animal recruitment into the Bay. The trophodynamic model has been specifically designed to reflect harvesting of various amounts, age/size classes, and locations so that a multitude of fishing scenarios can be simulated. As a continuation of the assessment of ecosystem changes from altered freshwater inputs into Biscayne Bay (both from redesign and re-management of the C&SF and from climate change), we are developing scenarios of fisheries management options. The utility of the verified physical and ecological models allows simulation of an enormous number and range of scenario conditions. From these simulations, with sensitivity analyses of specific parameters, input conditions, etc., we can map out the expected responses of this estuary to future changes. Models of other parts of the regional ecosystem, including the coral reef ecosystem, mangroves, the wading bird populations of the Everglades, endangered species like the Florida panther, and others, are currently being developed, calibrated, and validated; they will join the suite of analytical tools available for assessing the regional ecological risks of multiple stressors and linking these to specific management options and decisions.

Finally, the South Florida ecosystem restoration process (Figure 5-10) is supported by scientific inputs concerning cumulative risks, involving these key steps:

1) Assess the historical and present ecological systems of the region and determine from a weight-of-evidence and scientific judgment approach what the consensus hypotheses are about causal relationships between human activities and ecological changes.

2) Decide upon the societal goals and objectives for the regional environment, down to specific subregions and differing ecosystem types, and articulate those goals and objectives in ecologically relevant terms.

3) Identify a suite of management options, especially with respect to a rede-signed water management system, that might lead to improved hydrological conditions, which the causal hypotheses identified as critical to ecological restoration.

4) Use a suite of analytical models and statistical tools to assess prospectively the consequences from a suite of plausible scenarios of an altered water-management system, with the ecological effects characterized in terms of ecological endpoints.

5) Provide the scientific analyses to the decision-making process so that the appropriate management decisions are made that are commensurate with the desired ecological goals.

6) Design a monitoring and performance evaluation system to be put in place in the future if the selected management options are actually funded and implemented.

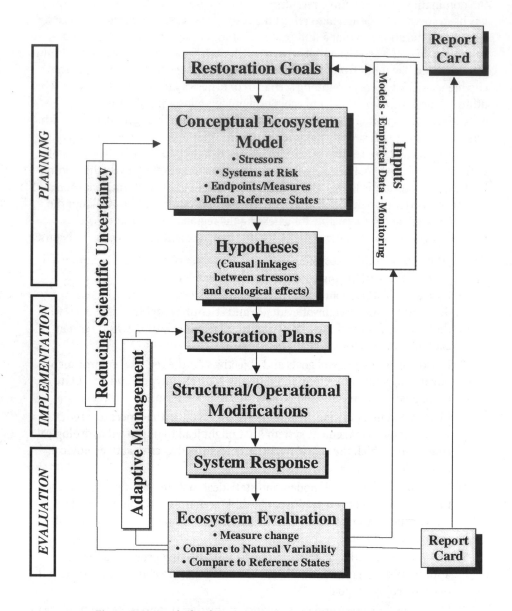

Figure 5-10 South Florida Restoration Strategy (Harwell et al. in press)

As we have noted elsewhere (e.g., Harwell et al., in press), the South Florida regional environment is poised on the edge of a successful application of ecological assessment and ecosystem-management principles in support of environmental decision-making, yet there are many political, economic, and other societal forces that yet may preclude success. However, unlike the severe degradation of the South Florida environment that has occurred over the past 50 years, this time there has been a systematic attempt to bring the best science to bear on assessing the health of the environment, determining how it got to its present unsustainable state, and predicting what the consequences will be from potential management options. This, indeed, exemplifies the critical need for reliable scientific methodologies for multiple-stressor, effects-based decision-making.

Assessing the effects of multiple climate change stressors on South Florida

Global climate change will likely affect South Florida via changes in the physical conditions that shape and dominate the region, including the following:

1) temperature changes—increased mean annual atmospheric temperatures, changes in frequency of episodic freeze events, changes in mean sea-surface temperatures, and changes in frequency of high sea-surface temperatures;

2) precipitation changes—changes in mean annual precipitation, changes in duration of wet season, changes in frequency of droughts and associated fires, and changes in frequency of floods; and

3) physical changes—changes in frequency or intensity of hurricanes and tropical storms and changes in rate of sea-level rise.

How does one assess which ecological effects such stressors might engender? Unlike single-chemical toxicity assessments, it is not possible to determine experimentally the "dose-response" relationships between these various physical stressors and the many ecosystems and ecological endpoints of the region. This is an obvious example of the need for the weight-of-evidence approach that builds upon a suite of lines of arguments about causal responses, including the following:

- Physiological studies—These are typical experimental studies that are characterized by hypothesis testing and standard statistical techniques for distinguishing differences in responses, following the inferential statistical techniques outlined in Chapter 3. An example of this type of information is experimentally determining, through laboratory studies, what are the optimal and limiting temperatures for corals.

- Spatial analogs—This involves examining the relationships between species distributions of productivity and geographical location. Chapter 3 also discussed spatially explicit statistical tools that are applied here. An example of this type of information is assessing the frequency of freeze events by latitude up the peninsula of Florida and correlating that distribution with the distribution of red mangroves (*Rhizophora mangle*) or with the locations of freeze-sensitive agriculture, such as citrus groves.

- Temporal analogs—This approach also relies on analogous relationships, but here with distributions that occur over time rather than across space. Again, the statistical tools described in Chapter 3 are applicable, especially the descriptive statistical tools. An example is understanding how the wading bird populations fluctuate in relation to inter-annual differences in rainfall, using a large number of years of data on bird populations and on precipitation to establish trends in the relationships.

- Historical analogs — This approach is similar to temporal analogs, except that the focus is on specific episodic events for exploring relationships rather than a series of past occurrences. This approach is much more qualitative and descriptive, and thus usually is not well-suited to statistical tools. However, in some cases, a simulation modeling approach may be taken to add rigor to the analogy, following Chapter 4. An example of a historical analog is deriving lessons from the effects on pineland communities of Hurricane Andrew, after which the natural recovery processes did not ensue because of the tremendous decrease in areal extent of pinelands from land conversion.

- Empirical models—This involves development of statistical models, such as regressions, between relevant parameters. The descriptive statistical tools described in Chapter 3 apply here, but not the dynamical models described in Chapter 4. A well-established example of this approach for climate-effects assessments is the Holdridge life zone model for assessing temperature/ moisture/habitat relationships. This, for example, could be used to assess the distribution of communities across a gradient of fire frequency or to assess the new expected communities if there is a shift along the Holdridge axis of mean annual temperature.

- Simulation models—Chapter 4 provides an excellent overview of the types and applicability of simulation models for addressing multiple-stressor situations. Such tools are the only feasible way to address mechanistically the multitude of potential combinations of stressors/endpoints, and thus are a highly desired tool for development. In the case of South Florida, an example of this simulation modeling approach is to use a calibrated and validated hydrodynamical model to simulate salinity regime in an estuary following changes in precipitation. The outputs from this model can then drive a seagrass ecosystem simulation model that predicts seagrass productivity and composition under different salinity regimes.

- Expert judgment—Expert judgment is essential to assess and weigh the various types of information available, each with its own degree of uncertainty. Examples of the use of expert judgment are provided in Chapter 1 and Chapter 2 and are fundamental to the South Florida case study. Moreover, this approach is essential to the implementation of an adaptive management strategy, suggested in Chapter 1.

* Scenario-consequence approach—Finally, the South Florida case example also illustrates the power of the scenario-consequence approach, in which the specific stressor combinations may be highly uncertain, but hypothetical scenarios allow exploration of risks, vulnerabilities, and information needs. For example, climate-change-induced alterations in precipitation are highly uncertain, so that even the direction of changes are poorly known. But a series of hypothetical scenarios of different changes in the mean precipitation, the timing and duration of the wet season, the frequency of high rainfall events, etc., can be evaluated, especially using simulation models, to define the range of system responses and sensitivities, as well as the importance of existing uncertainties in the context of making policy decisions.

Using the statistical and modeling tools and weight-of-evidence elements discussed above, following is a brief description of anticipated effects on the regional ecosystems from the multiple stressors of climate change.

Temperature

The greatest confidence in global climate-change predictions is for increased global mean annual atmospheric temperatures, with expected greater increases in higher latitudes and greater increases for nighttime values. General circulation model (GCM) outputs for regions on the scale of South Florida are less certain, particularly for this region because of its dominant maritime influence. Because the ecosystems of the region are already adapted to warm tropical conditions, one would not expect the sort of mass migration of habitats in the South Florida region that have been projected to occur in more temperate areas (e.g., Solomon 1986). For example, analyses by Harris and Cropper (1992) using the Holdridge life-zone model indicate little migration of habitats in South Florida, although the northern limits of the tropical and subtropical habitats would migrate up the Florida peninsula. Further, in what may seem to be a good question for *Jeopardy*, Miami is one of the very few cities in all of the U.S. that has never experienced a 100 °F temperature reading. On the other hand, South Florida is already ripe with exotic species that have invaded from more tropical areas, and climate change might favor highly opportunistic exotic species over native species (Malcolm and Markham 1997).

Changes in the frequency of episodic freeze events is another story. While one might expect that climate change would reduce the frequency of freezes (although that cannot be asserted based on GCM results), during the 1980s, which to that point was the warmest decade in U.S. history, there was a series of severe freezes in Florida, and many areas that for decades had been prime citrus production regions had their crops completely destroyed, forcing citrus production to move significantly further south. Reduced frequency of freezes would not be expected to cause a major impact on other ecosystems of the region.

Changes in sea-surface temperatures may affect South Florida. Presently, summer sea-surface temperatures are near the maxima of many marine species (above 30 °C) (Moore 1972; Albertson 1973, 1980; Roessler and Tabb 1974; Vicente et al. 1993; Milliman 1993). Thus, marine impacts are likely to be associated with transient elevations of sea-surface temperatures. Since many coral species live near the upper limits of their thermal tolerance, they are at risk to the stressor of elevated temperature episodes (Norse 1993). Recently, a series of such events caused extensive coral bleaching in the Florida Keys and elsewhere (e.g., Porter et al. 1982; Williams et al. 1987; Williams and Bunkey-Williams 1988; Glynn and de Weerdt 1991) resulting from rapid temperature changes or temperatures exceeding 30 °C (Milliman 1993). Other more subtle effects may occur from elevated water temperatures. For example, the gender of sea turtles is determined by ambient temperature at critical stages in embryonic development, with elevated temperatures leading to a preponderance of females (Mrosovsky and Yntema 1980; Mrosovsky and Provancha 1992). There is concern that individual animal species that are already stressed and have greatly reduced ranges, such as the Cape Sable sparrow and Florida panther, could be further stressed by higher temperatures, putting those populations at increased risk for extirpation or extinction (Harris and Cropper 1992). At the other end of the subtle scale, in very shallow water systems, such as in some areas of Florida Bay or in canal or other freshwater systems, high surface temperatures can lead to anoxia, thereby causing potentially massive die-offs of fish and invertebrate species.

Precipitation

It is unclear how mean annual precipitation would change in South Florida. If precipitation were to increase, the total annual rainfall could be important to coastal estuaries where much of the "excess" freshwater is presently discharged by humans. By contrast, Florida Bay has less freshwater inflows at present than it has had historically. Thus, increased precipitation, in the absence of changes in human water-management patterns, might return Florida Bay to more historical conditions and might reduce the frequency of adverse hypersaline conditions in Florida Bay. Another critical aspect of precipitation changes would be increases in the incidence of drought conditions, causing increased incidence of fire, which may increase risks to coastal mangrove ecosystems and hardwood hammocks from fire, making these ecosystems more vulnerable to exotic species invasions. On the other hand, a major restructuring of the water-management system will occur over the next two to three decades, making it difficult to distinguish how precipitation changes will affect the ecosystems of the region without much more extensive modeling analyses of the water budget and management regime for the region.

Hurricanes

South Florida historically experiences hurricanes once per decade, but some projections are that climate change could result in increased frequency, or even intensity, of tropical storms and hurricanes (Emanuel 1987; Gray 1993). If that were to occur, then the direct ecological consequences would be expected to be similar to the results of previous storms. Hurricanes can alter the plant communities; for example, Hurricane Donna, which in 1960 passed directly over the southern tip of the Everglades, destroyed mangrove forests north of Cape Sable that had massive, century-old trees. Hurricane Andrew (1992) took less than two hours to pass, but effects can still be seen (compare Armentano et al. 1995; Lirman 1997). In many cases following hurricanes, exotic species take over large areas, such as *Casurina* (Australian pine) following Hurricane Donna and the replacement of very large, old hardwood trees such as mahogany in hammocks by vines and other opportunists. Thus, if there were more hurricanes, there might be increased local damage to mangrove forests, transient increases of sediment and organic load to coastal waters, increased physical damage to coral reefs, and increased physical disturbance to pinelands. Mostly, of course, the ecosystems of the region are adapted to hurricanes, but the anthropogenic habitat alteration of the region has put many ecosystem types greatly at risk from hurricanes.

Sea-level rise

A critical issue is whether an increase in sea level would be in addition to the already accelerated sea-level rise rate in South Florida since 1930. There is clearly an interaction between sea-level rise and vulnerability to hurricanes, demonstrated by the significant subsidence of mangrove peat following Hurricane Andrew. This suggests that while the coastline may be able to keep up with present rate of sea-level rise if only average conditions existed all the time, the presence of episodic events like hurricanes and fires may undermine that ability to keep up (Wanless et al. 1994). Another critical interacting factor affecting the impacts of sea-level rise is coastal development, especially along barrier islands; these areas of South Florida are especially at risk from sea-level rise, again with exacerbation by hurricanes (Hendry 1993).

Summary of climate change risks

While there remains a great deal of uncertainty about the specific physical changes that will ensue in South Florida from global climate change, it can only be expected to exacerbate the effects of natural and anthropogenic stressors on South Florida. Many stressors would occur simultaneously, e.g., changes in temperature, precipitation, salinity, storms, sea-level, etc. Multiple endpoints and multiple effects can be expected to occur, ranging from adverse impacts on coral reefs exposed to episodic elevated sea-surface temperatures, to increased success of invasive exotic species, and perhaps to effects from more frequent or more intense hurricanes or from more frequent or more intensive periods of drought. The suite of analytical tools listed above—not only the statistical and modeling tools discussed in Chapters 3 and 4 but also analogs and expert judgment—are required to assess such a complex, Class 4 situation. From these considerations, one can expect that the greatest risk to the region from climate change may well be sea-level rise, particularly if global climate-change-induced sea-level rise is additive to the accelerated rates of increase of the 20th century.

Conclusions and Final Thoughts

In this chapter, we have attempted to address four issues in the cumulative environmental risk dialogue: terminology, problem categorization, analytical tools, and assessment and decision-making frameworks. While the first and third are self-explanatory, the second and fourth need further comment because of their implications for future cumulative assessments.

We are convinced that the next generation of environmental decision-making, if we are to make further progress in environmental protection, will increasingly focus on multiple societal drivers, multiple environmental stressors, with at least as great an emphasis on physical and biological stressors as chemicals, multiple at-risk ecosystems and ecosystem components, multiple societal goals, and multiple types of environmental management options. These characteristics are especially true for regional environmental management problems, such as South Florida, the Chesapeake, the Pacific Northwest, San Francisco Bay, Boston Harbor, etc.

We also are convinced that the ecological risk assessment paradigm not only is adequate but also is the appropriate and preferred organizing framework for addressing this class of environmental problems and that this framework works equally well, if done correctly, for prospective and retrospective risk analyses. Explicitly enhancing the current ecological risk assessment framework with the necessary steps and guidance for problem formulation processes, especially emphasizing the development of the conceptual model, will expand its utility as the assessment framework for the Class 3 and 4 classes of assessments. Thus, while it may appear that the more complex environmental decision-making problems require an integrated assessment framework rather than simply a "risk" framework, we contend that the ecological risk framework can readily be expanded to meet that need.

While semantics are sometimes important, this change in terminology from "risk assessment" to "integrated assessment" has more fundamental implications. What we are proposing in no way invalidates the current USEPA ecological risk assessment paradigm; in fact, it enriches and expands it to deal more realistically with Class 3 and 4 types of problems. In particular, we propose that the value- and effects-directed pathways of current problem-formulation phase of the ecological risk assessment process be expanded to address three questions explicitly: 1) What are the causes (drivers and stressors) for the current state of the system? 2) What is the current state of the ecological system. 3) What does society want the environmental system to look like in the future? To address these three questions will require the inclusion of biological assessments (e.g., field studies) of the current status and condition of resources, diagnostic and epidemiological approaches to identify potential causal linkages, as well as development of ecological benchmarks that describe the present and future states of the system.

This is illustrated in the South Florida case study, where the initial, retrospective phase of the assessment focused on understanding the causes of the current condition, establishing a baseline for the ecological health of the system, and selecting ecological benchmarks to describe the future state of the system. This process involved developing the appropriate conceptual models for the various ecosystems of concern, using diagnostic strategies to identify causal relationships between human activities and ecological changes, and assessing the current state of a wide variety of populations (e.g., wading birds, panthers, etc.), communities, and habitats (e.g., sloughs, mangroves, etc.). Using this information within the context of the conceptual models, we then set performance criteria for the stressor side of the equation, i.e., what specific stressor levels would be commensurate with the desired ecological conditions and, thus, acceptable targets for management. We also used this information to define ecological benchmarks to describe the present and societally desired future states of the ecosystems. This process sets the stage for the analysis phase of the ecological risk paradigm, where literally hundreds of spatially explicit scenarios were explored to forecast and optimize future conditions and identify management options that are consistent with the societal goals for the ecosystems of the region.

The South Florida case study is an example of an integrated assessment that demonstrates the flexibility of the current ecological risk framework. The USEPA framework is widely accepted nationally and internationally as an assessment strategy that explicitly engages the public, stakeholder, and managers in the process. This framework has a problem-formulation phase that can be stressor-, effects-, or value-directed, can be used either retrospectively or prospectively, and has a powerful forecasting and analysis component. The risk-characterization phase (e.g., current and/or future risks) synthesizes quantitative information, expert judgment, and uncertainty analyses into a weight-of-evidence or multiple-lines-of-evidence assessment of risk or environmental effect. Thus, this framework provides an integrated assessment strategy that is ideally suited to assessing the cumulative ecological effects for a wide range of scales and complexities.

Our South Florida and other experiences convince us that the development of a well-designed conceptual model is a critical initial step in assessing of cumulative effects from multiple stressors. The conceptual model illustrates the linkages among sources, stressors, and effects and is the basis for formulating hypotheses on potential cause-effect relationships. It also provides both the focus for scientific interpretation and research, and one of the most effective communication tools for interactions with stakeholders and decision-makers. In addition, we use conceptual models routinely to structure scenario-consequence analyses which, when coupled with extensive sensitivity analyses, offer a reasonable and transparent way to explore management options and system vulnerabilities and to provide the type of guidance needed to identify and select among management options.

We further propose that the ecological risk assessment framework, expanded to include the concept of regional integrated risk assessments, is positioned at the juncture of both scientific and decision-making activities. This is exemplified by the goals-driven selection of reference and desired ecological conditions and by the selection of ecological endpoints for both their ecological and societal values. An additional benefit of this approach is the recognition that expert scientific judgment based upon an interpretation of empirical data often is the ultimate basis of scientific input to the decision-making process at regional scales. This does not mean that quantitative information is not needed or useful, quite the contrary. In the ideal world a balance of expert judgment and quantitative analyses is the preferred option. However, as is discussed elsewhere in this volume, statistical and modeling of multiple stressors and cumulative risks at regional scales requires substantial amounts of data, which often are not available. We suggest that any attempt to bypass expert judgment in favor of an apparently more quantitative method may offer only the false security of precision at the expense of context and accuracy. Real confidence may be engendered through a goal-driven adaptive management process that provides exactly the same improvement in the likelihood of achieving the desired target as shifting one's system from a rocket to a guided missile.

Finally, we note that there is nothing fundamentally different about assessing multiple stressors and multiple effects; rather, the complex Class 3 and 4 problems involve application of the same tools developed for simpler analyses. These statistical and modeling tools are certainly stretched to their limits in the complex environmental assessments, and they must be utilized in a broader context that incorporates weight-of-evidence approaches and places greater reliance on sound expert judgment. However, because of tremendous advances in computing and in environmental sensing, we are confident that for the first time the scientific analytical tools and conceptual approaches are capable of tackling these complex and difficult environmental problems precisely at the time that we must move to that next generation of environmental decision-making.

Acknowledgments—The authors would like to thank Sue Ferenc, Anne Fairbrother, Kelly Munkittrick, Larry Barnthouse, and Jeff Foran for their thoughtful reviews. A special note of thanks is extended to Glenn Suter and Keith Solomon for their in-depth and insightful comments, which contributed substantively to the clarity and quality of the manuscript.

References

Ahlborg UG, Becking GC, Birnbaum LS, Brouwer A, Derks HJG, Feeley M, Golog G, Hanberg A, Larsen JC, Liem AKD, Safe SH, Schlatter C, Waern F, Younes M, Yrjanheikki E. 1994. Toxic equivalence factors for dioxin-like PCBs. Report on a WHO-ECEH and IPCS consultation, December 1993. *Chemosphere* 28:1049–1067.

Albertson HD. 1973. A comparison of the upper lethal temperatures of animals of fifty common species from Biscayne Bay [M.S. thesis]. Coral Gables FL: University of Miami. 79 p.

Albertson HD. 1980. Long-term effects of high temperature and low salinities on specimens of *Melonena corona* and *Nassarius vibex* [Ph.D. dissertation]. Coral Gables FL: University of Miami. 79 p.

Armentano TV, Doren RF, Platt WJ, Mullins T. 1995. Effects of Hurricane Andrew on coastal and interior forests of southern Florida: overview and synthesis. *J Coast Res* 21:111–144.

Ault JS, Luo J, Smith SG, Serafy JE, Diaz G, Humston R. 1999. A spatial dynamic multistock production model. *Can J Fish Aquat Sci* 56(Suppl 1):4–25.

Bancroft GT, Strong AM, RK Sawicki, W Hoffman, Jewell SD. 1994. Relationships among wading bird foraging patterns, colony locations, and hydrology in the Everglades. In: Davis SM, Ogden JC, editors. Everglades: the ecosystem and its restoration. Delray Beach FL: St. Lucie Press. p 615–658.

Barnthouse LW, Brown J. 1994. Conceptual model development. In: Ecological risk assessment issue papers. Washington DC: USEPA Risk Assessment Forum.

Baskerville G. 1986. Some scientific issues in cumulative environmental impact assessment. In: Canadian Environmental Assessment Research Council (CEARC) and National Research Council (NRC). Proceeding of the Workshop on Cumulative Environmental Effects: A Bi-national Perspective. Hull, Quebec, Canada: CEARC.

Beanlands GE, Duinker PN. 1983. An ecological framework for environmental impact assessment in Canada. Halafax, Nova Scotia, Canada: Institute for Environmental Studies, Dalhousie University and the Federal Environmental Assessment Review Office. 132 p.

Bedford BL, Preston EM. 1988. Developing the scientific basis for assessing cumulative effects of wetland loss and degradation on landscape functions: status, perspectives, and prospects. *Environ Manage* 12:751–771.

Browder J, Ogden JC. The natural South Florida system II: Pre-drainage ecology. *Urban Ecosyst* (in press).

Carruthers D. 1998. Air dispersion modelling. In: Douben PET, editor. Pollution risk assessment and management. Chichester, UK: Wiley. p 115–132.

[CEARC/NRC] Canadian Environmental Assessment Research Council and National Research Council. 1986. Proceeding of the Workshop on Cumulative Environmental Effects: A Bi-national Perspective. Hull, Quebec, Canada: CEARC.

Chen E, Gerber JF. 1990. Climate. In: Myers RL, Ewel JJ, editors. Ecosystems of Florida. Orlando FL: University of Central Florida. p 11–34.

Christensen NL, Bartuska AM, Brown JH, Carpenter S, D'Antonio C, Francis R, Franklin JF, MacMahon JA, Ross RF, Parsons DJ, Peterson CH, Turner MG, Woodmansee RG. 1996. The report of the Ecological Society of America committee on the scientific basis for ecosystem management. *Ecolog Appl* 6(3):775–747.

Cline EW, Vlachos EC, Horak GC. 1983. State-of-the-art and theoretical basis of assessing cumulative impacts on fish and wildlife. Washington DC: Office of Biological Services, U.S. Fish and Wildlife Service. 69 p.

Cocklin C, Parker S, Hay J. 1992. Notes on cumulative environmental change II: A contribution to methodology. *J Environ Manage* 35:51–67

Craighead Sr FC. 1968. The role of the alligator in shaping plant communities and maintaining wildlife in the southern Everglades. *Fla Nat* 41:2–7, 69–74, 94.

Craighead Sr FC. 1971. The trees of South Florida. Volume I. The natural environments and their succession. Coral Gables FL: University of Miami.

Cropper Jr WP, DiResta D. 1999. Simulation of a commercial sponge population in Biscayne Bay, Florida: Recovery following Hurricane Andrew and management implications. *Ecolog Model* 118:1–15.

Cropper Jr WP, Tosini SC, Snedaker SC, Koch-Rose M. Seascape-level simulation of mangroves adjacent to Biscayne Bay, Florida. (in prep.)

Dale VH, Pearson SM, Offerman HL, O'Neill RV. 1994. Relating patterns of land-use change to faunal biodiversity in the Central Amazon. *Conserv Biol* 8:1027–1036.

Davies KI. 1991. Towards ecosystem-based planning: A perspective on cumulative environmental effects. Prepared for the Royal Commission on the Future of the Toronto Waterfront and Environment Canada. Ottawa, Ontario, Canada: Minister of Supply and Services. 106 p.

Davis Jr JH. 1943. The natural features of southern Florida. Tallahassee FL: Florida Department of Conservation, Geological Survey. Bulletin No. 25.

Davis SM, Ogden JC. 1994. Toward ecosystem restoration. In: Davis MS, Ogden JC, editors. Everglades: the ecosystem and its restoration. Delray Beach FL: St. Lucie Press. p 769–796.

Davis, SM, LH Gunderson, WA Park, JR Richardson, and JE Mattson. 1994. Landscape dimension, composition, and function in a changing Everglades ecosystem. In: Davis SM, Ogden JC editors. Everglades: the ecosystem and its restoration. Delray Beach FL: St. Lucie Press. p 419–445

DeAngelis DL. 1994. Synthesis: spatial and temporal characteristics of the environment. In: Davis SM, Ogden JC, editors. Everglades: the ecosystem and its restoration. Delray Beach FL: St. Lucie Press. p 307–320

Douglas MA. 1947. The Everglades: river of grass. Revised edition (1988). Sarasota FL: Pineapple Press.

Duever MH, Carlson JE, Meeder JF, Duever LC, Gunderson LH, Riopelle LA, Alexander TR, Myers RL, Spangler DP. 1986. The Big Cypress Preserve. New York: National Audubon Society.

Duever MJ, Meeder JF, Meeder LC, McCollom JM. 1994. The climate of South Florida and its role in shaping the Everglades ecosystem. In: Davis SM, Ogden JC, editors. Everglades: the ecosystem and its restoration. Delray Beach FL: St. Lucie Press. p 225–248

Emanuel KA. 1987. The dependence of hurricane intensity on climate. *Nature* 326(2):483–385.

Fairbrother A, Kapustka LA, Williams BA, Bennett RS. 1997. Effects-initiated assessments are not risk assessments. *Hum Ecol Risk Assess* 3(2):119–124.

Florida Governor's Commission for a Sustainable South Florida. 1995. Final Report to Florida Governor Lawton Chiles. October 1995. Coral Gables FL: Florida Governor's Commission for a Sustainable South Florida.

Fong P, Harwell MA. 1994. Modeling seagrass communities in tropical and subtropical bays and estuaries: A mathematical model synthesis of current hypotheses. *Bull Mar Sci* 54:757–781.

Foran JA, Ferenc SA, editors. 1999. Multiple stressors in ecological risk and impact assessment. Pensacola FL: Society of Environmental Toxicology and Chemistry (SETAC). 115 p.

Fox GA. 1991. Practical causal inference for eco-epidemiologists. *J Toxicol Environ Health* 33:359–373.

Gentile JH, Harwell MA. 1998. The issue of significance in ecological risk assessments. *Hum Ecolog Risk Assess* 4(4):815–828.

Gentile JH, Harwell MA, van der Schalie W, Norton S, Rodier D. 1993. Ecological risk assessment: a scientific perspective. *J Hazard Mater* 35:241–253.

Gleason PJ, Stone P. 1994. Age, origin and landscape evolution of the Everglades peatland. In: Davis SM, Ogden JC, editors. Everglades: the ecosystem and its restoration. Delray Beach FL: St. Lucie Press. p 249–291.

Glynn PW, de Weerdt WH. 1991. Elimination of two reef-building hydrocorals following the 1982-1983 El Niño warming event. *Science* 253(5015):69–71.

Gray CR. 1993. Regional meteorology and hurricanes. In: Maul GA, editor. Climatic change in the intra American seas. United Nations Environment Programme and Intergovernmental Oceanographic Commission. London, UK: Edward Arnold. p 87–99.

Gunderson LH. 1994. Vegetation of the Everglades: determinants of community composition. In: Davis SM, Ogden JC, editors. Everglades: the ecosystem and its restoration. Delray Beach FL: St. Lucie Press. p 323–340.

Gunderson LH, Snyder JR. 1994. Fire patterns in the southern Everglades. In: Davis SM, Ogden JC, editors. Everglades: the ecosystem and its restoration. Delray Beach FL: St. Lucie Press. p 291–306

Harris LD, Cropper Jr WP. 1992. Between the devil and the deep blue sea: implications of climate change for Florida's fauna. In: Peters L, Lovejoy TE, editors. Global warming and biological diversity. New Haven CT: Yale University. p 309–324.

Harris HJ, Wenger RB, Harris VA, Devault DS. 1994. A method for assessing environmental risk: a case study of Green Bay, Lake Michigan, USA *Environ Manage* 18:(2):295–306.

Harshberger, JW. 1914. The vegetation of south Florida, south of 27_30' North, exclusive of the Florida Keys. Transactions of Wagner Free Institute of Science. Philadelphia, PA.

Harwell, MA. 1997. Ecosystem management of South Florida. *BioScience* 47(8):499–512.

Harwell MA. 1998. Science and environmental decision-making in South Florida. *Ecolog Appl* 8(3):580–590.

Harwell MA, Cooper W, Flaak R. 1992. Prioritizing ecological and human welfare risks from environmental stresses. *Environ Manage* 16(4):451–464.

Harwell, MA, Long JF, Bartuska AM, Gentile JH, Harwell CC, Myers V, Ogden JC. 1996. Ecosystem management to achieve ecological sustainability: the case of South Florida. *Environ Manage* 20(4):497–521.

Harwell MA, Myers V, Young T, Bartuska A, Gassman N, Gentile JH, Harwell CC, Appelbaum S, Barko J, Causey B, Johnson C, McLean A, Smola R, Templet P, Tosini S. 1999. A framework for an ecosystem integrity report card. *BioScience* 49(7):543–556.

Harwell, MA, Gentile JH, Bartuska A, Harwell CC, Myers V, Obeysekera J, Ogden J, Tosini S. A science-based strategy for ecological restoration in South Florida. *Urban Ecosyst* (in press).

Hendry M. 1993. Sea-level movements and shoreline changes. In: Maul GA, editor. Climatic change in the intra-American seas. United Nations Environment Programme and Intergovernmental Oceanographic Commission. London, UK: Edward Arnold. p 115–161.

Hill AB. 1965. The environment and disease: association or causation? *Proc R Soc Med* 58:295–300

Holling CS. 1978. Adaptive environmental assessment and management. New York: Wiley.

[IEMTF] Interagency Ecosystem Management Task Force. 1995a. The ecosystem approach: healthy ecosystems and sustainable economies. Volume I overview. Report of the Interagency Ecosystem Management Task Force. Available from: National Technical Information Service, Springfield, Virginia.

[IEMTF] Interagency Ecosystem Management Task Force. 1995b. The ecosystem approach: healthy ecosystems and sustainable economies. Volume II implementation issues. Report of the Interagency Ecosystem Management Task Force. Available from: National Technical Information Service, Springfield, Virginia.

[ISS] Interagency Science Subgroup. 1993. Federal objectives for South Florida restoration. Interagency Science Subgroup, South Florida Management and Coordination Working Group, Miami, Florida, USA.

Jaap WC, Hallock P. 1990. Coral reefs. In: Myers RL, Ewel JJ, editors. Ecosystems of Florida. Orlando FL: University of Central Florida. p 574–616.

Jacobs P, Sadler B. 1990. Sustainable development and environmental assessment: perspectives on planning for a common future. Hull, Quebec, Canada: Canadian Environmental Assessment Research Council. 182 p.

Kelly, JR, Harwell MA. 1990. Indicators of ecosystem recovery. *Environ Manage* 15(5):527–545.

Kooijmann SALM, Bedaux JJM. 1996. The analysis of aquatic toxicity data. Amsterdam, The Netherlands: VU University. 149 p.

Kushlan JA. 1989. Wetlands and wildlife, the Everglades perspective. In: Sharitz RR, Gibbons JW, editors. Freshwater wetlands and wildlife. Oak Ridge TN: U.S. Department of Energy. CONF-8603101, DOE Symposium Series Number 61, Office of Scientific and Technical Information. p 773–790.

Lane PA, Wallace RR, Johnson RJ, Bernard D. 1988. A reference guide to cumulative effects assessment in Canada. Volume 1. Hull, Quebec, Canada: Canadian Environmental Assessment Research Council.

Lee LC, Gosselink JG. 1988. Cumulative impacts on wetlands: linking scientific assessments and regulatory alternatives. *Environ Manage* 12(5):591–602

Light SS, Dineen JW. 1994. Water control in the Everglades: a historical perspective. In: Davis SM, Ogden JC, editors. Everglades: the ecosystem and its restoration. Delray Beach FL: St. Lucie Press. p 47–84.

Lirman D. 1997. Disturbance ecology of the Caribbean coral *Acropora palmata* [Ph.D. dissertation]. Miami FL: University of Miami. 250 p.

Lubchenko J, Olson AM, Brubaker LB, Carpenter SR, Holland MM, Hubbell SP, Levin SA, MacMahon JA, Mattson PA, Melillo JM, Mooney HA, Peterson CH, Pulliam HR, Real LA, Regal PJ, Risser PG. 1991. The Sustainable Biosphere Initiative: an ecological research agenda. *Ecology* 72(2):371–412.

MacVicar T, Van Lent T, Castro A. 1984. South Florida Water Management Model Documentation Report. West Palm Beach FL: South Florida Water Management District. Technical Publication 84-3.

Malcolm JR, Markham A. 1997. Climate change threats to the national parks and protected areas of the United States and Canada. Washington DC: World Wildlife Fund. 94 p.

Massachusetts Water Resources Authority. 1990. The state of Boston Harbor: 1990. Boston MA: Environmental Quality Department, Massachusetts Water Resources Authority.

McTaggart-Cowan I. 1976. Cumulative impacts of development of the Mackenzie Estuary/Delta, N.W.T. In: Mackenzie Delta: Priorities and Alternatives, Conference Proceedings; 3–4 December 1975. Ottawa, Ontario, Canada: Canadian Arctic Resources Committee.

Menzie C, Henning MH, Cura J, Finkelstein K, Gentile J, Maughan H, Mitchel D, Petron S, Potocki B, Svirsky S, Typer P. 1996. Special report of the Massachusetts weight-of-evidence workgroup: a weight of evidence approach for evaluating ecological risks. *Hum Ecolog Risk Assess* 2:277–304

Milliman JD. 1993. Coral reefs and their responses to global climate change. In: Maul GA, editor. Climatic change in the intra-American seas. United Nations Environment Programme and Intergovernmental Oceanographic Commission. London, UK: Edward Arnold. p 306–321.

Moore HB. 1972. Aspects of stress in the tropical marine environment. *Adv Mar Biol* 10:217–269.

Mrosovsky N, Yntema CL. 1980. Temperature dependence on sexual differentiation in sea turtles: implications for conservation. *Biol Conserv* 18:271–280.

Mrosovsky N, Provancha J. 1992. Sex ratio of hatchling loggerhead sea turtles: data and estimates from a five-year study. *Can J Zool* 70:530–538.

[NOAA] National Oceanographic and Atmospheric Administration. 1985. Climatography of the United States No. 20, Climate Summaries for Selected Sites, 1951–1980, Florida. Asheville NC: National Climatic Data Center.

[NRC] National Research Council. 1983. Risk assessment in the federal government. Washington DC: National Academy Press.

[NRC] National Research Council. 1996. Understanding risk: informing decisions in a democratic society. Washington DC: National Academy Press.

Norse EA, editor. 1993. Global marine biological diversity. A strategy for building conservation into decision-making. Washington DC: Island Press 383 p.

Obeysekera J, Browder J, Hornung L, Harwell MA. The natural South Florida system I: Climate, geology, and hydrology. *Urban Ecosyst* (in press).

Odum WE. 1982. Environmental degradation and the tyranny of small decisions. *BioScience* 32:728–729.

Ogden JC, Browder J, Gunderson LH, Gentile JH. Environmental management scenarios I: ecological implications. *Urban Ecosyst* (in press).

Porter JW, Battey JF, Smith GJ. 1982. Perturbation and change in coral reef communities. *Proc Nat Acad Sci (USA)* 79:1678–1681.

Preston EM, Bedford BL. 1988. Evaluating cumulative effects on wetland functions: a conceptual overview and generic framework. *Environ Manage* 12:565–583.

Robertson Jr WJ. 1955. An analysis of the breeding-bird populations of tropical Florida in relation to the vegetation [Ph.D. dissertation]. Urbana IL: University of Illinois.

Robertson Jr WJ. 1962. Fire and vegetation in the Everglades. *Proceedings of the Tall Timbers Fire Ecology Conference* 1:67–80.

Roessler MA, Tabb DC. 1974. Studies on effects of thermal pollution in Biscayne Bay, Florida. Washington DC: U.S. Environmental Protection Agency Office of Research and Development. EPA 660/3-74-014. 145 p.

Sanders FS, Adams SM, Barnthouse LW, Giddings M, Huber EE, Kumar KK, Lee D, Murphy B, Suter GW, Van Winkle W. 1978. Strategies for ecological effects assessment at DOE energy activity sites. Oak Ridge TN: Oak Ridge National Laboratory. ORNL/TM-6783.

Solecki WD, Long J, Harwell C, Myers V, Zubrow E, Ankersen T, Deren C, Feanny C, Hamann R, Hornung L, Murphy C, Snyder G. Human-environment interactions in South Florida's Everglades region: systems of ecological degradation and restoration. *Urban Ecosyst* (in press).

Solomon AS. 1986. Transient responses of forests to CO -induced climate change: simulation modeling experiments in eastern North America. *Ôecologia* 68:567–579.

Sonntag NC, Everitt RR, Rattie LP, Coplnett DL, Wolf CP, Truett JC, Dorcey AHJ, Holling CS. 1987. Cumulative effects assessment: a context for further research and development. Hull, Quebec, Canada: Canadian Environmental Assessment Research Council. 91 p.

Spaling H, Smit B. 1993. Cumulative environmental change: conceptual frameworks, evaluation approaches, and institutional perspectives. *Environ Manage* 17(5):587–600.

Stakhiv EZ. 1991. A cumulative impact analysis framework for the U.S. Army Corps of Engineers regulatory program. Draft Report (February 1991). Fort Belvoir VA: Institute for Water Resources, U.S. Army Corps of Engineers. 282 p.

Susser M. 1986. Rules of inference in epidemiology. *Regul Toxicol Pharmacol* 6:116–128.

Suter II GW, Antcliffe BL, Davis W, Dyer S, Gerristen J, Linder G, Munkittrick K, Rankin E. 1999. Conceptual approaches to identifying and assess multiple stressors. In: Foran JA, Ferenc SA, editors. Multiple stressors in ecological risk impact assessment. Pensacola FL: Society of Environmental Toxicology and Chemistry (SETAC). p 1–25

Suter II GW. 1999a. Developing conceptual models for complex ecological risk assessments. *Hum Ecolog Risk Assess* 5(2):375–396.

Suter II GW. 1999b. A framework for the assessment of ecological risks from multiple activities. *Hum Ecolog Risk Assess* 5(2):397–414.

Swartz RC, Schults DW, Ozretich RW, Lamberson JO, Cole FA, DeWitt TH, Redmond MS, Ferraro SP. 1995. PAH: a model to predict the toxicity of polynuclear aromatic hydrocarbon mixtures in field-collected sediments. *Environ Toxicol Chem* 14:1977–1978

Tuchmann E, Connaughton KP, Freedman LE, Moriwaki CB. 1996. The northwest forest plan: a report to the President and Congress. Portland OR: U.S. Department of Agriculture Office of Forestry and Economic Assistance.

[USCOE] U.S. Army Corps of Engineers. 1994. Central and Southern Florida Project (C&SF) Comprehensive Review Study. Jacksonville FL: U.S. Army Corps of Engineers.

[USCOE] U.S. Army Corps of Engineers. 1998. Central and Southern Florida Project (C&SF) Comprehensive Review Study. Draft Integrated Feasibility Report and Programmatic Environmental Impact Statement. Jacksonville FL: U.S. Army Corps of Engineers.

[USEPA] U.S. Environmental Protection Agency. 1987a. Unfinished business: a comparative assessment of environmental problems. Overview Report. Washington DC: Office of Policy Analysis, U.S. Environmental Protection Agency.

[USEPA] U.S. Environmental Protection Agency. 1987b. Unfinished business: a comparative assessment of environmental problems. Appendix III. Ecological Risk Work Group. Washington DC: Office of Policy Analysis, U.S. Environmental Protection Agency.

[USEPA] U.S. Environmental Protection Agency. 1992. Framework for ecological risk assessment. Washington DC: Risk Assessment Forum, U.S. Environmental Protection Agency. EPA/630/R-92/001.

[USEPA] U.S. Environmental Protection Agency. 1997. Guidance on cumulative risk assessments. Part 1. Planning and scoping. Science Policy Council, 3 July 1997. Washington DC: U.S. Environmental Protection Agency.

[USEPA] U.S. Environmental Protection Agency. 1998. Guidelines for ecological risk assessment. Washington DC: U.S. Environmental Protection Agency. EPA/630/R-95/002F.

[USEPA SAB] U.S. Environmental Protection Agency Science Advisory Board. 1990a. Reducing risk: setting priorities and strategies for environmental protection. Washington DC: U.S. Environmental Protection Agency Science Advisory Board. SAB-EC-90-021.

[USEPA SAB] U.S. Environmental Protection Agency Science Advisory Board. 1990b. The report of the Ecology and Welfare Subcommittee, relative risk reduction project. Reducing Risk Appendix A. Washington DC: U.S. Environmental Protection Agency Science Advisory Board. SAB-EC-90-021A.

[USEPA SAB] U.S. Environmental Protection Agency Science Advisory Board. 1999. Integrated Environmental Decision-Making for the 21st Century. Washington DC: U.S. Environmental Protection Agency Science Advisory Board (in review).

Van Leeuwen C, Biddinger G, Gess D, Moore D, Natan T, Winkelmann D. 1998. Problem formulation. In: Reinert K, Bartell S, Biddinger G. Ecological risk assessment decision-support system: a conceptual design. Pensacola FL: Society of Environmental Toxicology and Chemistry (SETAC). p 7–14.

Vicente VP, Singh VC, Botello AV. 1993. Ecological implications of potential climatic change and sea-level rise. In: Maul GA, editor. Climatic change in the intra-American seas. United Nations Environment Programme and Intergovernmental Oceanographic Commission. London, UK: Edward Arnold. p 262–281.

Wang JD, Cofer-Shabica SV, Chin Fatt J, 1988. Finite element characteristic advection model. *J Hyd Eng* 114(9):1098–1114.

Wanless HR, Parkinson RW, Tedesco LP. 1994. Sea level control on stability of Everglades wetlands. In: Davis SM, Ogden JC, editors. Everglades: the ecosystem and its restoration. Delray Beach FL: St. Lucie Press. p 199–223.

Westman WE. 1985. Ecology impact assessment and environmental planning. New York: Wiley.

Williams EH, Bunkey-Williams L. 1988. Bleaching of Caribbean coral reef symbionts in 1987–1988. *Proc. 6th International Coral Reef Symposium* 3:313–318.

Williams Jr EH, Goenaga C, Vincente V. 1987. Mass bleachings on Atlantic coral reefs. *Science* 238:877–888.

Abbreviations

ANCOVA	Analysis of covariance
ANOVA	Analysis of variance
ASMFC	Atlantic States Marine Fisheries Commission
CASM	Comprehensive aquatic systems model
CEA	Cumulative effects assessment
DELTA	Dynamic Ecological Land-use Tenure Analysis
DFA	Discriminant function analysis
DOC	Dissolved organic carbon
EEM	Environmental effects monitoring
EFPC	East Fork Poplar Creek
EIA	Ecological impact assessment
ESA	Endangered Species Act
FA	Factor analysis
GIS	Geographic Information Systems
GLM	Generalized linear model
MANCOVA	Multivariate analysis of covariance
MANOVA	Multivariate Analyses of variance
MLE	Maximum likelihood estimation
NCAA	Nonmentric cluster and association analysis
NMFS	National Marine Fisheries Service
NOAA	National Oceanic and Atmospheric Administration
NPPC	Northwest Power Planning Council
NRC	National Research Council

PATH SRP	PATH Scientific Review Panel
PATH	The Plan for Analysis and Testing of Hypothesis Project
PCB	Polychlorinated biphenyl
PCA	Principle components analysis
PCB	Polychlorinated biphenyl
SAV	submerged aquatic vegetation
SI	Sensitivity index
TOCs	Toxics of concern
USEPA	U.S. Environmental Protection Agency
USFWS	U.S. Fish and Wildlife Service

A

Abundance, 33, 45, 46, 47, 48
"Accumulated environmental state," 29–31, 37, 196
Acid deposition
    Chesapeake Bay, 15
    inferential methods, 69
    risk ranking in U.S., 170
Adaptive management, 21, 177
    experiments, 14, 23
    importance of, 22–23
    monitoring, 30
    role in decision-making, 194–196, 228
Additivity of risks, 124, 139, 146, 150, 173
Aerial photography, fixed-wing, 95
Age distributions, 42, 44
Age to maturation, fish, 45, 46, 48
Agricultural runoff, 4, 28
Air dispersion models, 96
Algae. See Phytoplankton
Alien species. See Exotic species
Anadromous Fish Conservation Act of 1979, 16
Analysis of Covariance (ANCOVA), 75, 77–78
    spawner-recruit trends, 9
Analysis of Variance (ANOVA), 69, 72, 74–79
    examples, 101, 102
    limitations of endpoints in, 75
ANCOVA. See Analysis of Covariance
ANOVA. See Analysis of Variance
Anoxic conditions
    Chesapeake Bay, 15, 20, 22
    South Florida, 224
Antagonistic toxicity, 139, 146, 176
Aquatic systems. See Comprehensive aquatic systems model
Aquatic vegetation. See Phytoplankton; Submerged aquatic vegetation
ARC/INFO, 94
Aristotle's law of the excluded middle, 121
Assimilation efficiency, 133, 134
Assimilative capacity, 31–32, 39, 61
Atlantic States Marine Fisheries Commission, 18
Atmospheric deposition, 15, 69, 121
Atmospheric temperature, in South Florida, 223–224

B

Backward regression analysis, 81, 88
Baseline historical data
    Columbia River flow, 13
    in ecological risk assessment, 201

    in reference site selection, 51
    South Florida, 222
Baseline information. See also Reference base
    biota, 37
    Columbia River Basin, 7
    to define the system, 38
    extant state of ecosystem, vs. disturbed, 208–210
    performance aspects for fish, 43
Bayes' theorem, 120, 125
Benchmarks, of ecological condition, 209, 227
Benthic invertebrate data, 39
Best Available Technology, 61
Bioaccumulation, 2, 46, 132
Bioavailability, 42
Biodiversity, in habitat degradation modeling, 95–96
Bioenergetics, 42
Biological assessment framework, 185
Biomagnification, 46, 132
Biomass, calculation of daily changes, 140, 142, 148
Birds
    population density, Multiway Frequency Analysis, 85
    reproductive studies, multivariate analysis, 76–77, 79, 99–103, 105–107, 111
    in South Florida, 224
Bonneville Dam, 7
Bonneville Power Administration, 6
Brundtland Commission, 34 n.1
Bycatch, 16

C

Cadmium, in Chesapeake Bay, 19
Calibration of model, 142, 144–145
Canada. Environmental Assessment Act, 27
Canada. Fisheries Act, 39
Canonical Correlation Analysis, 83–84, 97
CASM. See Comprehensive aquatic systems model
Categorical data, 69. See also Discriminant Function Analysis
Causative factors, identification of, 58, 60
Central and South Florida Flood Control Project (C&SF), 215, 218
Centroid, 89
Channelization, 2
Chesapeake Bay, 15–24
    current status, 20
    effects of turbidity on oysters, 2
    management actions, 19, 22–23, 195,